OUTBACK STATIONS

Evan McHugh is a journalist who has written for
newspapers, television and radio. His previous books
include *The Drovers*, *Bushrangers*, *Shipwrecks:
Australia's Greatest Maritime Disasters*, *Outback
Heroes*, *Outback Pioneers* and *Birdsville*. Evan's
book about true crime in the outback, *Red Centre,
Dark Heart*, won the Ned Kelly Award for best non-
fiction in 2008. He lives with his wife in the Hunter
Valley, New South Wales.

OUTBACK STATIONS

The life and times of Australia's biggest
cattle and sheep properties

Evan McHugh

VIKING
an imprint of
PENGUIN BOOKS

VIKING

Published by the Penguin Group
Penguin Group (Australia)
707 Collins Street, Melbourne 3008, Victoria, Australia
(a division of Pearson Australia Group Pty Ltd)
Penguin Group (USA) Inc.
375 Hudson Street, New York, New York 10014, USA
Penguin Group (Canada)
90 Eglinton Avenue East, Suite 700, Toronto, Canada ON M4P 2Y3
(a division of Pearson Penguin Canada Inc.)
Penguin Books Ltd
80 Strand, London WC2R 0RL England
Penguin Ireland
25 St Stephen's Green, Dublin 2, Ireland
(a division of Penguin Books Ltd)
Penguin Books India Pvt Ltd
11 Community Centre, Panchsheel Park, New Delhi – 110 017, India
Penguin Group (NZ)
67 Apollo Drive, Rosedale, North Shore 0632, New Zealand
(a division of Pearson New Zealand Ltd)
Penguin Books (South Africa) (Pty) Ltd
24 Sturdee Avenue, Rosebank, Johannesburg 2196, South Africa

Penguin Books Ltd, Registered Offices: 80 Strand, London WC2R 0RL, England
First published by Penguin Group (Australia), 2012

5 7 9 10 8 6 4

Cover design by Alex Ross © Penguin Group (Australia)
Text design by Cathy Larsen © Penguin Group (Australia)
Cover photograph © Scott Bridle
Maps © Michelle Havenstein
Typeset in Linotype Centennial 45 light by Penguin Group (Australia)
Printed and bound in Australia by McPherson's Printing Group, Maryborough, Victoria

National Library of Australia
Cataloguing-in-Publication data:

McHugh.Evan
Outback stations / Evan McHugh.
9780670075454 (pbk.)
Ranches – Northern Territory – History.
Beef cattle – Northern Territory – History.
Ranch life – Northern Territory – History.

636.01

penguin.com.au

CONTENTS

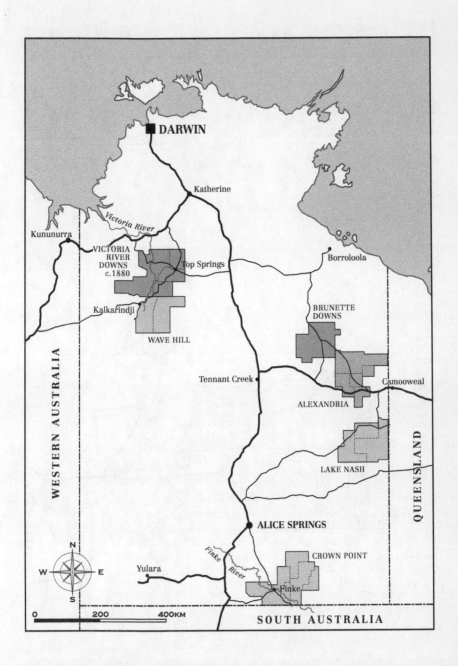

DARWIN

Katherine

Victoria River

Kununurra

VICTORIA
RIVER
DOWNS
c.1880

Top Springs

Borroloola

Kalkarindji

WAVE HILL

BRUNETTE
DOWNS

Tennant Creek

Camooweal

ALEXANDRIA

LAKE NASH

WESTERN AUSTRALIA

QUEENSLAND

ALICE SPRINGS

CROWN POINT

Finke River

Yulara

Finke

N
W   E
S

0   200   400KM

SOUTH AUSTRALIA

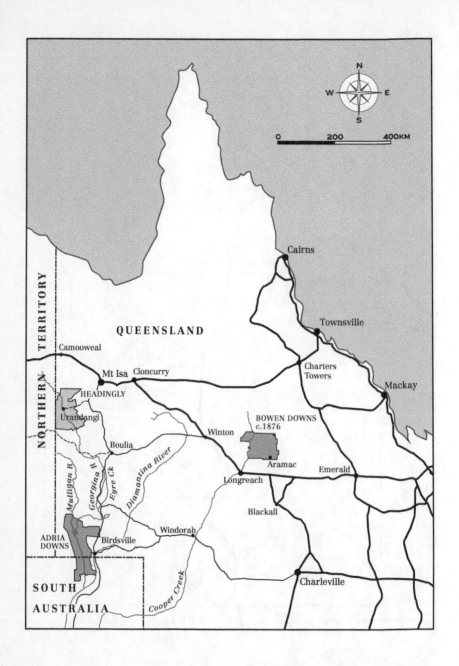

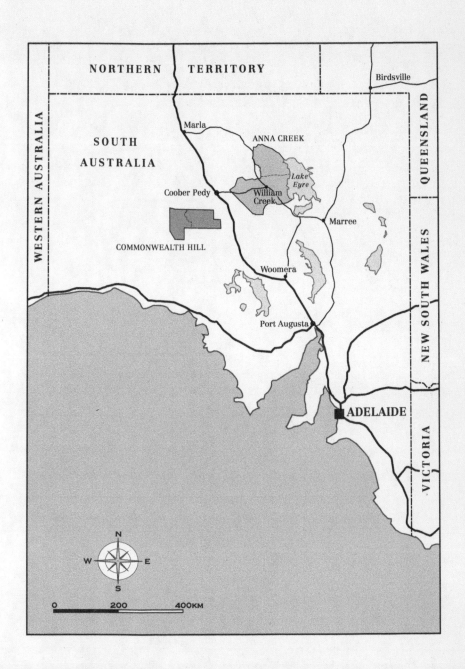

INTRODUCTION

'I would like to spread before you a world of rhythm and light; a world of beauty and fear; of rushing water and slow-burning dry-season fires: it is a realm where lightning strikes for nights on end, where clouds form ranks and phalanxes that stretch for hundreds of kilometres across flat plains, where rivers rush down bare savannah watercourses and enliven the dead earth.'
Nicolas Rothwell, 'Travels in the Northern Realm', *The Monthly*,
July 2008, (reproduced by kind permission).

In the midst of a wintry Hunter Valley dawn, I drove my LandCruiser past the still-sleeping cottage I called home, the leafless vineyard on one side and the hulking forms of cattle on the other, turned out of the driveway, and began the first of several journeys into the outback of Australia. I drove past the manicured estates that allowed moneyed Sydneysiders to feel like lords of all they surveyed, then on past horse studs that were a household name around the country. On through towns like Merriwa and Dungog, where pretence gives way to practicality, and the Great Dividing Range gives way to country that lifts and falls in gentle undulations like breathing.

By the time I reached Queensland, the skies were larger, the treeless plains more common, and red sandhills started to appear. When the fences disappeared and wandering stock lifted their heads to watch me pass, I felt the heart of the outback was growing near. When at last my wheels touched unsealed road, and the sense of freedom that permeates wide open spaces was inescapable, I was finally there.

My objective was to explore a phenomenon that doesn't exist anywhere else in the world. While many Australian stations are large, covering thousands of square kilometres, some are truly enormous. Nowhere else will you find not one but many places that cover more than a million hectares (or 2.5 million acres). By comparison, the biggest property in any other country is King Ranch, in Texas, which in 2012 covered just 334 000 hectares (slightly less than 1 million acres). In Australia, dozens of properties are bigger.

Originally, I planned to cover every million-hectare property in the country. However, to paraphrase T. S. Eliot, between the idea and the reality falls the research. I uncovered more and more of them, and more and more about them. I'd been hoping to discover rich histories while finding out what life is really like on those properties today, and I was far from disappointed. But it wasn't long before I realised I'd have to be selective and focus on those stations that had a special claim for inclusion. They ranged from Bowen Downs, the first giant station, and those stations that owed their genesis to the great outback pioneer Nat Buchanan – Brunette Downs, Alexandria, Victoria River Downs and Wave Hill (Bowen Downs falls under this category too). Nat wasn't just one of the best bushmen ever to mount a horse, he was also one of those intriguing individuals who treated the original inhabitants of the country he helped settle as people rather than ignorant savages. His respect for their ancient knowledge of the land was a key element of his success in the outback.

Then there were stations that were less well known but just as fascinating: the powerhouse Lake Nash Station; the family-owned and second-largest station in the world, Crown Point; and a personal favourite, the desert-challenging Adria Downs. I was particularly fortunate to be given access to the biggest sheep station in the world, Commonwealth Hill, which had only welcomed one writer in the last 80 years.

Unfortunately, I was refused access to the biggest cattle station in the world, Anna Creek. In the end, I went anyway, as explained in the final chapter.

One of the delights of a project like this was the occasional moment when what I thought I knew turned out to be totally different to the way things really were. For example, I'd assumed that stations in the same region would have a lot in common. What I soon discovered was that even stations that sit side by side can be surprisingly different. In the case of Victoria River Downs and Wave Hill, for example, the fact that one is closer to the Top End, even by only 50 kilometres or so, means that the climate and vegetation is noticeably different. While VRD is quite tropical, on the southern boundary of Wave Hill there is desert. Their histories also diverge. Aboriginal workers at Wave Hill were involved in the famous walk-off, while their colleagues at VRD were thwarted when a telegram stating their intentions was torn up instead of being sent.

Both these stations contrasted with those further south, such as Crown Point and Adria Downs. These two stations are in the arid 'dead heart' of Central Australia, one on the eastern side of the Simpson Desert, the other on the western side. While one enjoys the benefits of the regular floods of the Channel Country, the other has the advantages of being on the Ghan railway line. While one was carved out of the desert by one family over two generations, the other is a recent amalgamation by another family driven by the demands of the modern economics of cattle operations.

Not only were the stories of these stations markedly different, my responses to those stories, and experiences of them was also varied. As time went on, and my understanding grew, I recognised emerging patterns and examined them in more detail. Most often, I was exhilarated and inspired by the things I did and saw. At other times, however, there was also disappointment or disillusionment, which I guess is all part of life's rich tapestry. There were occasions when I was simply tired and homesick, driving alone and wishing my wife could share my adventures (and take the photos), gazing across an immense herd but wondering how our little 'herd' (Cassie and Barbie) were doing back home. Exactly which emotion described the moment when a wheel came off my vehicle and I couldn't wedge the jack underneath the axle, I'm not sure. What I can say is that at that point life's rich tapestry was looking pretty bloody frayed. Although, I was helped by a bit of advice once given to me a Birdsville cop, Neale McShane. 'When there's a problem, don't rush in to fix it,' he said. 'You could make things worse. Take a few minutes to assess the situation. Usually, you'll work out what to do.' I ended up digging under the axle with a spoon until the jack fitted.

Speaking of frayed, there are times when I tackled some massive drives that in the narrative might appear to push the boundaries of safety. In fact, these trips included regular rest breaks. The Trucka-saurus, as my Toyota LandCruiser 100 Series Wagon is nicknamed, was well equipped with coffee-making and nap-taking facilities. Indeed with a portable stove, 20 litres of water, two spare tyres, punc-ture-repair kit, compressor and power inverter, plus tools and a spare parts, there were few situations I couldn't handle, or at least survive.

In fact, the only time I really got caught was trying to reach Crown Point late at night. I have to admit I was too tired to keep going but I was expected. I was further delayed when a driving light blew and I didn't have a spare (I do now), which meant I had to slow down even more. Without radio or phone contact, I couldn't let anyone know that I was okay and not to come looking for me.

There was a lesson that came out of that: allow more time, and at the last available contact point make an honest assessment of how long a drive down an unknown track to an unknown destination will really take. I'm certainly not the most experienced outback driver there is, but it was easy, in hindsight.

· While visiting these extraordinary places, I was conscious that I was entering an intensely busy work environment and my presence wasn't helping to get things done. Nevertheless, many stations put themselves to some inconvenience showing me their operations and giving me access that was well beyond anything I could have hoped for. Some did so even as a major exposé threatened their industry.

Finally, if you really want to experience the big country, please remember that these are all working properties. It's best to keep to public roads, and to check first before entering private land. Of course, if you're really inspired, most of the stations are on the lookout for good workers. They advertise in all prominent rural publications. And as I found while visiting these stations, a life in the big country is one lived large.

Ultimately, while I jumped at the chance to explore these stations, I also got to return to the places in Australia that had long fascinated me. Visiting these stations to find out what goes on beyond the farm gate was certainly my main objective, but I have to confess I had other motives and sought other rewards as well.

It's no accident that this introduction includes words like 'breathing', 'heartbeat' and 'inspiring'. For me, the outback is a living thing. While making camp in the middle of nowhere might seem a lonely way to spend a night, when the stars begin to shine and all is silent, you can sometimes sense just how timeless this country really is. It's hard to feel lonesome when you're filled with awe.

Words may not be able to describe this feeling, but it's always worth a try. There are plenty of outback people who understand this, and you're about to meet some of them. Many of them share a bond, not just with each other, but with something much larger: the land itself. Once forged, it can never be broken.

1. A LAND OF OPPORTUNITY
Bowen Downs Station
38 000 square kilometres, 1863; 449 square kilometres, 2012

The Landsborough Highway between Barcaldine and Longreach doesn't have much to offer someone without a sense of history or place. It's flat, the road's pretty straight and the landscape on either side is monotonous – featureless grass that extends to a distant horizon, where it meets a sky devoid of clouds. Nothing to write home about here, you might think.

And yet, this is the country that inspired Banjo Paterson to write of a 'vision splendid of sunlit plains extended'. He peopled it with heroic figures like Clancy of the Overflow, who sang with the sheer joy of living as he rode along behind a mob of cattle.

Still, it does seem there's nothing out here but endless grass. Even the homesteads look deserted. It's hard not to start wondering 'are we there yet?' because there's ostensibly stuff-all going on where you are. At times it's impossible to imagine anything ever happening in such emptiness.

But this is country that operates on a grand scale. While Will Ogilvie wrote the wonderful line about a 'world bounded by a fence of blue', here you can actually see it. And when Banjo created his outback heroes, he wasn't making them up. This is Nat Buchanan's country, and for an idea of his stature, you can follow the tracks, trails, stock routes and stations he pioneered from here in central Queensland to the coast of Western Australia, 3000 kilometres away.

From the time I reached Barcaldine, considered the birthplace of the Australian Labor Party, I felt like my journey had really begun. It was my second day on the road and I was rolling along in the Truckasaurus, devouring the boiled lollies my usually health-conscious wife had given me, I suspected in lieu of the hugs and kisses I would be missing for the next few weeks.

My initial confusion over where to start my story had dissolved. I'd thought of arranging the stations in some kind of chronology, or in order of size, or even just alphabetically. Outside of Barcaldine, I realised there was only one way to begin. It was here, where Nat had established the first of the giant stations that would soon spread to the remotest corners of the continent. I would follow in the footsteps of Nat Buchanan. What better guide could there be?

It was here, in 1863, beyond the settled areas of Australia at the time, beyond anything worthy of the term 'road', that a party of overlanders with a mob of 5000 head of cattle slowly made their way deep into Queensland's heartland. They were bound for a place that was nothing more than lines on a map. Those lines delineated a leasehold of approximately 3.8 million hectares that would soon go by the name of Bowen Downs Station.

The overlanders were led by a man named Walter Kerr and included an assistant, Maurice Donohue, four stockmen, a woman and a boy. They were guided by one of the greatest-ever drovers and pioneers of the outback, Nat Buchanan, who had been appointed manager of the as-yet unformed property.

The drovers were following Buchanan, who had scouted ahead on his own, when they were surprised by a large number of Aborigines adorned with what Walter Kerr took to be war paint. The people had committed no aggressive act, but Kerr eventually opened fire on them. The rest of his men held back, perhaps mindful of one of Buchanan's previous admonishments: do not shoot Aboriginal people unless provoked.

Kerr shouted for help, some of his men joined in. Eventually they were all shooting. How many Aborigines were shot that day isn't known. Neither is there any record of the consequences for those involved in the affray, but the incident was typical of many that poisoned relations between Europeans and Aboriginal people in numerous areas of Australia during that time. The idea that Indigenous inhabitants had a claim to the country and a right to reside there unmolested never entered most Europeans' minds.

It hadn't entered the minds of those in government either. In Queensland, which had achieved Statehood just four years before Buchanan's group set off, the government had decided that the easiest way to bolster its fledgling coffers was to lease vast inland areas on extremely attractive terms to potential settlers, with no regard for its traditional owners.

Surveyor-General Augustus Gregory, who as an explorer had discovered the rich grazing lands of the Northern Territory's Victoria River district (see Chapter 5), became responsible for mapping the State and offering certain areas for lease or purchase. Between 1860 and 1864 an area covering one-eighth of Australia's landmass was made available to all-comers on 14-year leases. It was done without treaty or consultation with people whose connection to the country stretched back generations and thousands of years. Some were swept aside in the ensuing land rush. Others were hunted down for daring to resist their dispossession. A few managed to accommodate the run hunters, trading their labour for a continuing relationship with their land and culture, plus rations and/or low wages.

The conflict during that first trip to stock Bowen Downs was to be repeated throughout the establishment of nearly all the stations I planned on visiting. However, Bowen Downs was also the scene of some extraordinary and unique incidents.

Nat Buchanan was the common thread running through Bowen Downs and many other stations settled around the same time. He was born in 1826 in Ireland, his verdant, well-populated birthplace an antipodes in every sense to the arid frontier of his future home. It's hard to imagine how anything in his early years could have prepared him for the life he would lead. Buchanan arrived in Australia with his parents and four brothers aboard the *Statesman* in January 1837, and even their move to the pastures of the aptly named New England plateau of New South Wales was a gentle introduction to the harsh conditions of the Australian bush.

After a foray into the California gold rush in 1849 with his brothers Andrew and Frank failed to make his fortune, Buchanan took to the road. As a drover he moved cattle to the New South Wales and Victorian goldfields, while always on the lookout for an opportunity to set himself up on the land. However, as all the good property had been quickly seized by speculators and squatters, Buchanan eventually realised the only option was to go run hunting further out.

In 1859, with the explorer William Landsborough, Buchanan set off from Rockhampton, on the coast of Queensland, to examine the inland's potential for stock rearing. They penetrated to the present-day Thomson River and the site of what would become the town of Aramac, where they found superb downs country (grassy and undulating), which had the appearance of being well watered.

Buchanan returned in 1861 with a land speculator, Edward Cornish, who agreed that the land around Aramac was perfect for sheep. With Cornish, Buchanan pressed on across the downs to see how far they extended. The pair reached the Diamantina River, 500 kilometres west, where they found fresh tracks, which they realised had recently been made by Burke and Wills' expedition. The explorers may have been the first Europeans through the region but they were little more than a month ahead of Cornish and Buchanan.

On the run hunters' return, leases covering as much as 38 000 square kilometres [3.8 million hectares] of what was to become Bowen Downs Station were taken up by a consortium comprising Landsborough, Cornish, Buchanan and the Scottish Australian Investment Co. led by Robert Morehead.

For an idea of just how big Bowen Downs was, if it were circular, it would have a radius of 110 kilometres. Such a circle overlaid on

Australia's biggest capital cities would easily extend across all their residential areas. In Sydney, it would cover the coast to the Blue Mountains, down to Wollongong and almost up to Newcastle, and an area as large again out to sea. In Melbourne it would cover all of Port Phillip Bay, Western Port and Phillip Island, east to Drouin and north to Seymour. In Brisbane it would extend to Coolangatta, to Toowoomba, to Noosa and cover a similar area out to sea.

The partners may not have realised it at the time, but they had acquired some of the finest agricultural land to be found anywhere in the world. Many farmers from other regions still speak today of Queensland's blacksoil plains with reverential awe. That land can grow just about anything. The grasses that spring up there after the generally reliable rains are so nutritious that cattle almost grow fat just looking at them. In 1863, this paradise was completely open range; there wasn't a fence, a dam, a yard, or even a hut on any of it. Nat Buchanan had come from Europe, where agricultural infrastructure had been developed over centuries. Here, the slate was completely clean, except for the cattle and sheep that soon arrived in their thousands.

In the same year he established Bowen Downs, 37-year-old Buchanan married Kate Gordon, the daughter of a grazier with properties in northern NSW and Queensland. He was 16 years her senior. Kate had grown up on the land and could ride as well as any man. She was no stranger to the hardships of the bush, but even she must have been daunted by the prospect of following her husband to the isolation of Bowen Downs. When she arrived, the 21-year-old was the only white woman for hundreds of kilometres. Here, once more, Bowen Downs set the pattern for future big stations, of pioneering women living on the frontier as the settlement of the country was pushed further out.

Amid the feverish activity of stocking Bowen Downs, Kate discovered she was pregnant. When she was nearing full term, she moved back to her father's station on the coast, near Gladstone, where she

gave birth to Gordon Buchanan on 29 May 1864. When mother
and child were well enough to travel, they returned to the isolation,
dangers and basic amenities of Bowen Downs. We can only imagine
how Kate dealt with the challenges of being a new mother far from
the support of more experienced women and any hope of medical
support. Like many outback women, she didn't have time to write
her experiences down, yet the proof of her resourcefulness and
courage was her child: the youngster thrived at Bowen Downs.

Unfortunately Gordon was about the only successful venture on
the station. Drought, falling prices and the cost of operating such
an immense holding saw Bowen Downs falling deeper and deeper
into debt. In 1866 the price for cattle and wool fell to ruinous
levels, just as it was time to renegotiate the agreement between
the partners in Bowen Downs. By then the station had lost over
£100000. For members of the consortium who'd had little capital to
begin with, it was more than they could afford. In Buchanan's case, his
share of the debt was £14000. The company Scottish Australian paid
the debt, in return for Nat relinquishing his share in the station.

As Gordon Buchanan later put it:

The men who did the pioneering and bore the heat and burden of the
day [Landsborough, Cornish and Buchanan] went out without a penny.
The sleeping partners, city men, managed to hold on and eventually,
as shareholders in one of the most prosperous pastoral holdings in
Australia, reaped a rich harvest.

Nat's efforts in establishing and managing the station weren't
rewarded either. Later in 1866 Robert Morehead fired him and
replaced him with his 23-year-old son, Boyd Dunlop Morehead, who
was later to become premier of Queensland.

Nat returned to New South Wales to lick his wounds, and went
farming with his brother Andrew on a small selection in the moun-
tainous country along the Bellinger River near Coffs Harbour. When

that didn't work out, he moved on to a mining venture. It would be almost a decade before he returned to the country of far horizons, but when he did, it would be in the most impressive manner imaginable.

The owners of Bowen Downs continued to be plagued with problems. As the cost of operating the place was high, and tough times tested the finances of its investors, the property gradually shrank in size as leases were relinquished and the station was divided into smaller, more manageable blocks. Even so, by 1870, it was still barely developed: the buildings were still rudimentary, dams few and fences almost nonexistent. It was then that the duffers moved in. And not just any duffers.

From the early days of European settlement in Australia, stock duffing had ranked among the most common of crimes. Horses were taken for transportation. Sheep and cattle that had either strayed or been stolen were a ready means of sustenance for hungry settlers and convicts. There were considerable obstacles in catching and prosecuting the duffers, particularly when it came to identifying beasts cooked and eaten shortly after their disappearance. Fortunately, although stock duffing was rife, cases usually involved only one or two animals. However, all of that changed with the case involving Bowen Downs.

The first clue that something was amiss came in the middle of 1870 when another of the outback's great pioneers, John Costello, was scouting new grazing land in the south-west corner of Queensland. There, in the soft soil that followed a particularly good season of rains, Costello discovered the tracks of a vast mob of cattle being driven towards South Australia. Costello was immediately suspicious because the cattle were travelling what was far from an established stock route. Indeed, they were heading into country that only nine years before had killed the explorers Robert O'Hara Burke and William Wills. Costello suspected duffers and at the first opportunity alerted the Queensland police.

Costello estimated there were hundreds of cattle in the mob, and surmised that their most likely source was Bowen Downs. It was unfenced, and stock were allowed to wander. Between occasional musters that revealed the stock's condition and numbers to their young manager, Boyd Morehead, many of the stock remained unbranded and were left to their own devices.

Even so, it is still remarkable that the station owners initially did not believe the police's claim that they may have lost several hundred head of cattle. It was only when the station mustered at the end of 1870 that Morehead's men realised their numbers were well short. In particular, a prize stud bull, a pure-white Shorthorn known as the Duke of Marlborough ('Whitey' for short), was nowhere to be found on the sunlit plains of Bowen Downs. The station owners contacted police.

Before this time, it had been thought unnecessary to provide South Australia with details of Queensland brands – it was unthinkable that any cattle could have crossed the harsh, dry interior.

But in January 1871 evidence emerged that someone had succeeded in doing exactly that. A drover was arrested heading for Adelaide from a South Australian station with cattle branded 'LC5', the Bowen Downs brand that stood for Landsborough and Cornish, although neither was still a partner in the property. At the same time, Bowen Downs' stock agents, Elder Smith, reported that their Adelaide representative had seen LC5-branded cattle in the Adelaide saleyards. Inquiries soon revealed that all the LC5-branded cattle had come from just one South Australian cattle station – Blanchewater.

Blanchewater Station lies in the extremely marginal cattle country of South Australia's north-east, on the edges of Lake Blanche and Lake Callabonna. The lakes are fed by Strzelecki Creek, which flows (when it does flow) down from Queensland. Included among its tributaries is the Thompson River, which extends all the way to Bowen Downs.

Blanchewater was owned by a South Australian MP, John Baker, who'd briefly served as the state's premier. In February, Baker was contacted by Boyd Morehead and Robert Barr Smith, a partner in

Elder Smith. They wanted to visit Blanchewater to see if any LC5-branded cattle were still on the property. Baker responded that he was perfectly happy for them to do so, but insisted that he wouldn't be giving any of them back: he had a signed bill of sale for them and they were his. Although Baker seemed accommodating, when it came to arranging a time for the Blanchewater visit, he contrived a range of difficulties to thwart and frustrate the Bowen Downs men.

Morehead sought a legal opinion on whether he could go onto Blanchewater and take back any cattle he thought were his. The problem was that if he did so, and Baker really could prove that he'd bought the cattle, Morehead himself might be charged with duffing. Morehead thought better of it and ended up getting hold of some of the LC5 cattle by buying them at the Adelaide saleyards, where Baker and the butchers of Adelaide were turning them over as fast as they could.

Morehead needed the cattle as evidence in the trial of the duffers responsible for their theft, if they were ever apprehended. While Baker was evasive when it came to facilitating access to his station, he was more accommodating when it came to explaining how he'd come by the Bowen Downs cattle. Around June 1870, a man named Henry Collins had arrived at Blanchewater with two other men, driving no less than 1000 head of cattle.

At Blanchewater, Collins met the station's manager, J. Mules, who had seen most of his property's stock killed by a succession of droughts over the previous years. The rains that had helped the duffers bring the cattle down from Queensland had also helped Blanchewater, which was greener than it had ever been. Restocking, however, was a slow process. So when Collins offered to sell his mob at the bargain price of between £3 and £5 a head, Mules jumped at the chance.

Collins explained the LC5 brands as belonging to his brother, Lawrence Collins, who owned a property in Queensland. Mules didn't know any better, or wasn't so foolish as to enquire further, so the deal was done.

Baker gave Collins a promissory note for a figure of between £3500 and £5000 (sources vary), which could be cashed in six months. Collins left the cattle and continued south to Adelaide with his mates. Not only had they pulled off the biggest heist in Australian history, it was also one of the most extraordinary feats of overlanding cattle the country had ever seen.

On the way to Adelaide, Collins gave an interview to a newspaper in which he claimed the trip had taken four months. He reported that along the way they'd had to make 80-kilometre-wide detours to avoid floodwaters in what was supposed to be a desert. They'd also encountered friendly Aborigines (how could they be anything else but friendly to men in possession of such an immense amount of protein?), 6-metre-long snakes and 'alligators' (most likely desert goannas, which can grow up to 2 metres).

In February 1871, the information provided by Blanchewater enabled police to issue notices in South Australia and Queensland for the arrest of 'Collins, alias James Courtley [a name ascertained during further enquiries]: 32 years old, 6'1" [185 cm] tall with broad shoulders, large hands, high cheek bones, brown hair, dark whiskers, moustache, nose slightly hooked at the point; shows upper teeth when laughing'. The notices also stated that 'the management of Bowen Downs offered £200 for information leading to the arrest of the culprits'.

Enquiries soon revealed that shortly after Collins had arrived in Adelaide he'd cashed the promissory note with a money dealer and set sail from South Australia aboard the SS *Aldinga* on 20 July 1870, bound for Melbourne.

While Boyd Morehead was following Collins' trail in Adelaide, a party of stockmen led by Bowen Downs' overseer, Edmund Butler, was tracking that of the stock from Bowen Downs to South Australia. They may have had an Aboriginal tracker with them, although even the greenest city slicker could have followed the mass of hoof prints and cowpats extending south past the famous 'dig tree' on Cooper Creek, near which Burke and Wills had perished.

Along the way the men found the 'desert' in a state of breathtaking abundance, brought on by the rains and flooding river systems. Unfortunately, the abundance included a plague of rats that assailed them throughout their journey. However, their hardships were soon rewarded. At a remote outback store on Strzelecki Creek they found Whitey, the prize bull from Bowen Downs. Whitey was in the possession of storekeeper Allan Walke, who produced a bill of sale for it, signed once again by Henry Collins. Walke said he also knew the two men who were with Collins, and named them as George Doudney (or Dewdney) and William Brooke (or Rooke).

The names rang no bells for Butler but 'Henry Collins' meant plenty to one of his men. Stockman John Craigie had connections in Adelaide and had been there on family business in July 1870 when he'd run into an acquaintance from Queensland. His name was Harry Readford and he was one of several notorious central-Queensland small-holders who were a constant source of irritation for the big stations, as they were forever supplementing their herds with straying cattle. However, when Craigie and Harry met, Harry happened to mention that in Adelaide he went by the name Henry Collins. The description of the wanted Henry Collins matched Harry Readford exactly.

Notices for the arrest of Harry Readford were soon issued in Queensland, South Australia and Harry's home state of New South Wales. The possibility that he could be in any one of those states signalled a near-impossible task for police in tracking down a man who was clearly a highly skilled bushman and could be absolutely anywhere in millions of square kilometres of virtually unexplored country. Yet, as it happens, anyone who was in the habit of reading the *New South Wales Police Gazette* didn't need to look any further for the answer to the question of Harry Readford's whereabouts.

Harry, the son of a freed convict born in 1842, had in fact returned to his native New South Wales. In April 1871, having made his fortune, he married his childhood sweetheart, Bessie Skuthorpe. He also bought a pub near Gulgong, which meant that as a licensee he had to be listed in the *Police Gazette*. In a classic case of the left hand not knowing what the right was doing, the notices relating to his publican's license and the warrant for his arrest actually appeared in the same issues. Incredibly no one made the connection.

Months passed, and it wasn't until October 1871 that the law finally caught up with Harry. Even then, it wasn't the result of skilled police work. When it came to crime, it seems Harry just couldn't help himself.

On a tip-off from him, a couple of his mates, Fred Howard and Bill Osborne, had robbed a Mudgee store (near Gulgong) and stolen its safe. When they realised how heavy it was, they'd gone to ask Harry if they could borrow his horse. When they couldn't get the safe open, they'd asked him to help. Eventually the pair made off with £60 in cash and valuables.

Bill Osborne was never seen again but Fred Howard was caught soon after. Unfortunately for Harry, he confessed all.

Harry was arrested on 7 November 1871. He may well have beaten the charges he faced because the only evidence against him was from a man testifying to save himself. Yet a background check on Harry quickly revealed the warrants for his arrest on a much more serious matter. He was arrested again on 13 November and charged with cattle duffing. By the beginning of January 1872 he was on his way to Rockhampton, Queensland, aboard the coastal trader *Queensland*. He left behind his wife, who was nearing full term with their first child. Jemima Readford was born on 20 January 1872.

The sheer scale of Harry's crime, both in the number of cattle duffed and the vast distances of the Australian outback involved, meant that it took months to assemble the case against him. The Bowen Downs men had brought the white bull back from South Australia. Storekeeper Allan Walke was also brought to Queensland and accommodated at Bowen Downs for several months, at the station's expense. One of Harry's accomplices in the initial theft, 34-year-old itinerant labourer James McPherson, was tried, convicted and convinced to provide evidence in the trial.

Other problems presented themselves to the prosecution. One was a lack of proof regarding how many cattle had actually been stolen, since most of the evidence had long since assuaged the appetites of the good folk of Adelaide. Another was the track record of duffing cases at the Roma District Court where Harry was to be tried. Most juries returned verdicts of not guilty and the man who defended most of the cases, Ratcliffe Pring QC, was particularly effective in exposing the deficiencies in prosecution cases.

Even the weather conspired to delay the trial. At one point, the case was about to go ahead when massive floods hit Roma and the surrounding country. It was impossible for many of the lawyers, witnesses, jurors and others to reach the court, and the hearing had to be rescheduled. Finally, however, the case went before Charles William Blakeney, a judge who'd been forced to leave his native Ireland after being financially ruined by a chronic gambling problem. In Queensland, his son, solicitor Charles John Blakeney, had helped his father get back on his feet. As it happened, Blakeney Jnr was instructing Harry's lawyer, George Paul QC. Harry hadn't been able to engage the capable Ratcliffe Pring because, in an effort to counter the abilities he'd demonstrated in demolishing previous duffing cases, he'd been hired for the prosecution.

The trial began at 9 a.m. on 11 February 1872, according to the *Courier-Mail* correspondent whose report is the only surviving firsthand record of proceedings (other accounts suggest it was 10 February). The old Roma courthouse has since burnt down, but it was a wooden building that did little to combat the mid-February ferocious heat, especially as it was filled to capacity with eager spectators.

Plenty more heat was generated from the start of the trial in which 'Henry Readford was indicted that he, in the month of March, 1870, at Bowen Downs Station in the colony, 100 bullocks, 100 cows, 100 heifers, 100 steers, and 1 bull, the property of Messrs Morehead and Young, feloniously did steal, take, and carry away, and in a second count for receiving the same knowing them to be stolen.'

Throughout the morning and into the afternoon the prosecution witnesses built a strong case against Harry Readford. The prosecution even went to the trouble of bringing the Duke of Marlborough (the bull, not the man) to the trial as evidence. He was tethered outside the courthouse.

The prosecution even presented expert forensic evidence. The bill of sale Henry Collins signed for Allan Walke, and Henry Readford's signature on a recognisance of bail were both produced. *The Brisbane Courier* then reported that J.K. Cannan 'was examined as an expert, and gave it as his opinion that the signatures "Henry Readford" to the recognisance and "Henry Collins" to the receipt were written by the same person'.

Allan Walke took the stand and testified that:

He [witness] had no doubt whatever as to the prisoner being the man who sold him the cattle and signed the receipt, as he remained at his [witness'] place for some days afterwards; the bull he then purchased remained in his possession for over three months until delivered to the authorities, having been identified by Messrs Butler and Vernon [a Bowen Downs stockman] and claimed as the property of Messrs Morehead and Young, the owners of Bowen Downs in this colony.

Then the prosecution called James McPherson. The itinerant labourer gave the evidence that he, Readford, John McKenzie (a small landholder who'd previously been acquitted on charges of duffing), Dewdney and Rooke:

Went 25 miles [40 km] up the Thomson River, and there built cattle yards; when the yards were completed, he, with the others, mustered a large number of the Bowen Downs cattle, and filled the yards with them; the cattle were afterwards drafted off in mobs of two or three hundred at a time to Forrester's camp; the white bull outside the Court was amongst the cattle taken at that time, the object being that he would keep the cows and heifers quiet, of which there were a large number in the mob; ultimately the whole of the cattle were driven off by Readford, McKenzie [he probably meant Dewdney], and Brooke [actually Rooke], towards the southern colonies.

Up to this point the prosecution's case was formidable, if not unassailable. The evidence of Walke and McPherson in particular was crucial eye-witness testimony, while the evidence of the expert signature-witness Cannan was also strong. However, it was during George Paul's cross-examination of James McPherson that cracks started to appear. First, *The Brisbane Courier* reported, 'Mr Paul's examination of this witness occasioned some amusement. The witness stated that he was not a cattle stealer, although he might have stolen some, though not to his knowledge.'

Then Paul asked if McPherson had been charged with stealing cattle from Bowen Downs. Yes, he had to admit he had. Were they the cattle he'd just given testimony about? Yes, they were. What was the result of his trial? He'd been discharged on the grounds of insanity and sent to an asylum in Brisbane. Was that where he remained? No. He'd escaped.

James McPherson, star witness for the prosecution, was literally an escaped lunatic. He'd been recaptured at Armidale in New South Wales then brought to Roma to give evidence in Harry's trial. As Paul continued his questioning, the prosecution could only squirm. Was McPherson offered anything if he testified? Yes, 'a promise of a free pardon if he gave fair evidence at the trial; that he was there trusting to the honour of the authorities respecting the free pardon to be granted to him'.

By now evening was falling, but the trial continued into the night.

The prosecution finished presenting its case. Then the defence had its opportunity. Here there was another nasty surprise for the prosecution. George Paul didn't call any witnesses. He didn't even call Harry. Instead, after Ratcliffe Pring made his closing remarks for the prosecution in 'a very lucid and forcible manner', Paul got to his feet and started talking. It's a great loss that his exact words have not survived to this day (the court transcripts are thought to have been destroyed in the 1950s). However, the content was summarised by *The Brisbane Courier* as follows:

> Mr Paul addressed the jury and pointed out the many weak points in the case, and was particular in drawing attention to the evidence of the witness McPherson, who he designated as an approver seeking to escape the penalties of his own crimes, by giving evidence to convict his quondam mate. He argued that the Court should, under the circumstances, direct the jury to dismiss from their minds altogether the evidence given by the lunatic, or pretended lunatic, as being utterly unworthy of credit. He also pointed out the hardships his client had to endure for a period of twelve months since his arrest, during which time he was kept a close prisoner, and absolutely refused bail until an order had to be obtained from the Supreme Court for that purpose. His remarks occupied over an hour, and were listened to with marked attention by the jury.

Among the other weaknesses Paul may have pointed out was the degree of expertise of the 'expert' signature witness. Rather than being a trained forensic specialist, J. K. Cannan was a Roma bank manager. Another of the witnesses, named Birch, who'd testified to Harry's identity, was an alcoholic who police had kept in a stable prior to the trial to keep him sober. Then there was Allan Walke. Paul may not have needed to point out that during his stay at Bowen Downs and Roma he'd earned a reputation as an undesirable. He was described as 'a gentleman loafer' and 'a despicable character'. There was a story going around Roma that he'd suggested the way to deal with the case was to pay him a bribe or do the bull in.

Paul may also have pointed out that even if the case was proven, Harry Readford had done all of western Queensland a great service in opening a new stock route to the markets in Adelaide. The route had revealed vast areas of great potential for grazing (indeed it's now referred to as the Channel Country, some of the finest cattle fattening country anywhere in the world) and given many land holders a shorter journey to the Adelaide market than to Brisbane. Plus, the new market shortened the sea route for cattle being sent to Europe, cutting out the sailing time from Brisbane to Adelaide.

Clues to the content of Paul's address can also be found in the Judge's summing up. Reported *The Brisbane Courier:*

> He trusted that the jury would not be led away by the specious although clever address of the counsel for the prisoner; that they would dismiss from their minds the hardships said to have been endured by the prisoner, no doubt placed before them with a view to making him a martyr . . . He next would submit that, supposing that the jury accepted Mr Paul's recommendation, and gave no credence to McPherson, yet the case was plain against the prisoner.

The jury retired at 9 p.m., but none of the large crowd that had sweated throughout the proceedings for the entire day left the building. No one wanted to miss a thing. An hour later, the jury returned. The court was called to order and the foreman was asked if they had reached a verdict. James Nimmo rose to his feet to speak. An expectant hush fell over the multitude.

'Not guilty,' he said.

According to *The Brisbane Courier*, 'Much surprise was evinced at the verdict, in which the Judge joined.' Blakeney was so disbelieving he asked the foreman to repeat his verdict, in case he'd misheard. When Nimmo confirmed what he'd said, Judge Blakeney was moved to observe, 'Thank God, gentlemen, that verdict is yours, not mine.'

Harry Readford was a free man, and famous as well. He immediately returned to New South Wales, his wife and baby daughter. However, he left a devastated Roma legal system in his wake. Judge Blakeney wrote to the Queensland Attorney General attacking the jurors. The jurors attacked the judge, saying his intimidating manner didn't help their impartiality as they were put in fear of giving offence. Eventually, on 4 April 1873, the government withdrew Roma's criminal jurisdiction for two years. This only enraged Roma's citizens further, and shortly after Judge Blakeney was confronted by an angry mob. As it turned out, state elections were held in 1874 and the jurisdiction was returned early as a certain vote winner.

Harry enjoyed considerable notoriety in the wake of his exploit. He was immortalised in Rolf Boldrewood's epic novel of bushranging, *Robbery Under Arms,* published in 1881. By then, however, he'd done time on another charge of duffing cattle and horses. Ironically, when he went before the court in Toowoomba, in south-east Queensland, it was to find that George Paul had been called to the bench. When Harry was found guilty, Judge Paul gave his former client 18 months hard labour.

Harry eventually went straight, and enjoyed a more honourable connection with another of the outback's biggest stations, when he became the first manager of Brunette Downs, on the Northern Territory's Barkly Tableland (see Chapter 3). While managing another station in the district, he drowned in Brunette's Corella Creek in 1901.

Even before Harry's famous trial, the Queensland government had passed the Brands Act, seeking to regulate the use of brands as a means of curbing the activities of the duffers. Other states had done likewise, or did so soon after. The increasing use of telegraphic communications also meant that checks of cattle sales could quickly ascertain the ownership of stock. All of which meant the duffers had to become much more cunning if they were to succeed.

The route to South Australia pioneered by Readford and his companions Dewdney and Rooke (neither of whom were ever apprehended) was eventually dotted with vast outback stations, and became a preferred route for taking stock from western Queensland to market.

After the case, life returned to normal at Bowen Downs. A run of good seasons and an improving Queensland economy saw it prosper through the 1870s and 1880s. In his biography of his father, *Packhorse and Waterhole*, Gordon Buchanan claimed that it was eventually shearing 400 000 sheep. While that enormous figure may be exaggerated, in 15 October 1888, *The Brisbane Courier* reported the station was shearing 258 000. The station was also said to have been carrying more cattle than any other run in Queensland.

It wasn't to last. In the 1890s the worst recession in Australia's history to that date saw markets fall and many great holdings disintegrate. As it worsened, large numbers of unemployed carrying their meagre possessions wrapped in blankets or swags ranged the country in search of work. At the same time, unions were forming to protect the wages of agricultural workers and restrict the use of non-union labour at cheaper rates. As tensions rose, strikes and confrontations became violent. Shearing sheds and haystacks were burnt down. The steamer *Rodney*, carrying non-union labour up the Darling River, was attacked and burnt.

In 1894, the shearers (numbering between 50 and 75) at Bowen Downs went on strike. Eventually, the shearing was done by non-union shearers, and by members who defied their own union. The following year, the same men were the first shearers chosen to work at Bowen Downs. Unfortunately, someone was waiting for them.

In mid-July 1895, 57 shearers were poisoned, all within three days. An urgent telegram sent from Aramac, the nearest town to the station, reported, 'Strychnine is suspected, and it is believed the poison was put in the "meat and sago puddings eaten by the men". The poisoning only affected those who ate in the shearers' mess.'

A subsequent letter, reported in *The Brisbane Courier*, described the suffering at the station:

Scenes at the shed at Bowen Downs are beyond description, human beings contorting themselves in all shapes and forms in all directions.

A man called 'Thomas' has succumbed. He is unknown; it is thought that his name was an assumed one. Richardson, one of five brothers, reported to be the son of Mr W. Richardson, of the Hit-or-Miss Farm, near Barcaldine, and Christie Schulz, both well-known shearers, are said to be very bad. Sergeant Malone has passed through [Barcaldine] for Bowen Downs. He left Barcaldine at half-past ten this morning. The Aramac and Muttaburra police are already there.

John Henry Thomas had died screaming in agony. Within days, the Queensland government offered a reward of £2000 for information leading to the conviction of his killer. The station's management added a further £500. The station had employed 72 shearers, of whom only 28 were able to continue the shearing. Arsenic was eventually identified in the kitchen's flour and within a sago pudding.

At the end of August, three union shearers were arrested in connection with the poisoning: Robert Langhorn; Michael Maher, alias Baxter, alias M'Mahon, alias Alick Piper; and George William Bristowe, alias Porter. Bristowe was noted as a union activist, especially during the strikes of 1891.

In evidence given before Police Magistrate E. F. Craven in Muttaburra, the Bowen Downs cook, James Gordon, mentioned that 'Baxter', had once called the shearers at Bowen Downs 'a [expletive deleted in source] lot of scabs'. He also gave evidence that on the night of the second poisoning, shortly after serving the sago pudding, Bristowe had said he hadn't eaten any and was glad.

Shearer Charles Henry Egan testified that on the night of the second poisoning Bristowe had come to his tent just before dinner and had delayed him from going to eat the tainted meal. Cross-examined by Bristowe, Egan added, 'I don't remember saying I thought it was a put-up job for us *Rodney* coves.'

It emerged that the poisoning had been foreseen a year earlier. In his evidence, station manager Sydney Fraser produced a letter he'd been sent by the policeman in Aramac on 2 August 1894:

Sir, I wish to inform you that twenty men will leave the union camp here tomorrow and Saturday to shear at Bowen Downs. I am informed that three other men from the camp here will also leave for Bowen Downs, and if taken on there intend to poison the free labourer's food. I am unable to ascertain their names. Some of the twenty state they will leave immediately the three are taken on. Have a sharp look out for them, and inform the police at the shed. – Patrick Ryan, senior-constable

Fraser had taken precautions in 1894, but hadn't thought them necessary in the less volatile 1895. He also described the condition of the men who were poisoned. While Maher claimed to have been poisoned, and produced witnesses who saw him vomiting as violently as the other men, Fraser maintained that he wasn't affected in the same way; other sufferers were pale and sickly with bloodshot eyes.

Maher was subsequently released, while Langhorn and Bristowe were committed for trial. However, the cases don't appear to have proceeded, probably due to the evidence against them being circumstantial, if not speculative. In October 1896, a correspondent to *The Worker* noted that 'Bristow [sic], who stood his trial in connection with the Bowen Downs affair in Queensland, is now shearing for 17s per hundred at Yarralla Station, in N.S.W.'

Although the rainfall at Bowen Downs was more reliable than in many other parts of the outback, the station wasn't spared during the great drought that gripped much of Australia between 1895 and 1904. The desperate times were made worse by the lack of infrastructure. The inadequacy of water storages were soon revealed in an era before stations like Bowen Downs had begun to bore for artesian water, with stock perishing from thirst, and unable to travel stock routes that had long before been eaten bare.

The northern regions of Western Australia, the Northern Territory and Queensland also had to deal with the potentially fatal redwater fever (spread by cattle ticks introduced by buffalo imported from Indonesia in the 1870s), but as the drought eased, Bowen Downs faced another spectre: land resumptions.

In 1904, more than 100 000 hectares were carved from the station as part of one of many government initiatives (dating from the first days of European settlement to the 1980s) across Australia to encourage closer settlement (or raise revenue) by redistributing parts of leases to small holders. In many cases these led to impoverishment of the beneficiaries on what became known as 'starvation blocks', areas of land too small to be viable. Some blocks fell into a state of neglect as those who selected them lacked the capital for developing them. Some were sold at a profit as the selectors opted for a fast buck rather than a life of toil.

The Queensland government's timing in 1904 proved to be ill-judged. Of 25 blocks opened for selection, offers were made for only 11. Rockhampton's *Morning Bulletin* reported:

There was not by any means a rush, as is instanced by the fact that fourteen portions remain unselected. And the country up that way is looking splendid just now, having had a magnificent season. Unlike the times prior to the drought, when it was no uncommon thing to see thirty or more applicants for the one block, there were, on Tuesday last, only two cases where there was more than one applicant.

The drought may have been one reason for the lack of interest. Another reason may have been that the blocks offered were too small to be viable. Evidence for that came 25 years later, when Bowen Downs, described as 'an expired holding', was opened for selection under the Closer Settlement Scheme.

At the time there was considerable criticism of the Land Board's decision to make many blocks available to adjacent landholders first. Yet one Rockhampton businessman, quoted in *The Brisbane Courier*, supported the decision as, 'only reasonable in view of the Land

Administrative Board's fixed view that living areas must be provided. Many of these selectors have been battling along for years in face of terrible drought conditions, and some consideration might be expected for them. On the other hand, opponents of this view hold that all lands of this value and accessibility should be sent to public ballot, where the adjoining selectors would have equal chances with new applicants.'

Debates over resumptions of large holdings have raged throughout Australia's history, and the issue was resolved in a variety of ways, with varying success. The reaction at Bowen Downs was typical of many stations: discussion continued throughout 1929 and into 1930, by which time the Great Depression had begun. Nevertheless, when nine chunks of the Bowen Downs' resumption were opened for selection (ranging in size from 8800 to 17 000 hectares) in May 1930, there were 193 applications. All that remained of Bowen Downs, and continued to operate under that name, was an area of freehold and a block that was secured for stud purposes.

In 2012, the first of the Australia's great outback stations was still in existence, although greatly reduced from the days when it covered a sizable part of central Queensland and was the only station in the area. In 2011, when it was advertised for sale as an aggregation with another block, it measured 449 square kilometres, with a carrying capacity estimated between 5000 and 7500 head of cattle.

The last full-time manager was Ken Ross, who was there from 1998 to 2006. We'd crossed paths in 2011 at the ABC races at Brunette Downs, where he was a guest of the Lake Nash camp, the station for which his son Ed worked, and where his cousin, George Scott, was manager (see Chapter 2).

While almost nothing from the old days of the station remained, and though it was now the size of the house paddock compared to its early days, Ken still regarded the place with great affection. His observations gave tantalising glimpses of how Bowen Downs once was.

'In the old days the station used to have a pub,' he said. 'It was a little town, but it was all timber buildings, so now there's nothing left. There used to be a homestead dating from the 1880s. There are grave sites on Cornish Creek, possibly Chinese, and a sheepwash and steam boiler. There used to be old tram tracks to move meals from the kitchen to the dining room. The laundry is still there, the only historic thing left. The brands for sheep and rams are still there.'

He said the LC5 brand stood not only for Landsborough and Cornish, but for the five partners in the original consortium: Landsborough, Cornish, Buchanan, Walker and Scottish Australian.

The present house and shearing shed date from the 1980s.

Ken tried to renovate the old bore drains that had become choked with vegetation and when he was unsuccessful using modern equipment, he had nothing but admiration for the people who originally dug them in the horse-and-dray days. He eventually resorted to poly pipe and used 75 kilometres of it to replace the original drains.

When Ken was manager, the station was owned by an Englishman, Andy Joyce, who'd had it for 20 years. During that time, it ran 25 000 merino sheep and their progeny, with 21–22 micron bloodlines (a genetic disposition to yield wool of that thickness, a micron being a thousandth of a millimetre). It could also carry 2000 agistment cattle for six or seven months of the year, and it always had green grass in good seasons.

'It's naturally open downs, Mitchell and Flinders grass,' Ken said. 'We had prickly acacia and spent half a million eradicating it. The average rainfall was 18 inches [450 millimetres per annum], but we had bumper years, 30 inches [760 millimetres], for most of my time there. It gets northern rain but it does have dries.'

Like much of Queensland's blacksoil country, a good downfall in summer will see the pastures surge, but it will also bring up herbage if it gets 25 millimetres of rain in winter.

When the station was sold to a central Queensland couple, Ken left to work in the mines. He now lives in Longreach. The station was sold again after only a year to Queensland graziers Evan and Graeme Acton, who needed it for relief from the drought that gripped the Northern Territory and western Queensland up until 2008. They ran it as a beef operation, staffed only by a caretaker. At the time of writing, the iconic property was on the market again.

When I'd asked Ken what he liked about the place, he expressed himself in terms I'd come to hear often on my trip. Indeed, his words tapped into the experience of the outback itself.

'I loved the open spaces,' he said. 'And your time was yours. It wasn't a factor. There was time to get jobs done.'

LNT

2. THE QUIET GIANT

Lake Nash Station

16 936 square kilometres

It's not always easy to grasp the size of Australia's biggest stations. Numbers often reduce the reality to a kind of shorthand. Driving through or flying over a property only shows part of the whole. Every now and then, though, I came to recognise a station's scale in unexpected, often unforgettable, ways.

One of those moments came when I was sitting in an R22 helicopter, hovering above Lake Nash Station. Below was the 150 square kilometres of Blenheim Paddock's sun-browned grass. Pilot Erin Gibson and I were watching the muster of several hundred cattle, which were strung along several kilometres of fence line. Two hundred metres above the ground, we could hear the stockmen talking to each other on their radios: the two at the tail of the mob couldn't see the rider at the head, and they weren't sure what the middle was doing. There were no trees, the paddock was almost completely flat and the stockmen were on horseback, meaning they had unbroken vision over the backs of the cattle for as far as they could see. But they still had to ask Erin to report if the cattle were walking along the fence and not straying. The reason they couldn't see all the way to the front of the mob was because of the curve of the Earth. The lead cattle had disappeared below the horizon. My mind boggled at the thought. Yet Blenheim is nowhere near the largest paddock at Lake Nash.

Sitting on the Territory side of the NT–Queensland border, Lake Nash Station was developed by one of the great pioneers of this part of the country, John Costello. Costello is ranked by some as on a par with Nat Buchanan, yet his name is barely known. The same can be said for the property he built. At 16 936 square kilometres and carrying some 55 000 head, it's one of the biggest in size and capacity in the country, but its present-day owners and managers prefer to keep a relatively low profile. Hardly anyone outside the cattle industry has heard of the place, but throughout its history it has never been known for making a lot of noise.

John Costello was the first to develop Lake Nash but not the first to settle there. In November 1860, 20 years before Costello arrived in the district, John Sutherland took sheep to what would become the Northern Territory–Queensland border and set up Rocklands Station, upon which the town of Camooweal was eventually established.

Six years later, F. E. Nash took up a property to the south, on the Georgina River, called Stony Plains, home to a large waterhole to which Nash gave his name. To the south of Stony Plains, two brothers named Steiglitz squatted and also ran sheep. In many ways the country was ideal for sheep (nutritious grasses and a relatively mild climate meant they multiplied quickly and yielded good, abundant wool), but the high cost of transport, attacks on lambs by dingoes and hawks, and the shortage of water meant all the sheep men struggled. Within a few years of Nash's arrival, the enthusiasm for north-west Queensland as sheep country had faded, and when Queensland was hit by a recession in 1870, many of the remote western pastoralists were sent broke. At one stage the Steiglitz brothers reputedly boiled down 6000 sheep for tallow, the only way they could make any money at all.

By this time, John Costello was already making his mark in central Queensland. He was born in the NSW town of Yass in 1838, his Irish parents having been drawn to Australia by the hope of a brighter future. They first ran a store, then a property, Grabben Gullen, near

Crookwell, where they prospered and young John developed into a highly capable stockman. His sister Mary eventually married a young neighbour, Patsy Durack, whose fame was to be made by his grand-daughter's book *Kings in Grass Castles*. The book's title is based on Durack's prescient comment, 'Cattle Kings ye call us, then we are Kings in grass castles that may be blown away upon a puff of wind.'

In the mid-1860s the Costellos and Duracks pioneered stations around the now-cosmopolitan (by outback standards) Queensland town of Quilpie, establishing Thylungra and Kyabra, 40 kilometres apart on Cooper Creek and its tributaries. These men's achievements came at great cost. Facing drought, remoteness and hostility from the local Indigenous population, they buried children who'd died far from medical help, in 1863 they lost most of their stock and nearly their lives to drought, and sometimes spent night after night barricaded in their homesteads while the people of the Birria language group still haunted their ancestral lands.

However, both John Costello and Patsy Durack searched for land beyond their properties that might be suitable for grazing.

By the 1870s Costello had taken up 44000 square kilometres of land between Quilpie and the Diamantina River. As the Queensland economy improved during this decade, the hunger for land rekindled and soon Costello was selling or giving to friends and relatives parts of the vast tracts he'd taken up. These included Keerongoola on the Cooper, Stoney Point (site of the town of Windorah), Whichello, Morney Plains, Gilppie, Tanbar, Connamara, Mooraberri, Daroo, Mt. Leonard, Clashnamuck, Congabulla, Monkira, Davenport Downs, Milka Lake, Wombenderry, Springfield, Carawilla, Dalton and Tenham. Several are still operating under these names today and form something of a Who's Who of western Queensland stations.

Few would rival Costello in terms of the sheer number of outback stations established. Of course, while this record accords him heroic status for some, others regard this feat as unrivalled in its displacement of the original inhabitants from their traditional lands.

However, Costello and the Duracks were considered moderate
in their treatment of the Indigenous people they encountered
(compared to that of other settlers), both families seeing them as a
potential source of labour. The Costellos and the Duracks eventually hired Indigenous workers, who were intensely loyal and highly
capable in handling stock.

Costello's sales of vast sections of the Queensland outback made
him an extremely wealthy man. In 1877, aged 40, he was able to
sell Kyabra and move to the coast, where he bought a horse stud
and a cattle property, Annandale, near Gladstone. Having led such
an active life, an early retirement was never really an option. Only
two years after moving to the coast, Costello purchased Lake Nash's
lease from Frank Scarr, an explorer, lands commissioner and
surveyor, who had taken over the holding of the area that had long
since been abandoned by the Steiglitz brothers.

Where Scarr's acquisition had been speculative, Costello was
determined to develop. He went on to purchase other leases until his
property covered some 7750 square kilometres, and encompassed
great areas of the Mitchell and Flinders grasslands, gidgee country
and some timbered areas.

Costello started stock from his eastern properties on the road to
Lake Nash, with drays loaded with supplies and equipment, to begin
the work of developing the virtually untouched property. He installed
a manager, Tom Holmes, who began building basic accommodation,
huts and yards.

Developing the property was not without difficulties. Soon after his
breeding herd arrived, packs of dingoes descended 'in great numbers
and as ravenous as wolves', as Costello's son, Michael, subsequently
described it. They attacked newborn calves, of which few survived.

The dingoes were audacious, occasionally even entering the
huts of Costello's men. One night, the station's cook, a man named
Doolan, was woken in his hut by what he thought was an Aboriginal
warrior creeping up to kill him. He grabbed a shovel and lashed out

in the darkness, striking his assailant repeatedly until his colleagues heard his cries and arrived on the scene. In the light of a lantern they found a large dingo in its death throes. The dingo problem was only alleviated when Costello instituted an extensive baiting program. The dingo menace receded, but never completely disappeared.

As Costello developed properties deeper into the Northern Territory, around the Gulf Rivers and the future town of Borroloola, Lake Nash became his outback base. He built a substantial two-storey stone homestead shaded by a wide verandah that was able to withstand the Georgina's regular floods. On at least one occasion the Costellos were forced to retreat to the upper storey and eventually take to boats to reach higher ground.

During the early 1880s, the stock on Lake Nash increased rapidly during a run of good seasons, with up to 7000 calves being branded each year. By 1883 bullocks were travelling down what would become the Birdsville Track to Adelaide. That year cattle from Lake Nash and Headingly Station were achieving £8–9 per head, a couple of months' income for the average farmhand, in the Adelaide market.

The property was situated just inside the tropics and usually received the benefit of a wet season, if not directly then through flows down the Georgina. Costello also built small 'overshot dams' – stone and earth weirs that held extra water supplies. Even in dry seasons, the sheer size of Lake Nash (at the time around 7000 square kilometres) meant it was likely that at least a few passing showers would fall somewhere on the property, providing relief and keeping the stock's water supply up.

As Lake Nash prospered, John Costello could have been forgiven for thinking he had the Midas touch. He had opened huge areas to settlement, changing the face of the outback in the process. From Kyabra to Lake Nash his skills as a consummate bushman and pastoralist had made him a fortune. It may not have occurred to him that there was an element of luck involved, that he may simply have been the right man in the right place for a once-in-a-lifetime opportunity. Unfortunately, in the outback, luck can dry up faster than water from a billabong.

Rather than rest on their laurels, John and his brother-in-law Patsy Durack believed they could repeat their successes in opening up untamed country further afield. John Costello set his sights on the Northern Territory's Gulf region and Central Australia. Durack ranged further still, to the Kimberley in Western Australia.

John took up 5000 square kilometres near the Hart Range, in Central Australia, 500 kilometres from Lake Nash. He took up a further 750-square kilometre lease at Valley of Springs on the Limmen River, 150 kilometres north-west of Borroloola, on the Gulf. For a time he relocated his wife and children there and expanded his holdings to include Lake Ellen, Wickham and Wangalara. According to government reports this was 'despite the wild nature of the country and the fierce opposition of its Aboriginal population'.

It's not hard to comprehend how remote Valley of Springs was in those days because it's still almost as isolated today; it's at least an eight-hour drive to the nearest town with a supermarket. After several years of struggle, Costello withdrew his family from the blighted country, leaving his trusted manager, Jack Farrar, in charge.

It was a disappointing result for John, but worse was to come. In 1891, while Costello was still recovering from the considerable financial losses of his Northern Territory foray, the worst recession in Australia's history up to that time began. Rural regions were hit hard, especially those far from markets and vulnerable to dramatic falls in prices. While others lost everything, Costello managed to survive the difficult years that followed as the economy slowly recovered. However, by 1895, the worst drought in Australian history had taken hold. Over the next eight years, almost the entire country was drought-stricken.

C.E. Gaunt, a stockman at Lake Nash, wrote a vivid, though not entirely accurate, account of his experiences during this time. He described the action as taking place in 1890 (it was almost certainly much later) and named John Costello's son Michael as Martin. In any case, the situation he wrote about was doubtlessly desperate.

'Tragic news came up the river that Marion Downs was wiped out,' Gaunt wrote. 'Herbert Downs also, and the manager of Idamere (now known as Glenormiston) Lamond, wrote Jimmy Tyson, who owned Idamere at that time, asking for instructions.'

Tyson replied, 'Hang on as long as you can. If no rain, save yourselves at the last moment. Ride away and leave 'em.'

When Idamere's waterholes dried up, the station's stockmen left 35 000 head to their fate and, according to Gaunt, they all perished. 'The drought hung like a great funeral shroud over a vast extent of country. Roxburgh and Carandotta, having the only permanent water, held out. Headingly Station, adjoining Lake Nash, lost eighteen thousand head in four days – perished.'

Every day, the heavy clouds of the wet season gathered, the sky darkened and thunder rolled across the parched landscape, but no rain fell. This was a time when the only way to move cattle was by foot, but for most it was far too late for that. Animals died in their thousands. At Lake Nash, with its substantial waterholes, catastrophe unfolded more slowly. As water dried up, the cattle came to the Georgina and gathered around Lake Nash. According to Gaunt, 'The lake assumed the spectacle of a huge burying ground for stock, a mass of liquid mud with hundreds of cattle packed in that oozy slime bogged, dead and dying, with others roaming around the banks bellowing and maddened by thirst.'

At the time, there were roughly 15 000 head on Lake Nash, and it was decided that the station workers should take 4000 of the strongest up 120 kilometres of dry river channels to a water hole on the Ranken River, at Avon Downs Station. Downstream from Lake Nash, the river was completely dry for 180 kilometres.

The next day, young Michael Costello and his men loaded drays with supplies and water from the homestead tanks. They saddled their horses, and then with considerable difficulty, eleven men got the cattle moving away from 'that charnel house and lake of liquid mud'.

It was the height of summer, mid-January, with dry storms and hot winds whipping around them. The cattle seemed to sense they were being taken somewhere better, though it could hardly be worse. They walked along the dry river bed all day and into the night.

Gaunt described their grim progress: 'It seemed as if there was a spirit in the lead that said, "Further still! Further still!" There was no need to put a stockman at the front of the mob as the cattle kept to the river's channels.'

Just after dawn the plodding beasts reached the confluence of the Ranken and Georgina, three-quarters of the way to the Big Hole. Nearby was the Austral Downs homestead, abandoned.

Gaunt said to Michael Costello, 'I'll ride over and see if there's any water in the tank at Austral.' To his great relief there were four tanks, all full. He then went to look inside the homestead.

'When I did I got the shock of my life,' he recalled. 'Inside the room was a big red bull, sitting down, as cattle do, when resting. I slammed the door quickly and waited. Presently, very gingerly, I opened the door inch by inch and peeping in saw no movement. I soon found out the cause. The bull was dead. He must have been wandering around the house, probably smelt the water in the tanks, and possibly the door may have been open and he wandered in and in his dying moments had pushed the door shut.'

Gaunt also found the door to the station store wide open, the store still fully stocked, everything left behind after the inhabitants had decided to leave the station and escape with their lives.

After watering their horses, the Lake Nash crew found the head of the mob was already 5 kilometres up the Ranken, still trudging on. As the heat of the tropical sun beat down, stock at the tail were starting to drop. Yet the main body kept walking, silent but for a low moaning.

In the evening, Gaunt and another stockman, Mick Scanlon, rode 10 kilometres up the river to find the lead. As they did so, they saw cattle all along the mob dropping and dying, but still those that could kept walking. Strong bullocks were in the lead, and dangerous in their thirst-maddened condition.

As night began to fall, one of the bullocks spotted Gaunt and charged him and his horse. His horse was gored and fell. Gaunt was thrown from his saddle. Amid the ensuing chaos, Gaunt had no idea where he was in the mob but managed to make it to a tree. As he climbed up he shouted to Scanlon that he was all right and would spend the night in the safety of the upper branches.

He stayed in the tree all night as agonised, perishing beasts continued to stagger past below. Only when the first light of dawn silhouetted the trees to the east did he leave the safety of his perch. Gaunt quickly found his horse, which had died of its wounds. He took his saddle and continued up the creek on foot, covering 6 kilometres to reach the Big Hole, where the other men had made camp. The scene at the Big Hole was as distressing as that back at Lake Nash. Wrote Gaunt:

Maddened cattle, some blind with thirst, moan[ed] and walk[ed] through the water, being too far gone to drink. Up the bank they went and wandered out on the downs. After the drought broke we found that some of them had wandered six miles [10 kilometres] out from the river before dying. The tail-enders drifted in and these represented the last of the living.

Other cattle were so desperately thirsty that they gorged themselves to death. Some were seen to collapse on the banks of the waterhole with water pouring from their nostrils. When the men counted the cattle that had survived that terrible ordeal, they found that only 500 head were left from the 4000 that had started.

The day had yet another tragedy in store for young Michael Costello. One of his prized horses was disembowelled by a charging bullock as he watched, powerless to do anything. It was too much for the young man. With tears streaming down his face, he went and sat behind a dray, head on his arms, and poured out his grief.

His heart may have been broken by that day's events, but not his spirit. He eventually became the station's manager, and spent, by his own account, up to seven straight years battling severe drought. When the drought broke, he and his men took what remained back to the station and started to rebuild.

By 1903 they were branding 2300 calves annually, while other stations had branded none for several years, having lost bulls and seen those calves that were born soon die.

By the end of the drought, it was clear to those at Lake Nash that feed wasn't usually a problem. Water, however, was another matter. The property's 13 overshot dams and three wells had proved insufficient. After months without rain, the dams had dried up. The wells could only supply enough water for a few head, certainly not enough for tens of thousands.

In 1903 Michael Costello was interviewed by Townsville's *Morning Bulletin* during his first stint away from the property in nearly a decade. He explained how his and other properties were attempting to drill for artesian water.

He cited the optimistic view of a man named Cox, who had written in 1895:

[Queensland's] wealth of underground waters – liquid assets – lying as they do under the greatest part of the colony, are, there is every reason to believe, enormous, and so long as the rain falls will in all probability prove inexhaustible. The assertion that the underground water of Queensland will be of infinitely greater value to the country than all the gold mines that have yet been discovered may startle many who have not studied the subject, yet such is an indubitable fact. The discovery of artesian water has already saved stock to the value of many thousands of pounds, and when the immense water-bearing areas hitherto subject to drought have been tapped by boring, the saving in future years will amount to millions more, and, at the same time, make agricultural pursuits profitable in districts where scantiness of rainfall renders them too precarious to be thought of now.

This analysis was right on the money, as the next century would reveal, but the problem was that artesian water (and sub-artesian water for that matter) wasn't easy or cheap to get at. It still isn't. Each bore cost thousands of pounds to drill and the expense was reputed to have led to the ruin of John Costello. However, the earlier failure of his Gulf venture and the near-decade of drought had already put his finances in a precarious position; Costello's debts were reputedly as high as £200000 (many millions in modern values). He may have been able to struggle on but by 1904 the Queensland National Bank stepped in. Costello ended up walking away with nothing, even losing the family's original 400-hectare property, Grabben Gullen. However, he was able to cash in his life insurance, and after rear-guard legal action, was able to buy back Grabben Gullen.

It had been leased for many years and was suffering from neglect. However, Costello soon had it running properly, before he sold it and bought another property with unrealised potential, Tocabil, near Hilston in western New South Wales, which he expanded and developed until his death on 25 February 1923.

I drove down to Lake Nash from Camooweal, past Austral Downs Station and in places travelling alongside the Georgina and Ranken rivers, the scene of the terrible journey John Costello's son made in the drought-stricken 1890s. A run of good seasons in recent years made it hard to imagine the thirst-maddened cattle, staggering and dying along the route. Either side of road, thigh-high Mitchell grass swayed and bent as the ubiquitous south-easterly wind hissed through it. Flights of galahs and budgerigars rose up from the roadside as pairs of Australian bastards flapped off across the plain. The only landmarks were the occasional turkey nests that broke the horizon.

It was not hard to see why drovers considered the Barkly a paradise. The open grasslands meant cattle could graze at a steady pace and if they did rush there was more than enough room to head them off. In many places it was impossible to lose them because they were silhouetted against the horizon.

The grass was also of such high quality that in a good season stock rapidly put on weight. Interviewed in 1903, Michael Costello pointed out that bullocks from the area could travel long distances without losing condition. Meaning that when they reached the markets on the east coast, they were often sold at the top prices.

While Lake Nash built a reputation for the quality of its stock in those years, it was a different story when it came to the treatment of Indigenous workers. In 1949, the union-owned *Northern Standard* ran an article with the headline 'No Pay – Not Enough Food or Warm Clothing'. The article was based on a letter from North Australian Workers' Union organiser George Gibbs, who had visited the station and maintained that in February that year Indigenous workers had threatened to walk off the job if they weren't paid. The threat predated the famous Wave Hill walk-off by more than 15 years.

Eventually the then-owners, the Queensland National Pastoral Company, agreed to pay their Indigenous workers £4 per month, half in cash and half to be put into a trust account. That amount was still well short of what white workers were paid. There were other grievances. Bore-pumpers complained that they weren't getting enough food. One walked off the job three times to protest the conditions but it was only when all the pumpers downed tools that the food quality improved. Gibbs also found one boundary rider who was living under basic conditions, on his own, 130 kilometres from the station. He sometimes didn't see anyone for up to six weeks at a time.

Gibbs concluded: 'I believe this place made £38 000 profit last year – by the way it is using the natives the profit should be double next year. Protests must be made about the way this station is using the natives – if not all stations on the Barkly will be doing the same.'

A year later, little had changed. *The Northern Standard*, again reporting the investigations of union organiser Gibbs, told of pumpers only getting £1 a week while the equivalent rate for whites was more than £7. The article noted that:

> Years ago Lake Nash was one of the show places of the Territory and about 40 whites were employed. Cattle were then worth from £3 to £4 per head. Today, when prices paid for cattle are terrific, no white labour is employed in the stock camp. All cooking is done by natives on slave rates.

The workforce on Lake Nash was eventually unionised, although the result could hardly be called a victory.

The road I was travelling joined the Sandover Highway, and I passed by the township of Alpurrurulam. The town is often wrongly referred to as 'Lake Nash', and it's where the workers and their families from the nearby stations ended up in the mid-1960s after a period of dramatic social change. In that decade, the push for better wages for Indigenous workers coincided with the demise of droving as trucks took over stock transport. Aerial mustering also reduced the demand for station labour. The result was large-scale unemployment. Unlike the itinerant white workers who moved on to find other jobs, Indigenous workers had nowhere to go. Alpurrurulam is now one of many outback towns where welfare, known as 'sit-down money', is its inhabitants' prime source of revenue.

Not far beyond Alpurrurulam, and an unexpected pothole that woke me right up, I reached the modern homestead of Lake Nash. The property is an amalgamation of three leases – Argadargada, Georgina and Lake Nash – that tally to 16 936 square kilometres, approximately triple the size of the original property. Since the 1960s until just recently it was the second-largest cattle station in the world, after Anna Creek in South Australia. It has only recently been surpassed by Crown Point Station (Chapter 7).

In the 1960s and seventies, the property was owned by the Queensland and Northern Territory Pastoral Company, a subsidiary of King Ranch Australia, which stocked it with Santa Gertrudis cattle, a drought-tolerant breed. In the 1990s it was bought by Stanbroke Pastoral, a subsidiary of Australian insurance company AMP, which was one of the largest landholders in the country.

In 2003 Stanbroke was bought by a consortium that included former Stanbroke director Peter Hughes and former manager Bill Scott, both highly regarded cattlemen, who formed the Georgina Pastoral Company. In 2009 the families decided to disband the partnership, although Bill's son George continued as manager of Lake Nash and as group manager of all the stations in the Georgina portfolio, except Tierawoomba, on the coast near Mackay, where Peter Hughes runs 30 000 Wagyu cattle.

John Costello would hardly recognise Lake Nash Station today. The main homestead, built prior to 1924, was renovated by George Scott and his wife Dianne after they arrived there in 2004. They started by evicting the snakes that had taken to sleeping in a few rooms. The Scotts planted bougainvillea and hibiscus to break the relentless south-easterly wind, and the flowers lend a tropical feel to what were once unbroken grasslands. The modern station is located just above the peak flood level of the Georgina River. Most of the buildings date from the early 1970s, made of tin and fibro with corrugated-iron roofs.

George Scott found me shortly after I arrived. He was in his forties but looked younger, and while he didn't have the enormous build of your typical outback stockman, he was dressed like one: boots, jeans, long-sleeved shirt and work-stained akubra. We shook hands and his grip said 'even if you're a 500-kilogram bullock, you're not going anywhere until I let you'.

We started a tour of the station buildings and I soon realised George didn't walk anywhere, he strode. I struggled to keep up, but refused to break into a trot to match his pace. George's speech was deceptively laconic: behind the drawl there was an energetic and incisive mind that could be put to far more than how to run cattle.

I was pleased to discover that not only was George a fan of John Costello, his knowledge of Lake Nash's history reached back to the Steiglitz brothers as well. He asked if I had any information on where their original homestead might have been. He'd searched for it but had been unable to find any trace of buildings in the area he thought it might be, even when he'd flown over it in his plane.

George had another connection to John Costello. His family owned Thylungra, the station established by John's brother-in-law Patsy Durack, adjacent to his Kyabra in the Channel Country. He also, as it turned out, had his eye on Bowen Downs, which was up for sale at the time. While he was keen to own a slice of outback history, he thought the price was beyond him.

At the end of his tour George directed me to his office while he did a couple of odd jobs; I suspected I'd been slowing him down. In any case he turned up not long after I got there, and gave me a rundown on the station's operations.

Lake Nash sits in the southern Barkly region, with open grass-lands, gidgee timber in the creeks and some flood-out country around Gordon's Creek and the Woodroffe River, on the southern side of the property. The property runs Charbrais (a Charolais-Brahman cross), Ultra blacks that are seven-eighths Angus and one-eighth Brahman, Georgina Gold's, Senepols and Wagyu. There is a bull-breeding unit as well. The property normally carries around 55 000 head, including 30 000 crossbred breeders. In a good run, George estimated the station could carry as many as 90 000 head.

'Weaners (calves old enough to be separated from their mothers) are worked through the Georgina block,' he explained. 'We can basi-cally fatten and breed anywhere but we only breed on the downs country. It has the highest stocking rate, although the best dirt is in the gidgee creeks.'

There are myriad grasses on the property: soft curly Mitchell and Flinders grasses, and smaller annuals. There is also winter herbage. To some eyes, grass is just grass, but not if you've ever tried to feed cattle. Not surprisingly, George sang the praises of the great expanse of Mitchell grass that covered the property.

'Mitchell grass is like a haystack standing on end,' he said. 'It retains nutrient even when it's dry. The only thing that affects it is spoiling rain in winter, which causes it to fall over and rot.'

George's comment about haystacks was one of those passing remarks that can make you look at things in a whole new way. Up until then I'd seen paddocks full of grass. Now I saw hay from horizon to horizon. Hay! Back in the Hunter Valley good-quality hay costs $12 a bale, which I rationed out to my hungry heifers to get them through winter. Here, in a good season, there was more than 55 000 head of cattle could eat.

In a normal season Lake Nash Station runs three stock camps consisting of eight stockmen and women, and a cook. When it is busy there are 25 to 30 staff, plus contractors, all fixing windmills, mustering and building. Most staff are quartered at the station or stock camps.

George kept answering my questions as we got into a vehicle and drove to the airstrip. The station had one aircraft, a Cessna 206, and a chopper, a Robinson R22. At the hangar George refuelled and did his pre-flight checks, then we pushed the Cessna onto the strip.

'This is the best Toyota on the place,' he said, comparing the plane to the standard-issue farm utility vehicle used throughout the outback. 'Last summer it was the only way we could get anywhere. We were cut off from 17 December to 14 April. Nothing else could get in or out while the Georgina was in flood.'

We took off and flew west, over seemingly endless plains of grass/ hay interspersed at regular intervals with turkey's nest dams (round earth dams, usually at windmills or bores, which store water before it is distributed to watering troughs), towards Blenheim Paddock and the 1200 breeders and calves to be mustered the next day. We dipped to check the bores as we went. Keeping water up to cattle is a constant chore on any property but it's also crucial. While cattle can go without feed for a few days, they won't last long without water. So the supply system across the entire property is monitored and any breakdown repaired as soon as possible. In the meantime, staff will do anything to get their stock a drink.

As we flew we talked, in between radio calls to and from staff on the station. George even fielded calls from people needing help with paperwork. Communications were a major part of the station manager's work; at all times George knew the whereabouts of the grader drivers, bore runners and stock camps. To maintain contact the station had four radio repeaters, and all the staff carried radios.

When I asked how far it was from one side of the property to the other, George was stumped. 'I'm actually not sure,' he said. 'I do know you can fly for an hour and still be on it.'

I thought of the cocky who was told by a big landowner that he could ride his horse for a day and still be on his property. The cocky said, 'Yeah, I had a broken-down nag like that once.'

'So how fast is the plane?' I asked.

George gave me an odd look for a moment, then said, 'It'll do 110 knots.'

I figured Lake Nash was roughly 200 kilometres from east to west and 100 kilometres from north to south.

At Blenheim we dropped down to see where the cattle were.

'I'm checking out where to start mustering,' George explained. 'I've got two crews working here tomorrow and I want to make sure they'll be in the right place.'

The cows and calves looked to be in great condition, as did the country. At Lake Nash the grass went as far as the eye could see, and beyond – paradise for cattle. However, without the man-made dams, fed by over a hundred bores and many kilometres of piping, all of it established over the last century, much of the land would be unreachable by thirsty cattle. If they wander too far from water, they'll die. Ideally, they'll stay within 10 kilometres or less of a drink, which restricts how much pasture they can reach.

'There's actually not a lot of surface water on the downs,' George said. 'There's some in the timber country but there are not a lot of places we can trap water. If there was we could carry more cattle in the paddocks.'

As we reconnoitred, George pointed to distant smoke on the horizon. 'Those fires are bothering me,' he said. 'We have to keep an eye on them because grass fires can cost us millions. During the dry season [over the winter months] we have a dedicated grader for firefighting stationed in the middle of the property, ready to respond.

'A dropped match or the slag from a welder can start a fire that can cost a fortune. So we stress to staff that they have to be careful. We still have to manage the fires that nature causes. We fight with back-burns, roads, graders. We also have to educate kids: where to be safe, what to do. The local Aboriginal community is good with fire. We've had a few rows but we're good these days.'

After checking the paddock, we turned south to an area of gidgee ridges. 'This is sweet country down here. I grew up in the Channel Country and this is as good as anything there. I can relate to it.'

George made another radio call: 'Kevin King, can you give the airstrip at Churchill a sweep?'

Moments later the grader driver radioed back: 'Already done, boss.'

I got the impression that the property was run like a well-oiled machine. One with a mind-boggling abundance of grass. George was on the same wavelength: 'This is a magical property. It's really a principality. It goes on forever.'

We dropped down to 30 metres to have a general look around. I asked if he was relieved to see the place like this after the big drought a few years back.

'We can usually manage droughts,' he said. 'Even in droughts there'll be patches that will get a bit of rain, patches that are still workable.' His words were reminiscent of John Costello's experience back in the 1880s.

'In 2008, though, it was a wipe-out. At the climax of the drought, in '07–'08, we only got 9 millimetres all year. It didn't shut us down but it was very close. There was no effective rain after we had spoiling rain in '07. We were stuck in February 2008 and had to start turning cattle off. We could have tried to keep going but we would have had thousands of cattle too poor to go on the trucks. So we trucked out 47 000 head over four months.

'The Mitchell grass will last a few years, and keep its nutrient. While the grass is standing, you've got feed. Spoiling rain can make a dent in it. So you always only eat half what you've got, so you've got plenty in reserve. In '08 we still managed to hold 19 000 breeders, though.'

We passed over Abbadabbada stock camp, beside a waterhole surrounded by trees. George said the crew liked the site for the protection the trees gave: shade in summer, a break to the cold southeast wind in winter. On returning to the station, George circled the Georgina River. Some people from Alpurrurulam were fishing on the river bank. Technically they were trespassing but all George did was dip a wing in acknowledgement.

'I don't mind them fishing there but it's good for them to see that I know what they're up to.'

George executed a smooth landing and quickly taxied over to the hangar. He dropped me back at the homestead, leaving me time to talk to some of his staff before dinner.

I managed to corner the station's gardener, Jack Widgell, although George hadn't given me much hope of getting a lot out of him.

'When I got married, Dianne couldn't tell him what to do,' George had said. 'Now I can't tell him what to do either. You don't often see him, but you see where he's been.'

Despite the cold day Jack was in shorts. His fox terrier, Susie, who rode around on his quad bike with him, wore a pink windbreaker. Jack had worked for George's father as a ringer and stockman, and he came with George when he took up management of Lake Nash. George was wrong about my getting nothing out of Jack. Being an amateur gardener myself, we had a bit in common. So I got 18 words.

'Bougainvillea, messy bloody things,' he said when I complimented him on how good the garden looked. 'They're all right flowers,' he conceded.

'Lots of grass, too,' he said, when I asked if the gardens took a lot of work.

'I've got to move the hoses,' he said, before I asked anything else.

I had more luck over at the workshops where mechanic Reece Walker was changing truck tyres, blowing great clouds of dust out of them before putting on their rims. The 25-year-old was born at Dubbo in New South Wales but grew up in the Armidale area.

'I'm from big farms,' he said, 'but this is my first big property.'

His work mainly involved fixing Toyotas and trucks. Earlier in the day he and George had been aligning the wheels on the station's road train. Reece didn't mind being on a station that was far from the nearest town.

'It's not isolated,' he said. 'We've got a car and can go to Mt Isa.'

As we talked, a wizened bore-runner came in and joined us. Jonesy turned out to be as keen on the history of Lake Nash as George. A piece of history himself, Jonesy was a quintessential bushie with silver beard, weathered face, piercing eyes, battered hat and a head full of stories and knowledge.

The conversation veered off in a range of directions that revealed how the disparate pieces of the outback map were in reality closely linked. Stockman Ed Ross lit up when he learnt that I was including Bowen Downs in my book. Ed's father had managed the station for years and Ed grew up there. It turned out Ed's father had moved to Longreach to work in a mine after Bowen Downs was sold a couple of years ago. Ed was keen to work on a big property and turned to George, his cousin, for help. He'd been at Lake Nash ever since.

Eventually everyone made their way off to clean up before dinner, and I did the same as I was being entertained in the big house. The path from the spacious guest quarters, where I had been rattling around on my own, was pitch-dark but I managed to arrive at the kitchen door without mishap.

George's wife, Dianne, was putting together a salad and feeding their two sons, Daniel (eight) and Sam (four). Dianne, a qualified veterinarian who was involved in the station's breeding work (at very reasonable prices, according to George), professed that she didn't like cooking very much, but that certainly wasn't the fault of the well-equipped kitchen. The Scotts had done a great job with the renovations. The living areas were expansive and tastefully furnished without being overdone, giving an impression of comfort and style that wouldn't look out of place in an interior-design magazine.

After the boys had finished dinner, Dianne ushered them out while George fired up the barbecue to cook some prime station beef. He cracked open a bottle of red. He was distracted because the television program *Four Corners* was about to screen a program on the live-export trade. Among his many responsibilities, he also represented Georgina Pastoral's interests on several industry organisations, which were already going into damage control.

While the steaks were sizzling, I asked how he managed to fit so much in, and spend time with his family.

'That's an issue that we're trying to deal with,' he said, sounding uncertain of his ground for the first time since we'd met. 'I have to admit not always successfully. Often it's family life that suffers in a job like this. Managing all the properties as well doesn't help. I just try to do more. There's no work phone in the house.'

After dinner we sat down to watch the *Four Corners* report. Animals Australia, a rights group, had taken footage of cattle being tortured to death using methods that were supposed to be in compliance with Muslim law but in reality were far from it. *Four Corners* had obtained additional evidence which, while not as shocking, corroborated Animals Australia's footage. Many of the cattle were from stations I had visited or ones on my itinerary.

A curious aspect of the Animals Australia footage was that it was filmed openly, suggesting the organisation had been given access to the abattoirs. The footage also showed Animals Australia representatives making no attempt to prevent the cruelty they purported to abhor.

While the massive backlash was yet to hit the northern cattle industry, the reaction in the lounge room of Lake Nash Station was intense. It may come as a surprise to some, but animal welfare is a high priority on many cattle stations, in part because they want their stock treated humanely but also for sound commercial reasons. Mistreated animals lose condition and therefore value. Happy stock thrive.

At Lake Nash, staff were never allowed to raise a stick to an animal. Talking about the issue that evening, George said he took personal responsibility for any cattle killed on the property, ensuring that the animal was killed properly and humanely.

'I don't think there's anyone who honestly doesn't feel anything when they kill a beast,' he said. 'It's never done lightly.'

Anyone who thinks Generation Y is lazy, spoilt and unmotivated might change their opinion if they got up at 5 a.m. and wandered around the buildings of Lake Nash. The next morning I found men and women in their early twenties changing tyres on vehicles and loading equipment onto utes and trucks before heading out to work for the day. Generation Y was buzzing. There was no yawning, slouching or complaining. There was a quiet intensity as they went about their jobs.

Their manager, George, had been up since 4.30, answering emails, checking markets and talking to the other managers in Georgina

Pastoral Company's portfolio of properties. The impact of the previous night's TV program hadn't changed his routine; it just meant he was doing radio interviews and answering more phone calls than usual. By 5.50, though, he was changing tyres too, and getting the stock camp mobile for the day's mustering.

George had arranged for me to fly with chopper pilot Erin Gibson, who was helping muster Blenheim Paddock. Erin's R22 was parked literally at the back of his house. We couldn't take off until there was enough light, but it still meant fuelling up and doing pre-flight checks while it was dark.

Erin shot one look at my clothing and offered me a heavier jacket, which I took, not being sure I'd need it. The sun was still below the eastern horizon when we got airborne. It took about ten seconds to realise how wise Erin had been to make me bundle up. The R22's bubble did nothing to insulate us from the rotor's wind and, combined with the cold morning air, the chill factor was breathtaking. It was half-past six and I wasn't cheered when Erin, whose job I'd envied up until a few moments earlier, told me it usually warmed up by 10 or 11 a.m. There was some hope of respite because he'd added that if it got busy while he was mustering he would drop me under a tree somewhere until things settled down.

Good luck finding a tree, I thought as we shivered our way to Blenheim. My fingers were barely able to move as I took photographs. The consolation was the view in the early morning light. As the sun rose, the tussocks of Mitchell grass threw long shadows, accentuating their appearance as 'hay bales standing on end'.

When we got out to Blenheim, the ground crews were already in action and Erin got straight to work. We flew down the southern fence, flushing cattle out of a small belt of gidgee and heading them towards two horsemen who were gathering a mob around a waterhole, ready to walk them to the yards on the north side of the paddock.

We then flew down to the western end of Blenheim and flew long sweeps to push the few remaining cattle east. There was no dramatic swooping and diving, the preferred result being cattle walking in the right direction, calm and steady.

Erin was safety-conscious to the point of making me nervous. He did a quick check when he thought the engine was making a strange noise, then mentioned a recent fiery crash in the Hunter Valley, involving the company where he'd once worked, and another in the Gulf Country.

Occasionally a beast refused to cooperate, prompting Erin to call someone on the ground to assist, if they were nearby. The cattle quickly got the message when a horseman appeared.

Eventually the cattle were stretched in long lines across the paddock, walking into the yards. It was here that the curve of the earth blocked the view of the distant cattle.

From the chopper we could see the slowly moving threads of animals, hundreds of cows and calves spread across a plain deeply covered in grass, interspersed with man-made waters. It was a profoundly impressive sight, more so considering Lake Nash was one of nine properties that cover most of the Barkly tableland and carry between them 750000 cattle.

If John Costello or Nat Buchanan was looking down from above, they'd be impressed by what had been achieved over the 130 years since they'd opened up this country.

Shortly after we took off, Erin wondered aloud if George would remember to fly out to pick me up. He needn't have worried. It wasn't long before George came on the radio, asking where I was. He was about to land at the Churchill strip. Erin dropped me back and George and I were soon heading to the station.

The furore over the *Four Corners* program had been immense. Some managers had rung him and said that if that was how Indonesians treated their cattle, they didn't want to send them there.

He'd been fielding questions about the crisis all day and I suspected he didn't want to deal with more. I changed the subject and mentioned that his young staff had made quite an impression on me.

'These blokes can go all day,' he said. 'We used to have Barcoo rot, basically scurvy, because we saw nothing green. They can keep going because they've got the diet. And keep up the pace all through the day. They've got my admiration.'

As he talked, and flew the plane, he tuned the radio to pick up a news broadcast. He'd lost count of how many radio interviews he'd done today. The news opened with the latest developments in the *Four Corners* story.

'I don't suppose you imagined media skills would be part of your job description,' I said.

'It's a long apprenticeship to be a manager,' he replied, 'but big stations are a privilege.'

I'm sure he meant it. 'So where to from here?' I asked.

He laughed: 'A small place. Put my feet up.'

I subsequently read an interview where George ranked Lake Nash among the top-ten cattle stations in the country. He might have been biased but it might have been another example of Lake Nash understatement. For my money, the quiet giant was as good as it gets.

3. HEARTLAND

Brunette Downs Station

12 212 square kilometres

If I could have three wishes, one of them would be to own the Barkly Tableland. I came to this conclusion as I drove my LandCruiser, the trusty Truckasaurus, north on the Tablelands Highway, bound for the first of two great stations on the Barkly. It hadn't taken long for the country to work its magic on me. The land was like African savannah: a mix of gidgee trees and golden grasses that looked like giraffes or elephants should be grazing on it. Beyond the soft, rolling downs, the open grasslands began, and with them my sense of awe. The spaces out this way were immense.

Windmills peeked above the plain, rose up over the landscape as I passed by them on the road, and then in the rearview mirror sank into the endless grass. Anyone searching for Australia's heart might find it here, in the enormous whispering grasslands of the Barkly. They might even hear it softly beating beneath the great emptiness.

There was history here too. At Brunette, my first stop, and Alexandria, the one after, I would be walking in the footsteps of two great outback pioneers, Nat Buchanan and Harry Readford. The Barkly was the scene of both triumph and disappointment for one, and the burial place of the other.

Having been burnt by his partners at Bowen Downs in the 1860s, Nat Buchanan sought to settle newly leased parts of the Northern

The AACo name and its station brands, as shown in Chapters 3 and 9, are trademarks belonging to the Australian Agricultural Company Limited.

Territory and hopefully reap rich rewards, as his friends John
Costello and Patsy Durack had done in western Queensland. On
10 October 1877, Buchanan, 'Greenhide' Sam Croker, and an Aboriginal guide or possibly a man named Tetley, left Rocklands Station on
the Ranken–Georgina watershed and headed west. Before them lay
what they thought to be the well-grassed but poorly watered Barkly,
an unexplored 800-kilometre-wide 'wasteland'. However, the bushmen were undeterred.

After four days the party struck a large creek, which, according to
Croker, they 'named after our leader, Mr Buchanan'. The assumption
that the Barkly was bereft of water was proving wrong. As they went
on they found more creeks and lakes, some thickly surrounded by
lignum and bluebush that made travel slow and difficult. At one large
body of water, Croker wrote of 'wading for two miles [3.2 kilometres]
in water three feet [0.9 metres] deep'.

Buchanan's elation at finding well-watered country in what
was thought to be a desert was short-lived. According to Gordon
Buchanan, 'At a cost of eight shillings for twelve telegraphed words,
he [Nat] learnt that speculators and others sitting in city offices had
applied for country showing blank on the map, and on spec were
lucky enough to secure nearly all the good areas.'

Buchanan appeared to have been taken by surprise at the land rush
on the Barkly, yet the successes of Costello and Durack hadn't been lost
on those who knew of them. They had pioneered country at their leisure,
and then made their fortunes once its viability was established. These
were strokes of luck still very fresh in many minds.

On the Barkly, some leases were traded back and forth, including
the small lease to waterless country that Buchanan did manage
to get. In 1881, the South Australian register reported the sale of
Brunette Downs by the 'MacDermott brothers and Scarr' (probably
the ubiquitous western Queensland explorer and surveyor Frank
Scarr) to Walter Douglas. The area was given as 2000 square miles
(5180 square kilometres) and the sale price was £4000.

By 1883, Brunette was owned by John Macansh, Captain Charles Smith and John McDonald. That same year Harry Readford entered the picture. For all of his colourful history as a cattle duffer, he was still recognised as one of the best stockmen in the business. With John Macansh's son Tom, he drove 3000 cattle from western Queensland to stock Brunette Downs Station for the first time. Readford was appointed the first manager of what would become one of the greatest cattle stations in the world. Within a year, another 2500 cattle were en route to the run, and a further 1200 were brought in from Burketown the year after that.

Stores had to travel great distances to reach the station. They were shipped to Borroloola on the Macarthur River, 400 kilometres to the north, then transported upriver to Cape Crawford, where they were transferred to drays and carted 225 kilometres to Brunette. At other times camels brought loadings from Burketown.

As with many remote outback stations in those days, the spectre of death was never far away. Even so, as I drove the 80 kilometres between Alroy and Brunette Downs on a beautiful winter's day, it was hard to imagine that in 1893 stockman David McDay had perished travelling along the same route.

It was initially reported that David, two 'black boys' (locals aged anywhere between eight and 80) and 14 horses had perished. Searchers had set out from both stations to find them, hindered by a thunderstorm that had erased the missing men's tracks. Nevertheless, the search party found where the three men had taken the saddles from their horses and set them free. With the saddles was a note:

Blue bush, November 8 – My Dear Hutton – I am dying here for want of water. The horses are also dying. If any are recovered please sell them and send the proceeds to my mother with my love. Pay Jerry Connolly £5 out of them. The horses are all done, and there is no chance of escaping from perishing. Write to my sister, Mrs. Higgin. Give her my love for all. Good-bye, old friend. I am off. – DAVID McKAY.

A subsequent report revealed that David would have survived if he'd had enough respect for his companions to let them decide what to do. The Rockhampton *Morning Bulletin* reported that when found, McKay's remains were covered by bushes, earth and a rug. It was surmised that the two men who'd been with him had waited until he died before going off to find water.

While McKay died of thirst on the Barkly, Readford drowned. By 1901 he was the manager of Macarthur River Station, 200 kilometres north of Brunette. That year, while crossing Corella Creek, which lay between the two stations, he was swept to his death.

In 1902, the 'well-known manager of Brunette', J.C. Hutton, described conditions at the station. According to him, there was grass in abundance, but the lack of watering points meant cattle couldn't get to it.

Hutton described the lakes that make Brunette Downs one of the jewels in the Barkly, and an emerald-green jewel at that. According to him:

About half-a-dozen creeks flow into a huge swamp, about 100 miles [160 kilometres] in circumference. It is a very shallow area of water, and the wind, as it changes, blows the water in different directions over the surrounding country. As the water leaves the swamp in one part the country becomes covered with wild clover and crowsfoot. The wind continually irrigates the country until the water absolutely dries up. The country remains green for fifteen months after a flood without any further rainfall . . . The last flood occurred in March, 1901, and, though there is but little water in the swamp at the present time, there having been no rain since the date named, the country remains green. As a result of this natural irrigation, the cattle are living on the flood waters of last year.

Hutton conceded that the station had experienced dry runs for up to two-and-a-half years, and in 1892 and '93 the station had been forced to de-stock.

In 1904, the property was bought by brothers James Cobb White and Francis John White, from the Hunter Valley in New South Wales. J.C. had held separate leases in the Barkly area since 1878, while the White family had extensive pastoral interests in the Hunter that included two of the finest estates in the region. J.C. was a strong advocate of Shorthorn cattle and founder of the Aberdeen-Angus Herd Book Society. The Whites were also uncles of author Patrick White, and it was the family's beef-generated wealth that would provide the financial basis for Patrick's becoming Australia's first (and to date only) Nobel laureate for literature.

Station life, meanwhile, continued to take a toll on staff. A new manager at the station, a man named Kelly, had not long taken over before he died in a freak accident. He was cutting out some stock (separating selected cattle from the herd) when the horse he was riding fell over a blind calf. His grave is in the small cemetery near the present-day station homestead.

In 1912, the Whites went into partnership with northern cattleman A.J. Cotton, and together they invested heavily in improvements to the property and in the Shorthorn herd. Cotton also convinced the Whites to experiment with running sheep.

In the early years of Brunette Downs, there were references to mistreatment of the area's former owners, though not necessarily at the station. The policeman at Camooweal had accused some nearby stations, without naming any in particular, of mistreating Indigenous people and misappropriating their government handouts. Station managers, including Brunette's Hutton, had been incensed by the claims, which damaged the reputation of every station in the region, not just the culprits.

In 1926 a number of newspapers around Australia carried the report of a special correspondent who visited the Northern Territory and gave a firsthand account (albeit tarnished by prejudice) of conditions on Brunette Downs:

Huddled together in gunyahs and shacks in the country, just beyond the stockyard, the dependants of the station Aborigines appear to lead a care-free existence. They seem to be an appallingly primitive people, judged by their inability to make themselves even moderately comfortable. Breakwinds of gidyea [an alternative spelling of gidgee] are often inadequate, and they repose of filthy rags in filthy surroundings. An old man, 'plenty sick', coughing violently, yet clad only in an ancient sun helmet and a pair of bathing trunks, was a pathetic rather than a comic figure, and a toothless, blind old hag must have been endowed with extraordinary vitality to continue to live under such conditions. Piccaninnies were numerous. Mentally all the Aborigines seemed to be children. Station men, however, agree that a fair proportion of the 'boys' make efficient stockmen. Under the present depressed conditions of the cattle industry it is doubtful whether their services could be dispensed with.

The conditions described were in stark contrast to the White family's opulent estates in the Hunter Valley. The country's difficult economic circumstances – and there was far worse to come with the Great Depression looming – didn't stop the Whites buying out Alfred Cotton's share in Brunette in 1928. The family continued to invest heavily in the property, building yards and fencing, and putting in bores as quickly as money allowed.

While many of the large properties of northern Australia were seldom, if ever, visited by their owners, members of the White family visited Brunette Downs annually. While the Queensland and Northern Territory Aerial Service (QANTAS) was establishing services in the outback in the 1920s, the Whites preferred to drive. The journey of 4000 kilometres took more than a month, whereas for me, also based in the Hunter Valley, the round trip took under six days.

As properties like Brunette Downs successfully drilled for water and laid the piping that would carry it long distances, the threat of drought receded. Another advantage was that stock could be spread over a greater area, making more feed available and meaning it lasted longer. The improved infrastructure also allowed for higher stocking rates. In something of a chicken-and-egg scenario, increased stock numbers then helped pay for more infrastructure improvements. The only catch was that in the case of severe drought, there would be a lot more to lose.

In 1952, Brunette Downs got caught. As feed either withered away or was eaten, tens of thousands of beasts faced starvation. The situation grew steadily worse, and as the wet season failed, the animals were trapped: the stock routes away from the station were already eaten out. The feed on the station was fast disappearing.

In late March, Brunette got a lucky break. A small local storm broke on the property, bringing up enough feed to give the station a small window of opportunity. The Whites decided that as soon as their weaners had put on enough condition to start walking, they'd move them out.

It was such a large-scale gamble that it was reported by capital-city newspapers, with headlines like 'Desperate Cattle in Drought Trek'. In May 1952, two mobs, each comprising 1500 Shorthorn weaners, started towards Queensland, bound for the railhead at Dajarra, 600 kilometres away. From there, they were to be taken by train to properties beyond the drought-affected region. They would be followed shortly after by three more mobs numbering 5000 in total.

Company manager J.S. White explained that moving the weaners was a risk they had to take: 'Saving the weaners is urgent enough, but we must get them out to save the breeders at all costs. If the breeders go, we are lost. They are absolutely irreplaceable.'

To improve the weaners' chances, they were droved in easy stages of 15 kilometres a day. When the drovers found anything that remotely resembled feed, they stopped for a day to give the weaners sustenance. Trucks carried 200 tonnes of hay out to the stock routes to further supplement the available feed.

In the end, most of the weaners made it through. The first two mobs ended up on agistment at Jundah, on the upper Diamantina, 1500 kilometres from Brunette. Five months later, the other three mobs reached the Whites' properties at Muswellbrook. They had walked 700 kilometres to Mt Isa, then travelled 2700 kilometres south by train.

The courage, commitment and considerable financial muscle the Whites showed in saving their stock were matched the following year when they initiated a bull sale at Brunette Downs, the like of which has never been repeated. The Shorthorn Society and studs in Queensland and New South Wales provided the bulls, then took the extraordinary step of chartering an aircraft and flying them to Brunette to ensure they would be in 'show condition' when auctioned.

Unsurprisingly, the cost of flying bulls to the outback was far greater than the prices they attracted at the sale. Some sources suggest the exercise was a financial disaster but the sale was considered a success at the time. The price paid for each of the 31 bulls averaged £200 and ranged from £50 to £400. Even a distant Victorian regional paper, *The Benalla Ensign*, covered the event, reporting that the top price was paid for 'Woomargama Quick March, a son of the renowned Coonong Napoleon'. The buyer was Brunette Downs.

The sale was timed to coincide with the renowned ABC races. Inaugurated in 1911, the races brought together people from all the Barkly stations and were considered the social event of the year. Purchasers came from the Barkly and as far away as Alice Springs. The *Centralian Advocate* subsequently reported, 'Although it is understood that many of the prices paid were under the real value of the bulls considering the expense of getting them to the NT, the studs concerned did not view the sale as a commercial proposition. It was held as a means of introducing high-quality bulls to remote places.'

Flying the bulls to Brunette was the less significant of two unique aspects of the sale. At the time, outback stations made do with whatever bulls were available. This was one of the first opportunities they had to access stud bulls that would improve overall herd quality.

Improving herd quality (fertility, rate of growth and other factors) by bringing in stud bulls is now standard practice for outback stations. Breeding programs on some of the big stations now lead the world.

With the benefit of hindsight, it's clear the purchase of stud Shorthorn bulls was a waste of money for some stations, including Brunette Downs, because in 1958, after owning the station for more than half a century, the Whites sold it to the American millionaire Robert J. Kleberg's King Ranch Pastoral Company. Among the many improvements the new owners made was to introduce the Santa Gertrudis breed (a Brahman–Shorthorn cross) that had been established on the company's flagship Texan property, the 3000-square-kilometre King Ranch.

Within five years after its purchase of Brunette Downs, the company had reputedly spent twice the amount it originally paid (the equivalent of around $25 million in present values) on new buildings, 5000 kilometres of roads, 100 airstrips and 56 bores.

King Ranch claimed its expenditure significantly reduced stock losses. Around 25 000 head were lost to drought on the property the year King Ranch bought it. Within a few years, they had reduced the losses to almost none, albeit in better seasons.

By 1978, the station was valued at $50–60 million (in present values). Much had changed in the years since King Ranch had acquired the property. Modernisation on a large scale had transformed operations in the outback. Stock were mustered using planes, helicopters, motorbikes and horses. Stock were no longer walked to market; road trains rapidly moved beasts to meatworks or fattening properties, with the short journey time ensuring they arrived in good condition.

The only fly in the ointment was the price of beef. In 1973, producers were getting about 50 cents a kilo. Between 1974 and 1978 they were getting between 10 and 30 cents. In 1979, King Ranch threw in the towel and sold to the Australian Agricultural Company (AACo), which still owns the property in 2012. In the year of the sale the price rocketed to over a dollar a kilo.

AACo is Australia's oldest continuously operating company. Backed by the cream of British politicians and financiers, it was established in 1824 at the Port Stephens area of New South Wales with a grant of 400000 hectares [a million acres]. However, the AACo found the area unsuitable for agriculture, and obtained further grants in the Hunter Valley and Tamworth districts, where it concentrated on raising sheep. The company's sheep operations have gradually given way to cattle, and it is now Australia's largest beef producer, with just under 500000 head on 24 properties spread from the Victoria River district in the Northern Territory to Toowoomba in Queensland. The properties extend over 7.2 million hectares, 1.1 per cent of Australia's landmass.

I had timed my arrival at Brunette to coincide with the annual ABC races. The 'ABC' originally stood for Alexandria, Austral, Avon, Anthony's Lagoon, Brunette and Cresswell Downs (which is now part of Walhallow Station), but since the event started in 1911, several other stations have come to attend as well. The races, for me, were a mixed blessing.

Being the major social event on the Barkly calendar, everyone who was anyone was there. On the downside, they were so busy catching up with each other that the needs of a writer no one had heard of were prioritised accordingly. And while I was expected by Henry and Bernadette Burke, the manager of Brunette and his wife, first I had to find them in the substantial crowd.

The ABC races themselves, however, were worth seeing. The racecourse sits on a parcel of land purchased from Brunette Downs in 1951. On the day I turned up, all the Barkly stations (Anthony's Lagoon, Eva Downs, Lake Nash, Mittiebah, Soudan, Avon, Austral Downs, Alexandria, Helen Springs, Brunchilly and Walhallow) had occupied their permanent 'camps' at the course. The camp facilities ranged from rough and ready to rough and comprehensive, with kitchens, water tanks, toilet and shower blocks, stockyards and windbreaks. The latter were necessary as the races were held in mid-June, when winter's south-easterly was at its laziest, going through you, rather than around.

On the flats next to the course, hundreds of RVs, caravans and campers were lined up in neat rows. The racing was in true amateur style, with local riders rather than professional jockeys. The fields were small, with less than a handful of mounts, and while some horses had pedigree as racehorses, many were station stockhorses with a bit of pace.

When the horses weren't going round, novelty races were run, and jackaroos and jillaroos competing in events were auctioned to the crowd, raising money for charity. Rodeos and the ever-popular campdrafting were also on the program, and there was a dinner and an art exhibition.

As it happened, several members of the AACo board were attending the races this year. I wondered if their collective presence might have less to do with punting on the passing horseflesh and more with the federal primary industry minister's decision to suspend Australia's $350 million worth of live cattle exports to Indonesia. For northern Australian cattle stations, everyone involved in supporting their operations, and Australia's international reputation as a reliable beef supplier, the consequences were almost unimaginable.

It wasn't hard to find Henry Burke, manager of Brunette Downs and AACo's northern stations. I asked a passerby who told me to look for a big bloke in a big hat. I thought he had to be kidding as I approached a throng of men who could all be described in similar terms.

Nevertheless, I went up to the bloke with the biggest hat, introduced myself and asked if he was Henry. Sure enough, it was he. While he was middle-aged, he still had the physique of a pretty handy prop if the Australian rugby team ever tapped him on his broad shoulder. He had the hands and handshake of a man who still included hard physical labour among his functions as a company executive with responsibility for investments running into the hundreds of millions.

Henry explained that he was flying out to Canberra the following morning to lobby for the survival of the northern Australian cattle industry (and the easily erased notions of free enterprise and trade). He promised me a few minutes of his time before he left. I couldn't escape the irony that I'd driven 2000 kilometres for a brief interview when I could have whipped down to the national capital in an afternoon and got all the time I wanted.

Over by the main hall I found Henry's wife, Bernadette. I already knew her reputation as a tireless contributor to life on the Barkly but by that point, after a long day of socialising, I suspected I was the last thing she needed.

Bernadette apologised for not having a bed for me – the station was packed with visitors for the races – but I explained that all I needed was a place to roll out my swag. She directed me to an area back at the station, which she called 'the Brunette Downs caravan park'. It was usually a grassy expanse, but when I got there I saw Bernadette's description wasn't far from the truth. Family and friends of station staff were camped all over the lawn.

I spread my groundsheet, rolled out my swag among the giant RVs and caravans, endured the pitying looks of the more luxuriously accommodated and consoled myself with size of my carbon footprint compared to theirs.

Most homestead complexes on big stations are like small towns. At Brunette, the town isn't all that small. There are a couple of dozen houses, an office 'precinct', restaurant and entertainment area, and an industrial zone. While each AACo station operates independently, some resources are shared, and Brunette is part of a conglomeration of three stations that includes Anthony's Lagoon and Eva Downs and together covers 21 000 square kilometres. The three were the driving force for the company's operations across the outback.

Most of the buildings date from the King Ranch days of the early 1960s, although the main homestead was built by the Whites in the 1920s. The grounds surrounding the main house are a monument to the determined efforts of Bernadette and gardener Peter Mann, with lush tropical plants flourishing beneath enormous fig trees.

Early the next morning, Henry made good on his promise before he flew to Canberra. We both tried to ignore the sound of the company plane warming up on the airstrip just beyond the garden, where we settled down to business. Henry started by giving me a rundown on the property.

Brunette is the largest single perpetual lease in the Northern Territory, covering 12 212 square kilometres. This comprises those breathtaking golden-grassed downs I drove past, but there are also small areas of timber and, of course, the lakes – Sylvester, Corella and de Burgh – which when full can cover up to 25 per cent of the station, a watery expanse of nearly 3000 square kilometres. The lakes provide some of the finest fattening country on the Barkly and allow the station to carry more than 70 000 head of cattle in good seasons.

The station operates four distinct businesses: bull breeding, a commercial herd (cows producing calves), a trading herd (fattening and selling the station's and bought-in weaners), and a new Wagyu-breeding unit. Brunette also tends to be the proving ground for new ideas, due to its sheer size and central position.

'It allows us to put a lot of systems in place then take them out across the business,' Henry explained. 'We can do it here, we can understand how it works and where it goes, and we can then apply that out through all our northern properties.'

Stock from Brunette are supplied to the company's feedlots near Brisbane, or meatworks at Rockhampton or Brisbane. Almost every Australian who eats beef has at some time dined on a beast raised on the Barkly Tableland. And not just Australians. Stock are also part of the live-export market out of Darwin. Where once the Barkly was remote and cattle had to endure long marches to south-eastern markets, Barkly stations now have a range of choices.

'We're centrally located for that sort of stuff,' Henry said. 'We can either go to Adelaide, Brisbane, Townsville, to wherever the opportunity is. Live export is good for us because it's the closest. And it's a good early growth weight for weaners. You get 'em in as a weaner and you turn 'em off as 350 kilos into the Indo job. And the freight is only 1100 kilometres to Darwin against double that wherever else you go.'

Work on the property is restricted to an eight-month window. Around March the heat of summer starts to ease and the wet season draws to a close, allowing staff to start moving around the property again. By the end of October it is too hot to handle stock and by late December the first big storms break over the blacksoil plains, making it impossible for vehicles to move.

Just how much rain falls during the wet and at other times determines the stations' stocking rate during the dry. The calculations are remarkably sophisticated, particularly compared to the hit-and-miss methods of times past. Henry and the company's rangeland officer, Suzie Kearins, calculate how much grass the station has based on the amount of rainfall, when the rain falls and how much grass it brings up at a number of sites across the property. Each year, they arrive at a budget of useable kilograms of pasture per hectare, which tells them how many cattle they can carry to achieve the best result.

Not that the environment doesn't throw the odd spanner into the works. Issues that could affect the stocking rate throughout the year include fire or out-of-season rain that leeches protein from the pasture. While it still has the bulk, its quality as feed falls.

'The wet season will affect operations in terms of timing,' Henry said, 'when the wet season finishes that's when you can start mustering. But in northern Australia you also have a green window that you have to work in, which is the high-protein end. So you try and get your lactating cows mustered, get the calves off 'em, get them back, so when the dry, or the lower-protein part of the season takes over, your cattle aren't lactating. They're only maintaining their own body.'

The station doesn't completely shut down over the wet. From a regular staff of around 50, it reduces to 20, who still have plenty to do: maintaining equipment, overhauling gear in preparation for the next season, and making sure that stock across the property still have water. If necessary, staff are choppered to bores to repair them.

According to Henry, many of his staff like coming to Brunette for eight or nine months then going off to do something else for three or four months. I suspected avoiding the stifling heat and humidity of the northern wet would be uppermost in many minds.

In some years, though, the wet fails to materialise. I already knew about the several severe droughts in Brunette's 130-year history, and their colossal stock losses. However, the science behind big station operations in modern times means such disasters are largely a thing of the past.

'You can manage your droughts by knowing how many kilograms of grass you've got and matching that to your stock rate,' Henry explained, 'So you shouldn't wake up and get that "oh, shit" feeling, "I'm dry, got no grass". If you're having a series of dry years coming down, so this year is a little bit drier than last year, you'll match your stocking rate to that. I've got to lessen my herd by this number because I've only got this much. And then you get another dry year. You might start off running only one head to 20 hectares, and as the season is drying down you might be running one to 50 hectares. That sort of thing. So I've got to change my cattle numbers to suit.'

That said, the most recent drought, which culminated in 2007–08, tested all the stations in Australia's north. It was considered a one-in-50-year event.

'There's normally quite reliable rainfall up here,' Henry said, 'but we basically just got no wet in 2007–08. Within a four-month period, we had to move large numbers of cattle because it just didn't rain and the three years before were dry years also.'

Since then, the seasons have been sensationally good, from the north all the way down into South Australia.

Henry was clearly proud of his station's reputation as an employer. While AACo ran ads in rural newspapers and magazines, many of Brunette's staff come as a result of referrals from past staff. Many only come for 12 months but Henry said he believed that if they went back and talked about having a good experience, some of their friends always end up wanting to come too. Many use the experience as a gap year, before going on to higher education, and Henry is fine with that.

'There seems to be a lot more girls putting their hands up at the moment than boys,' he said. 'I think it's just working with the animals. Horses and cattle and that sort of stuff appeals to them. It's a self-test for some young people as well. They learn a lot of skills, there's a huge number of skills in being a competent cattle-stock person. If you take all those things into consideration, with machinery and vehicles and fencing and plants and animal husbandry and everything to go with it, there's a lot of skill.'

The days of large-scale employment of Indigenous people ended, as it did on most outback stations, with the mechanisation of the industry in the 1960s and the concurrent campaign for equal pay that conversely accelerated their unemployment.

In the 1990s, land from the station was set aside for a community at Corella Creek. Henry explained that while the native title process continued across Australia, the issue of ownership and tenure of Brunette Downs had been settled. The station still employed people from the community.

Henry was another manager impressed by the work ethic of Generation Y, who formed the bulk of his workforce.

'They have a go,' he said, 'particularly the type of people we get out here. I think they're getting more skilled. There's more knowledge.

You can jump on the Internet if you want to Google something and say, "Well, how does this work?"'

Of course, that means Internet access has to be available, along with opportunities to socialise, both face to face and on virtual social networks. When it came to what motivated people to work at Brunette, Henry admitted he didn't have all the answers. He gave me the names of two of his young staff who I could ask and explained: 'They're very highly educated people and you wonder what they're doing here. It would be interesting to hear what they say.'

He was also keen to learn why some of his other staff are still around.

'Find out what makes them stay here,' he suggested. 'Some of those guys have been here five or six years.'

After Henry posed for a couple of pictures with Bernadette, then headed for his plane, I took his advice. Jackaroo Jack Henry was over at the racecourse, one of a group of jackaroos and jillaroos burning off rubbish at the tip. I realised I'd seen Jack the day before, at the races, but almost didn't recognise him with his shirt on. He'd entered one of the novelty events and had been asked to remove his top while he was auctioned to a high-bidding group of women. He went for a handsome price in the end.

Jack was every bit as surprising as Henry had suggested. He was raised on a cattle and cropping property near Warwick in south-east Queensland. He then did a Bachelor of Commerce and Business Management in agribusiness only to find he wasn't ready to start a career in accounting. While I did a double-take, he explained further. He went to Canada and worked on a couple of ranches, backpacked around Europe, then came back to Australia when he was 24. He was still not ready to get behind a desk and wanted to work on one of the iconic properties: Brunette, Newcastle Waters or Victoria River Downs. He applied for jobs on all three. A friend whose father worked at AACo knew Henry and got him a start at Brunette.

'I love it here,' he said. 'I'm a first-year jackaroo in the bullock camp out on the lakes. There are five jacks and head stockman Chris

Keane, and we're often camping out and roughing it. ⁷
couldn't get the trailers out there so it was akin to the 19...
1960s-style stock camps. The old fellas reckon we were doing it old
style, which they hadn't seen for many years. We all really embraced
it. We swam in turkey's nest dams, cooked on fires.

'I thought I knew cattle but large mobs move differently, act differently. I had to relearn mustering. Dad and I could muster a mob back
home, but here it takes six or seven plus a chopper, communicating
by radio.'

In Jack's stock camp, most of the crew had only two years'
experience or less. However, he reckoned the head stockmen were
great trainers. He had also found that being so far from help made
him prepare better in case things went wrong; and this made him
more self-reliant.

'You'll get your orders in the morning,' he said, 'and you'll have
to remember them all day, because the boss might be 30 kilometres
away. You have to know when you're understanding and not understanding. And you can't say you can't do it, because you have to do it.'

Then there are the experiences you won't get anywhere else.

'You do get these "pinch yourself" moments. Like when I was on a
bike pushing cattle off a bore with a plane bombing them and coming
in only two or three metres above. You're riding flat-chat, you can't
see anything because of the dust churned up by 1000 head, then
there's the drama when the Cessna bursts through the dust, going
flat-chat, then it's gone.

'And the first time you throw and tie a beast and see you're able to
do it. There are moments like that.'

I was ready to sign up. However, Jack still wasn't sure about his
future.

'I'm at a bit of a crossroads,' he said. 'I've applied for a bank job,
with a six-month application process. That's been successful and I've
been asked to start. However, Henry has been talking to me about
having a future with AACo. So I'm still 50-50 as to which way I'll go.'

'If you had to choose today,' I asked, 'would you rather sit behind a desk or sit behind a mob of cattle?'

He said that he'd take the cattle in a heartbeat, but he still had to think about the long term. Whatever he chose, he'd certainly made an impression. Later, back at the homestead, Bernadette asked if I'd caught up with Jack. 'I've met the future prime minister,' I replied. She laughed and said, 'I know what you mean.'

I left Jack to burn rubbish and mooched over to jillaroo Annabel Guthrie, a fresh-faced sun-burnished young woman of about Jack's age. She was nothing like Jack, having been raised on a sheep and cropping property, rather than a cattle and cropping property, at Donald in Victoria. And her four-year degree was in exercise science and rehab, rather than commerce. I did another double-take. I wasn't expecting such seriously well-educated people to get down and dirty with livestock. After uni in Melbourne, she'd wanted a break from city life and applied for jobs around the country, including Brunette.

'I wanted to go to Kununurra but Dad's best mate breeds cattle for AA and knows Henry and Bernadette. I applied and got the job within a month. I found out I'd got it two days before Christmas. I started in the last week of February as a jillaroo. I'm in the com-mercial stock camp. There's a head stockman, two jillaroos and five jacks. We muster on horse or bike, depending on how rough the country is. We'll do yard work for two days with weaners, branding calves. You get to do everything, even preg-testing. Then there's a day or two trucking. Then we do it all again.'

She found the work challenging and at times frustrating. Not coming from a cattle background meant she sometimes struggled with knowing what to do. However, the job had plenty of satisfaction.

'It's a good feeling when you finish a big day's walk. You see the bore and the cattle arriving. After a big day you sit around the camp-fire and talk about being rolled by a cow or whatever. Half the days you can be hating your life, doubting yourself, but you get there. You get a sense of achievement, say, walking a mob 22 kilometres.'

While the company is an equal-opportunity employer, there is no discrimination when it comes to work.

'We do exactly the same as the boys,' Annabel said. 'In the yards you do the same. Mechanically, I'm probably not as good but I can do more with horses.'

One of things she enjoyed most about working at Brunette was the social life.

'You make a lot of friendships in the stock camp,' she said. 'I'm very lucky we're a good group, close as friends. The people are down to earth, connected. Henry's funny. He's hardly ever around but he's great with names and faces. Always good for a laugh. Bern is just so good, especially with us girls. She's a second mum. You can go to her with any problem, but she can be very direct.'

After four months at Brunette, Annabel was keen to do another year in the Territory. She also wanted to do more study, either in teaching or agriculture. One thing was certain, it wouldn't be at a city university.

'I've got no desire to go to the big smoke,' she said. 'It'll be a rural uni and a rural job.'

Back at the homestead, the workshops were a hive of activity. Vehicles were being serviced, equipment was being pulled apart. Any sense of order wasn't immediately apparent, especially to someone as mechanically challenged as me. However, there were two distinct groups, the bore mechanics and the general mechanics.

The head bore mechanic was 36-year-old B.J. Vankuyk, one of the guys who had been at Brunette for some years.

'I came for six months in 2003 and stayed,' he told me after I'd begged a few minutes of his time. He was wearing an oil-smudged sleeveless shirt and was fixing a piece of unidentifiable equipment that certainly looked broken, being in several pieces. B.J. was raised in

Wee Waa, in central New South Wales. He had a job there as a fitter but was tired of working in sheds. He worked at El Questro, in Western Australia, for three months, before moving on to Brunette.

I avoided any observations about the fact that, as we spoke, he was working in a shed. He explained that the station had 180 bores, which were spaced on average 10 kilometres apart. The goal was to increase the bores until they averaged 6 kilometres apart, giving a grazing radius around waters of only 3 kilometres.

Bore maintenance is one of the most important jobs on the station, and it never ends. B. J. had four bore runners working for him, six days a week, doing three bore runs (trips around parts of the station checking that bores are operating) of 200 to 300 kilometres each.

'The Toyotas [the station's workhorse utilities] take a beating, especially just after the wet season when the graders haven't been everywhere,' B. J. said. 'They're serviced every 5000 kilometres, which means every three weeks here.'

The maintenance schedule might be lighter if the boring equipment was more modern and reliable. However, the cost of upgrading equipment on the scale of a property like Brunette would be immense. So B. J. often found himself dealing with equipment that was well past retirement age. At the time we spoke, B. J.'s problems were compounded by the fact he was down to only three mechanics, which meant he had to prioritise what needed to be fixed. He turned to the job board.

'We've got nine problems at the moment,' he said. 'There's always a problem somewhere. We aim to do preventative maintenance. We could do it with the staff, men and gear, but things are always going to shit. You have a plan, then one radio call comes in and it all goes out the window. Things just go wrong. Since I've been here, I've had stuff-all cattle perish. You just do what it takes to get 'em a drink, even if you're there, still going at ten o'clock at night.

'I've got a good crew, reliable, a mix of personalities, but they get the job done. It's a constant battle getting staff – qualified staff – especially bore mechanics.'

I ventured a question on what it was that made him stay.

'These are good people to work for,' he said without hesitation. 'It's a great lifestyle. It's surprising how social it is. I think because there are so few people, and it's so far from anywhere, everyone tries harder.'

At the far end of the workshop, alongside B.J.'s bore pumps, head mechanic Dave Shearer was attempting to jump start an ancient ute, which would have made a good museum piece.

'It's just the vehicle for use around the homestead,' Dave explained, a rollie stuck between his lips never in danger of falling out. 'The butcher ute, it doesn't really go anywhere. It might be the alternator. It might not.'

Dave originally came from the Hunter Valley, where his family were dairy farmers. He did his mechanic's apprenticeship in Singleton, then joined the military with his wife. After 18 years, his wife was discharged, and they moved to Brisbane and separated. He started working for AACo five years ago.

'My brother was working on properties,' he said. 'I applied for a job and Henry offered me a position within 24 hours.'

It's an indication of the scarcity of qualified mechanics in the outback that the reaction from the general manager of AACo's northern properties was almost immediate. As I'd find out on other stations, such a reaction isn't restricted to AACo.

Dave started at Eva Downs, on the Barkly, then moved across to Brunette four years ago.

'I've got my son, Blair, who's 15, with me, and a house to live in,' he explained. 'Blair is now an apprentice heavy-vehicle mechanic. I'm also starting my pilot's licence. There are opportunities here if you're willing to take them. I know how to pull a bore. Henry and I pulled one together not long ago. When we're short staffed you end up mustering and yarding cattle. I ride as well. I've got nine horses.'

It turns out that the job description for a head mechanic ranges over virtually everything mechanical. As Dave detailed what that entailed, he encapsulated nearly everything on the station that didn't have hooves.

'Today we're fixing graders,' he said. 'One blew a hydraulic line at the track. We keep a grader at the track for firefighting. If the grass catches fire with the wind behind it, it could be pretty bad.

'Out here you make the best of what you've got. It's always a challenge. You can't run to the shop. You can't wait for four or five days for parts. The place doesn't stop. The cattle are still there.'

Therein lies the attraction. 'If it was mundane or boring,' Dave said, 'I wouldn't be here. You become pretty good at most things after a while.'

At half-past six the next morning I met with one of the few people on Brunette Downs with a desk job. Anthony Cox, the station's extremely busy assistant manager, was dressed like a station worker and wore the usual muck-spattered Akubra hat. The difference was he was sitting behind a computer screen.

Anthony, aged in his mid-thirties, was a bit coy about his background, saying that while he grew up and was educated in Brisbane, his family were from an agricultural background. How did that work?

'My father was involved with Stanbroke,' he admitted. 'He was CEO of Stanbroke Pastoral Company when it was up and running.'

Stanbroke Pastoral was insurance giant AMP's foray into grass castles that ended, as many similar ventures have, when experience revealed that the returns from big stations are long term and rarely compatible with the average investor's expectations.

After school Anthony completed certificates at Dalby Agricultural College, before starting with AACo in 2000. He worked at a number of company stations, including Brunette, in between trips overseas with stints on ranches in Argentina and Uruguay. He returned to Brunette in 2009 as assistant manager.

On the day I met him Anthony was just days from taking up his first appointment as a manager, at Delamere Station, in the Victoria River District.

With the four distinct operations on the property, much of Anthony's job involves directing traffic. Organising the various stock camps is less hands-on but has given him an extraordinary overview of the entire station.

The Brunette herd has also evolved since the Shorthorn days of the White family and the Santa Gertrudis days of King Ranch. The station now runs a breed known as the Barkly Composite which is 50 per cent Santa Gertrudis, 25 per cent Charolais and 25 per cent Senepol.

'The reason the breeding committee implementing the composite breed was to target MSA [Meat Standards Australia] grading and improve fertility,' Anthony said. 'As we speak that's where it is at the moment but it's being revised. It needs altering with the objectives of [improving] fertility, marbling, quality of meat and performance in a feedlot situation [through a better combination of attributes of the various breeds used to create the composite].'

Anthony was also responsible for the station's daily operations. Communication on the property was an important part of ensuring staff were safe and well. While mustering, everyone has a UHF radio to assist communication with the helicopter pilots. Stock camps have sat-phones, UHF and HF radios. All vehicles have HF and UHF. At all times, Anthony knows where all 54 of his staff are.

'I communicate with them every day,' he said. 'Communication is never-ending here. I really like talking to all of my head stockmen every night out at camp, just touching base. It sounds repetitive but unless you drive it, it becomes one day, two days you're not talking, and that's when things come undone.'

Not surprisingly, Anthony's favourite part of the property is the lakes area, where cattle being readied for sale dine on lush herbage and succulent grasses.

'The country that's there is ideal for fattening cattle,' he said. 'Your

breeder country is still very productive but our trading cattle, perfor-
mance-wise, are second to none – such is the feed that is available to
them, the quality. And you can imagine the scale of it. The vastness
and the variance of country here, even though a lot of it is blacksoil
plains and open flats, mean the difference in the quality of the feed
over there is quite substantial.'

Just before 7 a.m., I heard Susie Kearins, the rangelands officer
for AACo, in the office next door. Anthony established it was her by
yelling through the thin wall.

Susie was another AACo staffer who had started with the company
as a jilllaroo after completing a degree. Hers was in Environmental Science and Natural Resource Management at the Australian
National University in Canberra. She was now responsible for all
AACo operations covering the Northern Territory (with three properties in the Victoria River group, six on the Barkly and four in the Gulf)
and two Queensland properties in the Channel country. While other
companies had rangelands officers on staff, Susie was the only one
who lived 'in the field', based at Brunette Downs.

'That allows you to keep your finger on local issues,' Susie said.
'I'm also fortunate to have a general manager who is concerned with
environment and land issues, although you can find yourself being
pulled between on-ground local issues and public company stuff.'

According to Susie, the focus of her work is in the weaner and
steer paddocks, which is where the money ultimately gets made.

'If the wet is late, you have to move cattle to find pasture but you
don't want them to lose weight and you don't want to pressure the
paddocks,' she explained. 'The best rains come in early February;
it's a green time. In 2008 we had to hit the panic button because
there was no wet. Grass budgets help but we may have been a little
optimistic because they allowed for rain when it comes. Instead we
were just waiting. If you get it wrong, you start trucking to agistment
blocks or areas where there's been no grazing due to lack of water.'

When those moves are made across many properties, it's as if

Susie is playing a game of chess with nature that extends over a significant part of the Australian continent. Other factors make it even more complicated.

'The [AACo] board and shareholders are saying "make more money",' she explained. 'The media might be talking of rain. But you work out your strategy and decide afterwards whether it was effective. You might hit the nail on the head but this way [deciding stocking rates by calculating grass budgets] puts science behind it.'

It was getting hard to know which was more impressive: the scale of the operation at Brunette Downs, or the level of sophistication.

After leaving Susie I headed over to the big house to find Bernadette. I asked how things were going in Canberra.

'They're not listening,' she said.

The ban on live exports appeared to have become a political hot potato. As she put it, 'Well, there were no politicians at the ABC races this year. Last year they came in planeloads.'

As most of Bernadette's numerous guests had departed, she had started to get her life back. She was in her element dealing with the usual station issues: a staff member who was unsuited to every job he was given; an English backpacker who at age 22 couldn't cope on her own, yet was travelling around the outback with little money and less common sense. Bernadette even had time for a writer who wanted to know all about her life.

Bernadette found a spot in her garden away from phones and questioning staff. Our conversation moved to the work that had gone into her oasis.

'I share the garden with Peter Mann,' she said. 'He's worked on it for the last six years. There are beds, annuals, flowers for races. The veggie patch is planted in Easter. We've got birds nesting in the trees. We were trying to create a tropical feel. We even have roses in the cool months and we've got a special spot, the Sunset Tavern, with a table and chairs where we watch the sun go down.'

She and Henry had been at Brunette since 2002, having managed stations with AACo since 1988. They have four children, three of whom were working in the rural industry, in contract mustering. Their fourth child was still in boarding school.

'That's one of the toughest things for mothers in the outback,' she said. 'They leave when they're only 12. You're expecting it but then there's an empty bedroom, an empty place. And it's hard to hand over to other teachers.'

Bernadette explained that her role at Brunette actually has a job title: manager's assistant.

'We're a husband-and-wife team,' she said. 'I look after people, the homestead complex, the clinic, first aid for everyone. Human relations is an issue in the role. I'm pretty astute on people's feelings. I take an interest in them. It's a part of the job I enjoy and take pride in. I try to ease people through rather than have them hit brick walls.'

It was a job that didn't come with a training course. Some manager's wives prefer to keep some distance from staff. Bernadette, on the other hand, was confident in her people skills. As jillaroo Annabel Guthrie put it, she was like a second mum, but one who knew how to dispense tough love when required.

'What I like about it here is that people care about each other,' Bernadette said. 'They care. The station and Barkly are my community. We all support each other.'

She noted that none of the stations is privately owned, so everyone is working for one corporation or another. Once made, many of her friendships have endured, even with staff who were working in subordinate roles. Rank tends to be less important when everyone has to roll up their sleeves to get jobs done.

Henry and Bernadette have been married for 32 years and his career progression has meant spending long periods apart. When he is away, though, he could feel confident that the station was in good hands. And Bernadette worked out that in an average year she hosts 400 guests.

When they can get away they go fishing together: Henry fishes,

Bernadette kicks back with some reading. It sounded like a good life but I couldn't help wondering whether she ever felt like she was spending her best years far from the centre of things.

'We think we live in the real world,' she answered. 'It's not like the city, and even when you're tired and exhausted you know you've done a good day's work. We really don't know what we'll do next but I don't think it matters if you're happy, if you're not looking for the next stage. Maybe that's naive but I have a sense of contentment. I'll go wherever he goes.'

I'd driven to Brunette Downs with a head full of history, of great pioneers who risked perishing from thirst, and of those who followed and faced calamity as drought ravaged the land. Leaving Brunette, the impression I had was of one of the most progressive cattle operations in the country, with hundreds of water bores and plans for yet more, and with elaborate operations that ensured the business could survive in a tough, competitive environment.

The days of horrendous stock losses may have passed but they'd been replaced by different challenges. Scientific approaches to pastures and herd management meant that big stations were no longer overstocked, but the drive to maximise their efficiency and returns meant they were always working close to their limit. The result was that they were like giant production lines, constantly turning off large numbers of cattle. Any interruption to the supply chain could have an immediate and potentially disastrous effect.

If the cattle stayed on the station, instead of being turned off, it would rapidly arrive at the point where it exceeded its pasture budget, while more hungry cattle poured down the production line.

The decision to ban live export of cattle to Indonesia was one of those unexpected interruptions to the supply chain. Not only did it mean the loss of markets and income for some stations, but many lost a necessary outlet for the cattle they produced.

It didn't occur to many observers in south-eastern Australia, and surprisingly not to the minister who made the decision to ban exports, that within a short time stations would be forced to shoot stock or risk losing their entire herds. They were so finely tuned that the crunch would come in weeks, rather than months.

I'd come to Brunette looking for pioneers; I left having met professionals. The gap between perception and reality was as wide as the open spaces of the Barkly. Unfortunately, the misconception wasn't mine alone.

4. THE LONG HAUL

Alexandria Station
16359 square kilometres

It is only a short drive – 90 kilometres – along the old stock route from Brunette Downs to the second of the great jewels in the heartland of the Barkly, Alexandria Station. In its time it had been the largest cattle station in the world, and even now ranks among the top five.

Alexandria had been the scene of many history-making moments in the development of the outback, including in aviation, communications and the cattle industry itself. However, it was also unique among the giant stations of Australia: it has had only one owner in its entire history.

While Nat Buchanan was en route to becoming the first to cross the sparsely watered Barkly in 1877, large tracts of it were already being leased, site unseen, by city speculators. However, not all those taking up leases were fly-by-night operators. In the same year as Nat's epic journey, William Collins, Thomas McIlwraith and William Forrest formed the North Australian Pastoral Company (NAPCO or NAP) and acquired leases on the Barkly that would become the nucleus of Alexandria Station. The three men would prove something of a 'dream team' in the development of the Barkly.

Collins was a pastoralist whose family's holdings included the Cooper Creek property Whitula, bought from the pioneering John Costello in 1874. William and his brother Robert would assess the quality of land the fledgling company sought to acquire, travelling extensively to inspect properties or take possession of them. They were also invaluable in judging and acquiring the stock best suited to that land.

Thomas McIlwraith was a shrewd political operator and capitalist with extensive holdings and investments throughout the Australian colonies. In 1879, he became premier of Queensland. McIlwraith lent political muscle and savvy to the company, although in later years he was to become a controversial figure, dogged by financial scandal and eventually driven from office. He was described by one contemporary as 'the only public man in Australia who, by any stretch of the imagination, one could call great'. Yet another characterised him as 'an able bully with a face like a dugong and a temper like a buffalo'.

William Forrest was a pastoralist, company director and politician, and a colleague of McIlwraith from their days on the Bendigo goldfields in the 1850s. McIlwraith may have been a visionary who proposed grand schemes. Forrest was a details man (he originally trained as an engineer) who could make them work. The initial float of the company, for example, was handled by Forrest, as was the delicate negotiation with the South Australian Government, which controlled the region at the time.

Alexandria Station was NAPCO's first acquisition, and while some of the surrounding properties were acquired purely for speculative purposes, the new owners appear to have bought with an eye to the future. The property was put on the market in its early days, but no offers, if there were any, were seriously considered. They named the property after the Egyptian town near the mouth of the Nile that was pivotal to the British Empire's military ambitions in the Middle East. In 1878, the partners set about getting an idea of the terrain of the new station, contracting Frank Scarr, who had sold Lake Nash to John Costello, to carry out a feature survey of the property.

Plans to stock Alexandria were advanced with the purchase of two properties near the Queensland coast, from which breeders could be sent. In addition, two English investors joined the NAPCO partnership: John Henry Boyer Warner in 1879 and newspaper proprietor Sir William Ingram in 1880. These five partners formed the core of the family-owned private company, today the oldest of its type and size in Australia. It has held Alexandria throughout its history.

In 1882 further blocks on the Herbert River were acquired and the outstation Soudan (the then spelling of the Sudan, south of Egypt, scene of further British military expeditions at the time) was eventually established, possibly as early as 1886.

As with Brunette Downs and other Barkly properties, Alexandria's proximity to the Gulf of Carpentaria, some 400 kilometres to the north, made it more economical to ship stores to the remote outpost of Borroloola, near the sea on the Macquarie River, from where they were carried upstream to Cape Crawford. From there drays carried supplies the remaining 350 kilometres to Alexandria. The arrangement worked well in dry times; however, in particularly wet seasons the trip was known to take up to five months.

The concentration of powerful interests among its partners gave NAPCO a degree of security, as they had the resources to deal with the inevitable setbacks of drought, flood, depressed prices and more. Even so, before it really had a chance to get its business off the ground, from the late 1880s this formidable conglomerate was to be tested to the limit.

Redwater fever had been spreading across the Northern Territory since it arrived in Australia on a shipment of cattle from Indonesia around 1880. The disease, affecting cattle and carried by a parasite found in ticks, was so-named because one of the symptoms was blood in the afflicted beast's urine. Eventually waterholes would be turned red as the disease took hold and infected cattle came in to drink. By 1883, it had spread to Wave Hill in the west and Queensland in the east, and stock losses soon grew to the point where the rush to offload properties depressed prices of land and stock. Many stations, big and small, faced ruin. According to Ernestine Hill, author of *The Territory*, during this period NAPCO relinquished 2.6 million hectares of its holdings in a single day. It was to be some years before the cause of redwater fever was understood and the practice of dipping cattle to remove ticks alleviated the problem.

The problems for NAPCO didn't end there. At Alexandria, the watercourses on the property were ephemeral at the best of the times. They ran in the wet season, but would eventually give out during the dry. When the rains failed completely, the situation rapidly became dire. Well-sinking had been going on since 1885, despite a man named Ross being speared to death while sinking a well on the property. Three wells were completed by 1892, the year the first attempt was made to drill for artesian water.

Artesian water was a newly discovered resource in the outback but NAPCO partners McIlwraith and Forrest wasted no time pressing the South Australian government for money to assist with the first search for supplies on the Barkly. It's a mark of their effectiveness as lobbyists that they obtained £4000 towards the cost.

Work started in August 1892, 3 kilometres south of Buchanan Creek, the nearest water source for the steam engine that powered the drilling rig. The nearest wood was 6 kilometres away. Four men were employed to haul wood and water to the drilling site.

In 1893, at a depth of 75 metres, sub-artesian water was struck. While it was usable, it required a pump to bring it to the surface. An artesian source (usually struck at greater depths and rising to the surface under pressure) would flow of its own accord, so the drillers continued deeper. By April 1894, NAPCO had spent £4698 pounds on the drilling; the South Australian Government had spent £3328. Almost a year later, in March 1895, disaster struck. The bore jammed at a depth of 507 metres. After having been drilled for nearly three years with costs in the vicinity of £10000, the bore had to be abandoned.

There is no record of what happened next but by 1900 the same bore had been salvaged and was operating. The detail may be missing but the motivation isn't hard to find. From 1895 onwards, drought gripped the property. The water courses turned to baked mud, the Mitchell grass withered to dust, and stock perished in increasing numbers. Necessity and ingenuity somehow got the No. 1 bore working.

Alexandria's No. 1 bore is the oldest artesian bore on the Barkly and is still operating on the station today. In the intervening period, the government assisted with sinking a further six wells.

While the drought tested NAPCO's resolve and resources, the major economic downturn of the 1890s also put pressure on the more entrepreneurial of the partners. William Forrest was greatly reduced politically and financially, and his holding in the company fell accordingly. For a brief period Patrick Perkins, the businessman who gave Queensland XXXX beer, was a partner with a 20 per cent share. However, when he was unable to meet a call for more funds, he was forced to relinquish his share.

With the turn of the century came a turn in the fortunes of the outback stations. Around 1904 the drought broke and by that time the scourge of redwater fever had receded. For anyone who had managed to battle through with any cattle left, there was growing demand as markets recovered and properties restocked. Soon cattle were walking across Australia from stations as far away as Wave Hill and Victoria River Downs, some on the Gulf Track, while increasing numbers took the Barkly stock route, passing through Alexandria in their thousands.

The station became such a popular thoroughfare that in 1904 a man named George Watson established a store near the Ranken River. In the tradition of outback localities, the only reason for the Rankine Store (as the river was spelt at the time) ending up in its location was that it was where George, a hawker from Cloncurry, happened to get bogged while travelling along the stock route. He started selling his goods on that spot and finding business good, stayed on.

In the store's early days it didn't seem to bother George that he was on Alexandria's land. He put up two buildings, yards and made other improvements. He eventually applied for and was given a lease to the immediate area around the store. He took up with an Aboriginal woman and had a number of children, many of whom eventually went to work on the surrounding stations. As at 2012, his grandson, Johnny Rankine, was the road-train driver on Alexandria.

The Rankine Store became notorious not long after it started trade. Stockmen who had endured monotonous months of hard conditions droving stock or working on the surrounding stations were drawn to the store to blow their cheques on grog and spend their days in idleness. Many drovers and station managers found it almost impossible to get them to return to work, especially if they still had money.

A sense of how lucrative the Rankine Store was in its early days comes from George Watson's manoeuvring over his lease. In 1925, his annual rent was £20. He complained that it was too high in 1927, and it was reduced to £15. In 1929 he sold the store to Herbert Lloyd for £5000.

The profitability of the store was helped by the fact that the ABC races moved there in 1914, after being established at Brunette in 1911. Brunette's manager had been a keen horseracer and organised the meetings until he went to fight in World War One. George Watson, secretary of the club, then moved the races to the Rankine Store. They remained there until 1949, when they returned to Brunette, where they've been ever since.

The track at the Rankine Store was a rough bush affair, with bore casings used as posts to mark the track. When jockey Len Lloyd was killed in 1939 after he fell and landed against one of the posts, they were replaced with roofing downpipe.

As previously detailed, from their earliest days the races have been the biggest event on the Barkly's social calendar. When they were held at the Rankine everyone paid a 'grog levy' that included all meals. A cook was hired and everyone ate together.

The Rankine Store also became something of a base for stock

thieves. In 1911, a police station was established nearby, in particular to deal with a duffer named Paddy Lemmy. Lemmy specialised in stealing horses and added insult to injury by building yards on the stations and using their bores to water his ill-gottten stock.

The first policeman at the Rankine Store, South Australian Mounted Constable James Kerin, enjoyed immediate success. Shortly after his arrival he managed to apprehend Paddy Lemmy, and because a lock-up had not yet been built, he chained him to a log in the wood pile. Unfortunately, during the night the log disappeared, with Paddy Lemmy still attached. After that, until cells were built, prisoners were chained to posts or had their boots taken from them.

During the years when droving along the Barkly was at its peak, the Rankine police station recorded a river of cattle, up to 80 000, being put through the Rankine dip to remove ticks. The police station continued to operate until 1963, when trucking effectively ended droving on the Barkly. It was then relocated to Avon Downs, on the Barkly Highway. The store itself didn't close down until 1968.

Well before that, Alexandria had become the heart of the NAPCO business. In the post-World War One period, drought and poor prices meant that for some time it was the only station in the NAPCO portfolio. However, the fact that it wasn't sold, despite occasional attempts to do so, reflects the high value that was put on it by the company.

The pattern of development at Alexandria reflected that of many properties I would visit. The expense of developing the property meant that for decades the returns from the place were never great, but every improvement added value or security to the operation. Fast city operators might find such investments unattractive. Those on the land recognise it as the way things have always been.

In 1918, NAPCO expanded the station with the purchase of the property to the east, Herbert Vale. It was renamed Gallipoli, in keeping with the convention at Alexandria of commemorating battle-grounds associated with Anglo-Australians. The rationale behind the purchase was to curb the predations of duffers, who had been using Herbert Vale as a base for their operations.

In 1919, Alexandria was again a trailblazer, when the first plane to land in the Territory touched down at the station. The pilot, named Wrigley, was flying to Darwin to greet Ross and Keith Smith on their epic flight from Britain. He beat them to the record landing by two days.

Aviation delivered another first for the station some years later. On 25 February 1930, *The Brisbane Courier* published a letter from John Owen, who wrote from the station on February 21:

> I feel I should give you a little news by the first air mail plane from the Northern Territory. Yesterday saw the inauguration of the service from Camooweal to Daly Waters. The Wattle Bird arrived here on time, making a good landing on the aerodrome, and I received the first official air mail for Alexandria and district. To-day, at about 1 p.m., the first air mail leaves here for South, and will carry approximately 75 letters from this port alone, and weekly this mail will be greatly patronised. The stride made in aviation makes one feel quite in touch with the world; for the past week one or two planes have been passing daily. We can now leave Brisbane on Tuesday morning and have breakfast on Thursday morning at Alexandria. From a business point of view Brisbane firms can keep up a wonderful service with their Northern Territory clients, and it is hoped the American idea of supporting the air services will not be forgotten. No doubt there are people throughout the Commonwealth who would like to know what we outback think of the service. It is the dawn of a new era in the history of North Australia.

Not all of the events on the station were as pleasant. In 1933 Ernest Baker, the owner of an adjacent station, reported as 'Binmarch', was in a relationship with one of the young Indigenous women employed on Alexandria. Phyllis, aged 19, had borne him two children and he'd proposed marriage to her. She not only turned him down, she took up with another man, Walter Collis.

On 18 October, Baker was droving cattle near Alexandria. After making camp for the night, he sent one of his stockmen to the station with a message for Phyllis. At 10 p.m. the boy returned and told Baker that Phyllis still refused to have anything to do with him, and wasn't going to leave Collis. Baker saddled his own horse and galloped to the station.

When he got there, around 2 a.m., he went straight to Phyllis's room. She refused to let him in. When he tried to climb in the window, she escaped through the door, probably in company with Collis. Baker fired a shot at her, which missed, then pursued the man. He fled into another room, that of drilling engineer Palmer Brushe. Not surprisingly, Baker found his entrance barred.

'Open the door,' he shouted, pounding on it with his fists.

When Brushe or Collis refused, Baker fired a shot through the wood. The shot hit Brushe in the throat, killing him. When Baker realised what he had done to the much-liked Brushe, he said, 'I have shot the wrong man. That other mongrel was the man I wanted.'

At Baker's trial, Phyllis testified that she had decided not to marry Baker because she 'was not fond enough of him'. However, she didn't tell Baker of her decision, despite Baker giving her a phonograph, a gold watch, furniture and other gifts.

In November, Baker stood trial for the murder of Brushe and was found guilty. The verdict meant Baker was facing a death sentence but the jury strongly recommended mercy on the grounds of 'ill health, business worries, and disappointment in affections all tending to an unbalanced mental state'. Brushe was buried on the property and his grave is one of two near the former quarters for Indigenous staff.

Baker was apparently spared the death penalty. At the time he wasn't the only one with financial worries as the Great Depression was devastating lives all around the world. However, the 1930s was to mark a period of expansion in NAPCO's properties and a new direction in the company's operations.

NAPCO purchased Marion Downs, between Boulia and Bedourie in the famed Channel Country of western Queensland, in 1934, and Monkira and Coorabulka, in the same area, five years later. From then on, Alexandria became the engine room of NAPCO's expanding operations. Cattle were bred on Alexandria in large numbers (at its peak the property stocked around 62 000 head), then shifted to the Channel Country to fatten until they were ready for market. Fashions in beef may have changed, supply-chain integration may have become more fully developed and the company's operations may now reach from the Barkly farm gate to south-east's Australia's dinner plates, but Alexandria has always been pivotal to the whole operation.

The 1930s also saw the departure of the Forrest family from the partnership when Philip Forrest sold his shares in NAPCO to Francis Foster, a university friend of a member of the Collins family, Douglas Fraser. The Foster family was based in Tasmania, about as far from Alexandria in terms of climate and agricultural style as it was possible to get. Nevertheless, further acquisitions of land around Alexandria, including part of Rocklands Station, saw it continue to grow in size until 1943, when it reached its maximum extent, 29 281 square kilometres. This made it the largest cattle station in the world at that time.

It was then a vast holding of seemingly endless Mitchell and Flinders grass, plus a great diversity of other plants that flourished after wet season rains, belts of gidgee scrub and small areas of flood-out country along the watercourses. The usable areas of the property had been greatly increased by successful boring for artesian water and construction of dams and tanks that spread water to areas previously too far from water for cattle to reach. Extensive fencing, yards and other infrastructure works had also been carried out. The property was still not fully developed but over the preceding 67 years Alexandria had been transformed into one of the most highly prized properties of the Northern Territory and the nation.

Not that many people knew much about it. Beyond the stock pages of the nation's newspapers, the company made few headlines as it went about the gradual process of improving the place as good seasons yielded the money to make more improvements. The 'slow and steady' approach might not have been as spectacular as the rapid acquisitions of a cattle king like Sidney Kidman, but it had laid the foundations of one of Australia's largest cattle producers.

While Alexandria was the centrepiece of NAPCO's operations, it was still remote from just about everything else. In 1952, fencing contractor Bill Crawley understood as much when he was driving from Alexandria to Borroloola and broke a bearing in a front wheel of his truck. He didn't have a spare, and he was on a very infrequently travelled road, 100 kilometres from the nearest help. So he sat down with a knife, a file and a piece of gidgee tree and started whittling. Three hours later he had carved a wooden bearing that he then fitted to the truck. He went on his way and covered the distance to Borroloola without further incident.

Others weren't so fortunate. In December 1947, Ted D'Arcy, a pumper on the station, had been working on the No. 21 bore. The Gallipoli outstation manager, Doug Harris, was supposed to pick him up but had gone into Camooweal for Christmas drinks and ended up in jail. When he didn't turn up, Ted started walking to the homestead in the furious heat of high summer. He didn't make it and was eventually found, lying dead by the road, by Harris. Ted was buried where he died, 19 kilometres west of Gallipoli, his grave one of many grim reminders of how easily death can come in the outback.

In 1956, pumper Fred Lehmann also perished, between the No. 38 and No. 7 bores. Alexandria manager Bill Young found him and later wrote, 'Having no water with him it looks as though he must have panicked and by the tracks did quite some running about in circles and as time went on, he shed his clothes, and finally died out on the plain. From indications death by perishing is not a very nice way to go.'

In 1965, as the company moved to grow by acquiring more property, the federal government moved in the opposite direction, resuming 12 873 square kilometres from Alexandria, reducing the property to 16 359 square kilometres, its current size. The resumed land was divided into Mittiebah, Mount Drummond and Benmara stations, with 1400 square kilometres remaining Crown Land, which would be subjected to a native title claim in 1978.

In the mid-1980s, the era of corporate takeovers, it wasn't surprising that NAPCO was targeted. A quiet giant, with solid success resting on the bedrock of stations like Alexandria, it was seen as fair game. Attempts to seize control came from former prime minister Malcolm Fraser (who had a family connection to the company and a small share), acting with a consortium called Far North Pastoral Holdings, Kerry Packer's Consolidated Press Investments, cattleman turned cattle baron Peter Sherwin and John Elliott's Elders IXL. While some of the offers were attractive, all of them would have dramatically altered the way the company operated.

Given the company had been operating perfectly well for a century, there was plenty of merit in keeping things as they were. Ultimately, the dilemma was resolved when those who wanted to sell their shares in NAPCO were bought out by those who didn't want to sell. The result was that the Foster family ended up taking a controlling interest in the company.

At the time the company also took the opportunity to expand its holdings. From the mid-1980s to the mid-1990s it acquired the Wainui Feedlot (100 kilometres west of Brisbane), Connemara (a former John Costello property in the Channel Country), Kynuna and Dagworth on the headwaters of the Diamantina River (and the sites of incidents that inspired Banjo Paterson's 'Waltzing Matilda'), Boomara and Coolullah in the Queensland Gulf Country and Roxborough Downs (in the Channel Country).

The company grew to become the fourth-largest cattle producer in the country, with almost 200 000 head and properties extending over more than 6 million hectares. Some properties have been sold and others acquired since, but if the conglomerations of adjoining stations were taken as one, Glenormiston, Marion Downs and Coorabulka would be the world's biggest cattle station at 25 750 square kilometres and Alexandria–Mittebah would be the third biggest at 23 354 square kilometres. The current largest cattle station, Kidman and Co's Anna Creek, arrives at a figure of 23 677 in combination with the Peake Station.

Some years ago, I had the pleasure of interviewing Dr Amar Bose, sole owner of the audio-products company that bears his name. Sitting in his office overlooking the shimmering lakes and autumn-coloured forests of Massachusetts, the affable billionaire explained how many of his contemporaries had publicly listed their companies for short-term gains, only to regret the accountability to shareholders that subsequently haunted their every move. The BOSE corporation, he said, could take greater risks and make short-term losses in order to achieve long-term strategic goals. In essence, it was his money and he could do what he liked with it.

Considering the operations of the privately owned NAPCO, the similarities were obvious. Since the 1980s, the company had embarked on a number of long-term initiatives that drove innovation in the cattle industry. Much of the pioneering work was carried on the broad shoulders of the mighty Alexandria. As the property branded 28 000 calves a year, even small gains could produce significant differences to the bottom line.

In the early 1980s the company became an industry leader when it recognised that Alexandria's Shorthorn herd would do better if it was crossed with Brahman cattle. It began a composite breeding program that took a decade before it showed the desired results: cows with good 'motherability' (the ability to carry and rear a healthy calf) that were adaptable to harsh conditions. The result was a moderate-sized, low-maintenance cow with high fertility, even when times are tough. In all but the most exceptional circumstances, they would keep breeding.

Along the way, the cattle were criticised for the colour variations in the hide (which was a bit like inventing gold only to cop flack because it glittered). It was a view Ross Peatling, who had managed the property since 1991, dismissed. As he told the ABC's *Landline* in 2005, at the meatworks they all look the same with their shirts off.

Subsequently, the company has turned its attention to male cattle and has developed the Kynuna composite, to improve meat quality. It has since been seeing what happens when the two breeds are combined.

In an effort to closely assess what's working and what isn't, NAPCO introduced the use of gene-marker technology. The tail hair from of all the top stud and bull-multiplier groups at Alexandria and Boomarra stations was taken and logged, and the station could monitor the meat traits and growth rates of all the animals. It allowed the company to judge animals with various genetic traits against the quality and quantity of the meat they ultimately produced. The use of gene-marker technology and the composite program were regarded as part of the most sophisticated breeding program in beef cattle across the world.

It was an expensive program but NAPCO CEO Nigel Alexander, great-great-grandson of Sir Thomas McIlwraith, believed that over time it would produce the best return on investment compared to other options the company could explore.

When Alexandria cattle near the end of the supply chain, at the Wainui feedlot near Brisbane, the company's leadership comes to the fore again. The feedlot, purchased in 1985, was one of the first of its kind in Australia. The feedlot handled 8000 head at a time, fattening heifers for two months and steers for just over three months. The steers could put on 2 kilograms a day while growing to 650 kilograms for the Japox (Japanese bullock) market.

Wainui has also achieved a number of firsts. The property was built on a 3-degree gradient on 1 axis, one degree on another, to aid runoff. Its effluent was processed into fertiliser for resale. Feed was pre-processed to optimise digestion, which also reduced methane emissions from the cattle. As a consequence Wainui became the first feedlot in Australia to achieve the ISO 14001 environmental standard.

In 2005 NAPCO also created Australia's largest nature refuge, 21 500 square kilometres, in the Channel Country. The refuge covers much of two of its properties, Glenormiston and Marion Downs, and by agreement with the Queensland Government balances the requirements of the Department of Environment with its operations in fattening cattle. Environmentally and culturally sensitive areas of the land have been identified and fenced off so cattle can't damage them. Areas where cattle graze are closely monitored to ensure they aren't badly affected. In many ways, the environmental monitoring and pasture monitoring are complementary, as overgrazing is undesirable from both perspectives.

In a tough industry where spectacular rises are as common as dramatic falls, NAPCO's innovative approach to its business has seen its survival. In an interview on the ABC's *Landline* in 2005, Nigel Alexander reflected on the reason the company has thrived: 'I think part of the core philosophy of the business is sustainability, and if you let that guide you in your decision making, you're always going to be making decisions based on the long-term outcome rather than the short-term.' (Reproduced by permission of the Australian Broadcasting Corporation (c) (2005) ABC. All rights reserved.)

During my visit to Alexandria, I didn't have to look far to find that kind of long-term thinking. After Robyn Peatling, the manager's wife, showed me to the guest quarters and invited me to dinner that night, I started reading the history of NAPCO she lent me, appropriately titled *You Can't Make it Rain*.

The book detailed much of what I'd heard before when I'd been reading up on the station's history, but it also contained a letter from an Irishwoman named Charlotte Fitzmaurice, whose great-grandfather was Thomas Harding, the first manager of the station. Writing in 1999, Charlotte thanked Robyn for her hospitality during her visit to Alexandria, and her letter included her impressions of the station. 'It's a way of life, not just a job,' she wrote, 'and a life of strength and determination.'

It was certainly a way of life for the Peatlings, who'd managed the station for 20 years. And the possibility of making it a way of life could still attract new staff. With us at dinner was a new recruit to NAPCO, project officer Sam Harburg. He'd been with the company since January 2011. After working in government for a few years, he'd considered working for several other agricultural companies before choosing NAPCO. Why? 'Because of their stability compared to other companies,' he said.

Ross and Robyn were perfect hosts, although I didn't feel it was appropriate to bring my notebook to the table and pepper the conversation with questions about cattle. As it happened, it was the last I saw of Ross, who had his hands full giving Sam an introduction to the property and running the station, and was unable to make time for a chat during my stay.

Over dinner, Ross told me he was approaching retirement, although he didn't look like a man in his sixties. His conversation was forthright and authoritative, which seemed right given the impressive track record of achievements at the station, many of them during his tenure. Robyn was more approachable, with a likeable mixture of commonsense and an easy enjoyment of life.

Stability became something of a recurring theme with nearly everyone I talked to the following day. For Robin Jenkinson, the station's cook and a woman who was in her middle years, it was a stability she wasn't expecting. We got chatting after breakfast. She had known nothing about cattle stations, but when she got the job at

Alexandria, on a three-month trial, she decided to give it a try.

'I was homesick and considered walking on the first day,' she said. 'When I was first driving in I thought: there's nothing, what am I doing here? I started in October and was offered Christmas holidays, but I was still homesick so I didn't go home because I knew I wouldn't come back.'

She eventually went home in March, after she'd been at Alexandria six months. Shortly after she got home, Robin realised she couldn't wait to get back.

'I'd enjoyed the six months; I'd enjoyed the job and made friends. When I saw home, I realised I didn't need to be there. People come and go but Facebook amazes me. Kids who used to work here are my friends on Facebook: their weddings, christenings; they keep in contact. This place touches people, it really does.'

Before coming to Alexandria, Robin had worked for 18 years in kitchens across Victoria and Tasmania.

'I'm a cook,' she emphasised. 'Chefs decorate plates. I used to cater footy dos. Then I got a back injury and ended up on a pension because I couldn't work. I was suffering from asthma and spending time in hospital and then I decided to apply for a job I saw in *The Land*.

'I tell the young ones, "I'm not your mother." I don't give them advice. I listen but tell them, "Call your parents. If you're not happy, you have to decide what you want to do." I might point some to the flying padre.'

When I asked about the food she cooks, she laughed and said, 'They get beef seven days a week. Every now and then they get chicken.'

When I arrived, the station had just built a butcher's shop. Each week they kill two beasts, enough to feed up to 50 staff on the property and its two outstations. All the cuts are used for steak, casseroles, roasts, stews. Robin had about 33 basic recipes that ranged from roasts to beef-and-bacon rolls and beef with olives.

Some might find it surprising but fresh fruit and vegetables were very popular at the station. Having lived in the outback for a year myself, I was surprised at how quickly you missed them when they weren't there. At Alexandria fresh fruit and vegetables are flown in on the company plane, based in Mt Isa. A truck delivers heavier and non-perishable items once every couple of months.

Robin tries to balance variety with favourites. 'I do a roast every Wednesday when there are fresh vegetables,' she said. 'And one of the bore runners told me, "You can't change it; I won't know what day it is."'

Robin's favourite times are Christmas and Easter.

'At Easter I brought in fresh fish and grilled it and gave them battered prawns. Sometimes they all put in for lamb. They will ask for variety, but nutrition is the top of the list. I'm diabetic so if I can't eat it, they can't eat it. We have a nutritionist and dietician come around to check what we're serving and it turns out the food is great. Not much is deep-fried. On Saturday night they might get chips.'

Robin had worked at Alexandria since 2001 and thought highly of the company. 'You are well looked after here,' she said. 'The company does a great job; I'm always impressed by them. In some places, you're just a number. Here, they know you by name.'

Stock-camp cook Rowena Brown had been with the company for four years. She cooked for up to seven in a mobile kitchen, usually between March and November, for periods of a couple of weeks to several months. The mobile kitchen has a chest freezer and dry store that is topped up by bore runners and pumpers on their weekly rounds.

Rowena was originally from the Hawkesbury district, near Sydney, where she'd started out feeding firefighters from a 6-tonne truck. Of working in the stock camps she said, 'You are cut off but it's quite interesting work. You can get aggravated when people are sitting in the caravan keeping warm and dry but it's also the dining room. If anyone gets too annoying, I throw them out for five minutes to run around in the rain until they settle down.'

Over in the main office, head stockman Pam Gobbert was grappling with a malfunctioning computer. I actually knew how to fix it, in return for which she took a few minutes to talk about what she did. At 26, she was another long-term employee, having been with the company for seven years.

Pam grew up at Mitchell in central Queensland on what had been a sheep property but was now running cattle. After finishing ag college in 2004, she started out as a jillaroo, then became a leading hand and was now head stockman for the stud operation.

'I work solo but the camps help with the yard work,' she said. 'A lot of the work is entering data into the computer. There are 750 top stud cows, 2000 bull breeders, 1500 stud-bull growers and 1500 heifer growers ready to join. I've also been doing things on the composite [breeding] side and I'm in charge of the station's stallion.'

Pam said that much of the work she was doing wasn't being done anywhere else.

'There's a lot of forward thinking,' she said. 'We do estimated breeding values, tail-hair sampling, feedlot trials, progeny testing. I've learnt on the job and done training courses.'

Pam has seen the results of composite breeding literally in the flesh. 'Composite breeding means cattle are more uniform and uniformly better. And that's the whole 60 000 on the property, not just one herd. Their temperament is better. At Alexandria the focus is on fertility, adaptability and temperament.'

And she's another fan of the company. 'They have a good attitude towards young people. If you prove you can do the job and know what you're doing, they listen. I have encountered a bit of chauvinism, but I'm still here and they're not.'

I caught up with Robyn Peatling for morning tea. Over a cuppa, she told me that her family was as deeply involved in the cattle industry as it was possible to get. She was the manager's wife here on Alexandria, and her brother managed NAPCO's Marion Downs Station in the Channel Country.

Her family was from Clermont but left in 1953 to work for the English cattle company Vesteys. Robyn was born on Limbunya

Station, near Victoria River Downs, in 1956. She showed me one of her treasured possessions, a coolamon given to her mother by the station's Aboriginal women to use as a cradle. Robyn had eventually used it as a cradle for her two sons, who both now work in the cattle industry: Richard on Alexandria and Warwick for Elders in Winton.

Her husband, Ross, was originally from Childers, in Queensland, and they met when Robyn was working as a bush nurse. They were married in 1977 at Fort Constantine, where Ross was head stockman. Ross applied to manage Wondoola in the Gulf Country but ended up being sent to Mt Bundy on the Adelaide River in the Northern Territory, then a feedlot in New South Wales, then to Arcadia Valley. In 1991 he was made manager of Alexandria, and has been here ever since.

Robyn's boys were educated by the School of the Air, then went to boarding school at Scots in Warwick, near Brisbane.

'I went back there this year,' Robyn said. 'I had the same horrible feeling when I got close to the school. The kids find the first year hard but by the end they love it. As they grew up you knew it was going to happen. It's just another way of life. They meet people and get used to it.'

Our conversation was interrupted when a newly employed stockman entered, requiring an orientation, which was part of Robyn's job.

The stockman, Jonathan Ward, told us he was the son of Cyclone Ward, who had once worked on the station. Jonathan, a solidly built young man, was schooled at Alexandria as a boy and recalled playing on the rocket cone that was once a feature of the place. It had landed on the property at the end of a flight from the Woomera rocket range, 2000 kilometres to the south.

I tagged along with Robyn and Jonathan as she explained how the store, canteen and bar operated, the Sunday barbecue and the rules of the kitchen: the need for good hygiene, courtesy, being presentable, washing up and putting things away. There was no smoking in the building or vehicles. Robyn explained that if Jonathan got sick or injured he should tell the head stockman immediately: even a tiny scratch could become infected if not dealt with.

The orientation done, Robyn explained that her position was station services coordinator, with pay equivalent to a head stockman. It essentially involved supervising the community and living arrangements while the work of the station was carried out by the manager. She said it was the nature of big stations that managers' wives were drawn to support their husbands' work. The responsibilities were too broad for one person. If a manager isn't married, they need staff to support them, a view that I'd hear repeated at nearly every station I visited.

'I'm a mentor only if I have to be,' Robyn said. 'We have an employee assistance program, and if necessary I refer them to that.'

When she and Ross first arrived at Alexandria, they said they would review their situation after five years. When they did, they realised how happy they were. Once again, the style of the company's management was a key factor.

'It's a family company, it's stable and here for the long haul,' she said. 'I love that it's fully Australian owned.'

The other attraction was the open country. And there was certainly plenty of that.

'I don't like being fenced in,' she said. 'We've got two or three favourite picnic places. One of our favourite things is, when the stock camp is tailing cattle, to go out and put the billy on. As each one takes a break, they come in to have lunch. We just go out there and enjoy things.'

Towards the end of the day, I caught up with the man who was one of NAPCO's longest-serving employees, and a legendary figure on the Barkly. Johnny 'J.R.' Rankine was the grandson of the Rankine Store's original owner, George Watson, and has lived on Alexandria station since 1965, when he was 16.

J.R. was keeper of many of the station's stories, some of which he told with delight. I'd been coached to ask him about ghosts, and he lit up at my question.

'There's a ghost here on the station. He used to be a boundary rider on Soudan. Someone had run a cable between two trees and when he was out galloping it chopped his head clean off. I've seen him at no. 41 gate. It was night and he came up and asked for a smoke. He just came up beside me. I said, "I don't smoke", and he went on his way. The second time I saw him was at Gidgee, when I was watching stock. I saw this bloke open a gate and let the cattle out. I thought, That's crazy, and took off after them.'

J.R. had an easy manner about him, a ready smile, and an obvious pride in his work. As we talked, we sat on a pile of old tyres, down in the shed where he kept the prime mover for the station road train that he drove. His hair was grey and dishevelled, his clothes were smudged with grease and dirt, but his truck was immaculate. It looked like it had just been driven off the showroom floor, not over 100 kilometres or more of station tracks.

'A few blokes have seen that ghost,' he continued. 'Usually it happens when they're driving trucks and opening gates. He asks for a smoke. You know that feeling when your hair goes on end? He just gets up alongside, on your side when you're not looking. Sometimes I go a long way round rather than go through that no. 41 gate at night. It depends on the moon but sometimes you just get that feeling.'

I told him he had just ensured that I'd never feel comfortable opening a gate at night ever again. He laughed. It may have been his plan.

'There's others walking around too. Spirits of my people. But they're all right. You hear them sometimes, outside the door at night making a noise. They're just keeping an eye on things.'

J.R. was born on 27 November 1949, 'somewhere on the station'. He had worked his way up from being a stockman. In 1974 he started driving trucks, then spent a year on a grader and a year on a bore truck. Eventually he became the road-train driver. While mechanics were responsible for most of the other vehicles and machines on the station, the road train was his domain. His initials, 'J.R.', are painted on the side.

'I'm mostly moving cattle around paddocks,' he explained. 'RTA [Road Trains Australia] take cattle away to other stations.'

Driving around the station suited him, he said. He didn't even like going to town any more. However, station life isn't like it once was. He started to talk about the changes, and his smile faded away.

'There used to be an old Aboriginal camp,' he said. 'Not many whitefellas. Then they got all these new ideas, got civilised and took them all away. My father was a bore mechanic. My mother was cooking in the kitchen. I was one of eight kids. They all started off here but all went away. I'm the only one who stayed at home. My wife and I had five kids. My wife died six years ago, cancer. Two of the kids are in Katherine, one is a teacher. The other three are in Tennant Creek. They all grew up and went to school. Now they're all working for the government. One of my girls played basketball for Australia and for the Northern Territory.'

I asked him what it was like at the station in years gone by.

'I've known all the managers,' he said. 'Bill Young was the first one: Bill, Long John Olsen, Ross. Bill was a lively old fella. He kept an eye on us. We had to stay out of pubs. We had to stay away from the old Aboriginal people. We couldn't go chasing their daughters. They'd watch us. As soon as the sun went down, we'd go to sleep but there were some, they'd still go down. You know how it is.'

We talked about the challenges of driving a road train on the unsealed roads of the station. He said, and he seemed a bit surprised himself, that he'd managed to get bogged just the day before.

'All three trailers bogged,' he said. 'I had to unhook and take one load, then come back. It's been 11 or 12 years since I did that. There was some ground that was spongy from the rain a couple of months ago. The trailers were digging in. With a load of heifers, 120–130 tonne is a bit too heavy.'

When he wasn't driving the truck, or doing the maintenance on it, he turned his hand to just about everything, from pulling bores to fighting fires.

'We give the young people a bit of help,' he said. 'We show them how to load cattle onto the truck. The young fellas change tyres, do bearings, drive forklifts, but we teach them a little bit when we can. We put them on the right track.'

When I asked if there was anywhere on the station that particularly appealed to him, he replied, 'This place is pretty good everywhere: there's a bit of scrub gidgee, a bit of desert, timber in places. With three stations it's not really boring.'

J.R. didn't have an answer to what the future held.

'The company has looked after me well,' he said. 'I don't know about retiring. What would I do? I'm happy to keep going while I can.'

The sun was setting over the Barkly grasslands as J.R. posed for a couple of photos with his truck. We had a laugh when I asked him to act like he'd seen the ghost from gate 41.

When we were done, he went back to his chores while I took advantage of the golden light to get more photos of the station buildings and the nearby yards, where several thousand weaners were being earmarked and branded.

Weaners had been going through those yards on Alexandria for close on 133 years. In all that time, they'd belonged to just one company. It was the longest tenure of any big station by an outback mile.

As I walked around, something J.R. had said struck me. He reckoned he'd known all the managers in his 46 years at Alexandria but he'd named just three: Bill Young, Long John Olsen, Ross Peatling. While Alexandria and NAPCO had an enviable reputation for innovation, from the first bore on the Barkly to its breeding programs, it was achieved within a corporate culture of extraordinary stability. Perhaps the secret to successfully thinking long term is if everyone is thinking the same way. At Alexandria, they were all there for the long haul.

5. THE BIG RUN

Victoria River Downs Station
41 155 square kilometres, 1882; 2824 square kilometres, 2012

The vessel that sailed into Joseph Bonaparte Gulf, on the north-west corner of the Northern Territory, in 1839 was perhaps the most famous ship of its time. HMS *Beagle* had already carried naturalist Charles Darwin on the global voyage that would make him the greatest scientist of his age. However, in 1839, under the command of John Clements Wickham, with first officer John Lort Stokes, it was about to become instrumental to another discovery with far-reaching consequences.

In the south-eastern corner of the Gulf, the ship ventured into a large inlet whose current suggested that here, at last, was a major river that might provide access deep into the interior of Australia. Further exploration amid spectacular bluffs of deep red stone, enlivened by the huge crocodiles that at one point attacked an incautious Stokes, gave those aboard sufficient confidence to name the waterway after Britain's monarch: the Victoria River.

Despite the significance of the discovery, it wasn't until 1855 that an expedition was mounted to investigate further. Led by surveyor Augustus Gregory, a party travelled far up river, establishing a base at the highest navigable point, a site now known as the Depot. From there, Gregory and his men travelled on foot and horseback, and were rewarded with the discovery of expanses of lush, well-watered pasture, with excellent potential for raising cattle and sheep. Gregory didn't know it at the time, although the country might have suggested as much, but he was standing on what would become the greatest cattle station the world has ever known: Victoria River Downs. Nevertheless, he explored the Victoria to its headwaters, finding good country the whole way, though as he went on the land became increasingly dry He then decided to head east, eventually crossing northern Australia to reach the Queensland coast.

Gregory's report of extensive grazing country didn't cause a stampede to settle the north. This was a mark of how remote the location was, and how few Europeans there were in Australia at the time. In the Victoria River district, for the moment, the estimated 4000 Mudburra, Billinara, Ngariman and other tribal groups continued to enjoy their ancestral country in peace.

The potential for settlement in the region increased in 1863 when Colonial Secretary Newcastle ceded the Northern Territory to South Australia. As detailed elsewhere, several early attempts were made to settle the area. Nothing came of them until the completion of the Overland Telegraph Line in 1872 (and gold rushes in the north, particularly around Pine Creek, 200 kilometres south of the tiny port of Darwin) provided a tempting market for beef producers.

Some leases were taken up along the telegraph line during the early 1870s, but it wasn't until leases to much of the Territory were offered on excellent terms, as described in previous chapters, that the land rush to the Top End began.

The first lease on Victoria River Downs was taken up in 1878 by a Territorian, Albert Sergison, and a drover, Roderick Travers, who were enticed by what they considered the best grazing country in Australia, just 150 kilometres from the Overland Telegraph and the anticipated (by more than a century as it turned out) transcontinental railway. However, Travers was murdered by local inhabitants on the Gulf Track in December 1878, and his partner never took up the country.

A year after Travers' death, southern financiers Charles Fisher and J. Maurice Lyons took up their first leases in the Victoria River district. By 1882, they had formed Victoria River Downs, with leases covering 41 155 square kilometres. In typical outback understatement, it came to be known as the Big Run.

While Fisher and Lyons enjoyed the distinction of establishing the largest cattle station in history, they were also the first owners the place sent broke. The pair were astute pastoralists and financiers from southern Australia, and the example of the Duracks and Costellos, who settled large areas before selling them for handsome profits to late comers, may have inspired them to join the great push 'further out'. However, the luck of the Irish in western Queensland wasn't to be repeated in the north-west of Australia.

Fisher and Lyons were among the most ambitious landholders in the Top End. Their total holdings amounted to more than 100 000 square kilometres and it was their money that backed the largest single movement of cattle in history: 20 000 head taken by great outback pioneer Nat Buchanan in 1881–82 to stock another of their Top End stations, Glencoe.

It soon became apparent that Glencoe wasn't suited to cattle and in 1883 Fisher and Lyons moved all that had survived, only 6000 head, onto the Big Run. The cattle were taken there by Nat Buchanan's brother-in-law, Willie Gordon. Nat also recommended Lindsay Crawford to C. B. Fisher, who made him the Big Run's first manager. Nat had met Crawford when he was putting together the 20 000 for the Territory and bought cattle from Richmond Downs in Queensland, which Crawford managed. Nat had been impressed by how well he mustered and prepared his stock for the road.

Fisher and Lyons' losses of cattle, the massive cost of the operation they'd undertaken and the gradual realisation of the immense logistical difficulties of stocking and marketing cattle in such remote stations soon had an equally substantial impact on their finances. They were in trouble as early as 1883, and when their attempt to float a pastoral company to spread their risk failed, their bank took mortgages on their properties as collateral.

Meanwhile, Lindsay Crawford was discovering the problems of running cattle on what was effectively open-range country, just as the local inhabitants were discovering a taste for prime grass-fattened beef. The cost of freight to bring supplies to the station was also breath-taking: £250 pounds per ton. Eventually a dock was established at the Depot to allow coastal vessels to ship supplies from Darwin, greatly reducing costs.

By that time, the Big Run was already considered a port of call for travellers heading to and from the goldfields. Not all of them were welcome. In 1886, the station was visited by a group of vagrants who became known throughout the north as 'the Ragged Thirteen'. They called at the homestead at Centre Camp (now the head station) while the manager, Lindsay Crawford, was away. When their request for rations was refused by the storekeeper, they tore sheets of corrugated iron from the storeroom's walls and helped themselves. They also pilfered the station's free-range beef. As such, they were at the vanguard of poachers and duffers who found the growing herds of the Big Run, spread over an enormous area virtually unsupervised, too tempting to resist.

Meanwhile, Fisher and Lyons were going through the death of 41155 cuts. Not only were the Big Run and their other northern properties costing them prodigious amounts of money, but the markets for their beef simply weren't there. Gold strikes provided temporary windfalls but the mining camps were only there as long as it took to extract the precious metal. Over time, the partnership relinquished or defaulted on some of their leases, bringing the Big Run's area down to just over 20000 square kilometres. Unfenced and barely developed, it was still an unmanageable size.

For all the northern pastoralists, now including Nat Buchanan at Wave Hill, just south of the Big Run, the search for markets was becoming a matter of survival. Exporting to Asia was one option,

shipping cattle to Fremantle another, while in 1886 Nat Buchanan
and his colleagues pioneered a stock route that would open up access
to the markets of south-eastern Australia.

Buchanan's efforts were too little, too late for Fisher and Lyons,
who tried to stitch together another land deal. When in 1888 that too
failed, the company that had held most of their debt, Goldsborough
Mort, took control of the Big Run. At the same time, the South
Australian government got around to dealing with the cattle-
spearing locals and cattle-duffing blow-ins by establishing a police
station on Gordy Creek, near Wave Hill. The creek was named after
Nat Buchanan's son.

When Goldsborough Mort realised it was going to become the
owner of the Big Run, it sent one of its staff to assess the place. He
reported that it was capable of running 100000 cattle and 400000
sheep. That was, after improving the provision of water, properly
fencing the place, building yards and eradicating the dingoes. In
other words, after fully developing the almost totally undeveloped
property. Still, it was good to know.

Sheep might yet thrive on the Big Run, but the 1890 experiment
with them was short lived. A flock of 2000 grew to 6000 within two
years, at which point the sheep were sold to a neighbour, whose country was unsuited to them, and they soon perished. The reason for
abandoning the sheep wasn't clear, but it may have been due to the
cost of freighting the clip, the quality of the clip, the extra labour sheep
involved and the liking dingoes and the locals acquired for lamb.

There was better news in 1892 when the steamer *Darwin*, built
by Goldsborough Mort and supported by an annual subsidy from the
South Australian government, started exporting cattle from its name-
sake port to Asia. It was capable of carrying 2000 head a year, which
wasn't much, but was better than nothing.

By that time, the Big Run was being managed by one of the
most colourful characters in its history: Jack Watson. The former
drover became famous while a passenger on a vessel in the Gulf of

Carpentaria. When a crewman fell overboard and was attacked by a shark, Jack pulled a knife, dived into the sea, stabbed the shark and saved the sailor.

Jack also had a reputation for punching out crocodiles that tried to devour him as he swam in the Northern Territory's rivers. At the Big Run he made it his habit to leap with his horse from the 10-metre cliffs where the Wickham and Victoria Rivers meet. In her book *The Territory*, Ernestine Hill related that he solved the problem of cattle slaughter on a station near Burketown in Queensland by riding out and killing eleven of the suspected culprits, before returning to the station with their skulls in a bag.

Jack was managing the Big Run in 1894 when a trooper on patrol named Willshire came across a breeding cow that had been recently speared. Willshire hunted down the suspects, encountering the party near the southern boundary of the Big Run. He later wrote, 'It's no use mincing matters. The Martini-Henry carbines [rifles] at this critical moment were talking English.'

Jack Watson eventually met his end swimming in the Katherine River in 1896, dragged under by a crocodile that, presumably, knew how to roll with a punch.

His job was taken over by his brother, Bob, whose wife was the first white woman in the Victoria River district. Their son George was the first white baby. If anything, the Big Run was becoming wilder as time went on. With something in excess of 30 000 head (an 1894 estimate), the station was thought to be losing 7000 calves a year – speared, stolen or strayed.

The developments suggested by Goldsborough Mort's inspector back in 1888 were all but forgotten as the 1890s saw an economic downturn matched only by the Great Depression 40 years later. In 1895 heifers were selling for £1, making the exercise of disposing of them financially impossible. The Depression coupled with the prevalence of cattle tick spelt the demise of the steamship *Darwin*'s trips to Asia.

Goldsborough Mort was well down the track to appreciating what

Fisher and Lyons had gone through a decade earlier. In 1896, the company attempted to sell the Big Run for £75000 pounds but was unable to secure a deal. In 1900, they were only too happy to sell to a consortium that comprised Sidney Kidman, Alexander Forrest (brother of the WA premier), Isadore Emmanuel (Goulburn-based financier of the Duracks, Costellos and others), and William Buchanan (Nat's wealthier brother). The price: £27 500.

Kidman couldn't understand why such a well-watered, well-stocked property was so cheap. The reason was that it was still almost completely undeveloped, still open range, surrounded by duffers and cattle-spearers, and as far from markets as it was possible to get. There was a large but indeterminate number of stock on the place but they were practically feral, rarely experiencing contact with stockmen that might accustom them to being handled.

One analysis of the situation was that the Big Run was simply too big to be profitable. It was something of a catch 22. The Big Run wouldn't make money until it was developed but it was so big that the cost of developing it was prohibitive. The station's first two owners had both tried and either gone broke or lost a fortune.

Fortunately, the new owners and subsequent partners had the advantage of access to some unexpected markets. Forrest, with his Western Australian political connections, played a key role in opening access to WA markets but the syndicate was dealt a blow with his death in June 1901. However, as the combination of stock losses from cattle tick and the great drought that extended over Australia from 1895 to 1904 decimated herds in the eastern states, the Big Run was largely spared. When the drought broke, there was an opportunity to move cattle across the country to restock the devastated properties in south-eastern Australia. There was money in rising prices as well. The increasing numbers of cattle on the Big Run even stayed ahead of the duffers.

In 1904, the partners in the Big Run attempted the experiment of droving cattle down the Murranji and Barkly stock routes to their properties in Queensland and beyond. It was an expensive exercise droving cattle such a long way but it proved sufficiently lucrative in a good market for them to persist. Soon, up to 15 000 head a year were on the road from northern Australia, joined by cattle from the Northern Territory's Barkly and Queensland's Channel Country to become a river of cattle flowing to eastern stations and markets. In addition, 1906 saw the Big Run shipping 3500 fat bullocks to Fremantle via the port in Wyndham and branding 14 000 head a year.

By 1907, droving cattle from the Big Run down the Murranji was gathering momentum. In fact, the track had always been a trading route from the Top End to Central Australia, with stone spear and knife blades from Newcastle Waters being exchanged for boomerangs made from Murranji bulwaddy, bamboo spear shafts from the Daly River and pearl shell from the Kimberley coast.

In 1908 manager Richard Townshend estimated the station was carrying about 74 000 cattle and could accommodate 50 000 more. That year 17 000 head were branded and 8000 turned off. The profit for the year, from the station that now measured 31 235 square kilometres, was £25 000, almost as much as the syndicate had paid for the whole place back in 1900.

The following year, 1909, English beef conglomerate Bovril was given the opportunity to buy the Big Run. Sidney Kidman went to England to secure the sale, for £165 000. Kidman sold only half of his then 6/16 share, retaining nearly a quarter share and taking a seat on the Bovril Australian Estates Board. The Fisher and Lyons G10 brand, which had adorned Big Run stock for nearly 30 years, was replaced with Bovril's bull's head brand, based on the bull's head used on its containers of beef extract at the time. Its beef broth was and is still a staple of English football fans.

Little did Bovril's management and shareholders realise that the canny Kidman had sold at the top of the market. By 1909 most of the stations in the eastern states had restocked and prices were starting to normalise. The next year the Big Run's profit was down to £17 000.

It would be years before even that figure was repeated. Meanwhile, the Big Run was about to cost Bovril far more than that.

In 1911 the federal government looked into the management of the Northern Territory, or the lack of it, and decided it could do a better job than the South Australians. The Commonwealth subsequently assumed control. The decisions on the fate of the north moved from Adelaide to Melbourne (the seat of federal government until 1926 when it moved to Canberra). In hindsight, Adelaide probably had its finger closer to the pulse of the Territory, but back in 1911, who was to know?

One of the first projects the new potentates of the south proposed was a meatworks in Darwin. When the federal government's proposal proved to be all talk and no action, establishing a pattern that was to be repeated well into the future, Bovril and Vesteys (owners of Wave Hill and other northern stations) stepped in to build their own. Work started in December 1914, with a budget of £250000. However, as expectations of a swift resolution to World War One faded, the cost of materials and labour escalated. The project ended up costing £1 million and wasn't completed until 1917.

There was worse to come. As soon as the meatworks opened, the membership of the Australian Meat Industry Employees Union repeatedly went on strike for better wages and conditions. Between 1917 and 1920, operations at the meatworks were constantly disrupted. It closed for good in 1921. The debacle resulted in a loss of confidence in Territory investment for years after. It's worth noting that, in 2012, there are no meatworks operating in northern Australia.

For the Big Run such setbacks had become almost a way of life; this in a place where progress was slow at best. The provision of medical services was another example, and it took a crisis to provoke a response. In 1922, a malaria outbreak killed 11 per cent of the station's population, which at the time was probably more than 100.

The Reverend John Flynn, who may have visited the region in the 1890s, sent one of his Australian Inland Mission nurses, Sister E. M. King, to treat the survivors. Fundraising in the Victoria River District and the distant Wimmera region in Victoria, topped up with a small grant from the federal government, paid for what became known as the Wimmera Hospital on the Big Run.

Sometimes it was a struggle to get the basics. In 1926 Alf Martin reluctantly agreed to take up the management of the Big Run, probably because he knew how hard the job was and that it was getting harder. In November that year, his plight was documented in newspapers around the country after he gave an interview in Darwin.

The station was paralysed because supplies of food and clothing hadn't arrived. Local Indigenous people who worked as stockmen had 'gone bush' to find food. The white stockmen had been living on nothing but beef and damper for the whole year. Alf's wife and seven children were also on basic rations.

According to the reports: 'The only thing which had saved this vast property from being abandoned was the loyal conduct of the men employed, who had lived on miserable rations for months past; but, knowing that the station owner had made every possible endeavour, loyally stuck to their post.'

There was also no progress with such items as the railway line from Darwin to Adelaide, promised shortly after Federation in 1901, and still not completed when Lord Luke, chairman of Bovril, visited Australia in 1929 (the year the Ghan reached Alice Springs). After meeting with prime minister James Scullin, and trying to convince him of the benefits of taking cattle by rail rather than droving them two-thirds of the way across Australia, he summarised the attitude: 'I am afraid they are so busy looking after eastern Australia at the moment that they have not much time for northern Australia.'

Lord Luke also admitted that, after 20 years, Bovril hadn't made any money from the Big Run.

Meanwhile, life on the station continued to exert a fascination on the rest of Australia. The work of the AIM nurses was a particular focus. Their dedication is one of the most inspiring stories of life in the outback. While Lord Luke was in Canberra, the *Sydney Morning Herald* interviewed two AIM nurses, Sister Norman and Sister Wood, who had just returned from their two-year tour of duty at the Big Run:

There is a mail every six weeks, but the service does not link up very satisfactorily, so that letters are often two months old before they are received. There are no telephones or telegraphic service. A wireless station at Wave Hill, [160 kilometres] away from the hospital, kept the nurses in touch with the world around them, but unless the set was in perfect working order the reception was not good, so that they could not absolutely depend upon this link with civilisation. Yet despite this isolation the sisters look back on their two years at Victoria River Downs with many happy memories. The A.I.M. hospitals are something more than mere nursing homes in these outback parts of Australia. They are social centres for the lonely bush people, many of whom live a nomadic life, travelling up and down the vast tracts of country. At the hospital there is always music, reading matter and some of the refinements of home life, which are denied the average bushman.

In 1932 the Big Run became one of the first stations to have a wireless transceiver installed; it was put in by the AIM at its Wimmera Hospital. The first Morse code message was directed to the AIM office in Brisbane, 'proclaiming to the world that at last this lonely outpost was in communication with civilisation'. The pedal radio, designed by Adelaide radio engineer Alf Traeger (and featured on the Australian $20 note), was one of 20 installed at locations across the outback to enable calls to be made to the Royal Australian Flying Doctor Service, established at Cloncurry in 1928. Other transceivers were at Innamincka, Birdsville, Betoota, Bedourie, Borroloola, Anthony's Lagoon, Hermansberg Mission and Mornington Island in the Gulf of Carpentaria.

In 1933 the Big Run's Wimmera hospital was staffed by Sister Grace Francis and Sister F. G. Hurley, who at the end of their two-year tour at the Big Run could claim the distinction of having only lost one patient, from old age. No visits from the flying doctor were needed because the nurses coped with every emergency, including further outbreaks of malaria.

One patient had a bad cut on his foot that had become infected. The two nurses managed to deal with the infection, talking to a doctor up to three times a day by Morse code. They saved the patient, and the foot, and the flying doctor never needed to visit. According to *The Queenslander* of 29 June 1933:

High tribute to the efficiency of the Australian Inland Mission nurses was paid by the ship's surgeon on the *Marella* [which did the Darwin–Singapore run], Dr. Stanley Jamieson, who said that, in the face of many difficulties, they solved problems that often would perplex a doctor.

Grace Francis in particular was one of the unsung heroes of the Australian outback. In the mid-1920s she established the first AIM hospital in Birdsville, and in her two years there delivered the first white child who survived to adulthood. One of the locals wrote of the contribution Grace Francis and her colleague, Catherine Boyd, made to the community: 'If ever angels came on Earth, I would say these were two.'

Unfortunately, there wasn't much they could do for Bovril, whose difficulties at the Big Run continued. In 1933, the federal government decided the problem with the lack of development in the Northern Territory was that vast areas were locked up by a few interests who lacked the resources or motivation to develop their land. The government's solution – piecemeal resumptions of parts or all of leases – soon saw what little enthusiasm there was for developing properties evaporate.

When the Big Run, which was carrying an estimated 170036 head, had 8521 square kilometres cut from it, the resumption was described as having been done with a ruler. There appeared to be no reference to topography, let alone commonsense. This while in 1933 the Big Run only returned a £1890 profit from the sale of 10000 head.

In 1938, with cattle fetching £4 a head, VRD managed a profit of only £51. In World War Two the station was contracted to supply 400 head a month to Darwin at £5 a head, which could have meant a bonanza, but the station had only five white stockmen and struggled to supply the required numbers. The woeful lack of infrastructure, long promised but never delivered, made supply difficult, while also hampering the war effort.

When in 1942 the Japanese threatened to overrun northern Australia, the government's response was to sacrifice it cheaply if it came to invasion while focusing defence on the south-east of the country along the Brisbane Line. The scorched-earth policy that ensued actually benefited stations like the Big Run. For years, there had been calls to improve stock routes and water supplies and when defence planners looked at marching hundreds of thousands of cattle out of reach of the enemy, the reality dawned: it couldn't be done.

Not long after, giant bulldozers, the like of which the Northern Territory had never seen, tore a 400-metre wide swathe through the Murranji. The stock route was formerly a harrowing track winding through the bulwaddy and lancewood scrubs. Here, cattle were often spooked into rushes, seeing some impaled on timber and many more lost. Tanks were also built and pumps were installed and soon thousands of cattle were being evacuated. The bulldozed route was to prove beneficial to the northern stations for years after the war, although the scrub encroached once more as the years went on.

The Big Run's proximity to the coastline meant that it was within range of enemy aircraft and so a bomb shelter was built for those on the station. It remains at the homestead to this day, used after the war as a movie theatre.

In 1948 Lord Luke became the first chairman of Bovril to visit the Big Run since the company bought the place in 1909. He probably wanted to see for himself what it was that had cost so much and yielded so little. However, it was also an opportunity to get firsthand experience in order to understand what it would take to get the place operating efficiently.

Only a year later, the Big Run's manager, Mr Magnussen, told the Minister for the Interior, H.V. Johnson, that Bovril had already set aside the funds for extensive fencing and other works, and that it was intended that three blocks would be designated for use fattening bullocks, breeding and weaning. A new meatworks would also be built in Katherine, the debacle at Darwin having faded in most memories. However, there was one catch. As *The Northern Standard* reported: 'The rapidity with which the work proceeded depended largely on the amount of labor which could be obtained.'

Much of the material for the work was duly delivered, stockpiled and remained there for years to come. The meatworks in Katherine was started, hit with union disputes, and ended up costing two-and-a-half times the original estimate.

Then the federal government, which had assured Bovril that it would be able to supply the electricity to run the meatworks, failed to deliver. At that point, in 1950, Bovril pulled the plug on the meatworks project, powerless though that plug might be.

In the early 1950s, drought hit much of the country. The Big Run faced a situation similar to 1904 – an opportunity to get good prices for its cattle, as other stations would need to restock when the drought broke. However, the normally reliable wet season failed, and the station found itself 'almost completely bare of feed', as one report put it. Meanwhile, neighbouring property Wave Hill, owned by British competitor Vesteys, was reported to have Mitchell grass a metre deep.

The year 1952 was the Big Run's driest on record. It seemed things couldn't get any worse. Not so. At the end of the year, the federal government resumed three more blocks of the property, reducing it by 40 per cent in size, to a mere 12 359 square kilometres. The Big Run now existed in name only.

Bovril's reaction wasn't surprising. In 1955, after struggling with the Big Run for 46 years, the company threw in the towel. The property was sold to a Melbourne businessman, Lionel Buckland, the quintessential Collins Street farmer. Buckland may have envisaged himself as a budding king in a grass castle but his core business was making money, not raising cattle. While the price paid for Victoria River Downs wasn't clear, it was almost certainly a buyer's market, particularly where the financially scarred Bovril was concerned. Buckland spent as much money as he did time on the Big Run, which was precisely zero. Then, in 1960, he sold most of his pastoral holdings to L. J. Hooker, at a significant profit.

Hookers were the sort of company the Big Run had needed throughout its history. Well-managed and well-financed, it was also based in Australia and knew how to deal with local conditions, including its parochial politicians. Despite further drought hitting the Big Run in the early to mid-1960s, the company commenced an extensive development program.

Just about the only thing Hookers didn't do while it was developing the Big Run was make any money. In fact it lost substantial amounts during the crisis in beef prices in the mid-1970s, which saw values fall dramatically year after year.

In 1984, when prices recovered rapidly and beef on the hoof ticked over $1 a kilogram, the Big Run made a profit of $3.5 million. Hookers promptly sold. It was a good time to get out, but after so much effort for so little reward their exit was surprisingly hasty. However, the company's management believed its skills and assets could be better used elsewhere. As many had discovered before them, becoming kings in grass castles more often than not came at a price, rather than a profit.

The new buyer, for $12 million, was one of high-flyers of the 1980s, Peter Sherwin. Unlike most corporate raiders, however, Peter Sherwin was outback born and raised. The former stockman had drawn Wallamunga Station in a land ballot in the late 1950s and never looked back. He added two more stations to his holdings in the 1960s, one more in the 1970s, then 11 stations in the financially deregulated years between 1980 and 1984. The speed of his growth in the early 1980s was only matched by the rapidity of his fall.

Several bad seasons, losses due to the Brucellosis and Tuberculosis program (a disease-eradication scheme known as BTEC that involved culling large numbers of cattle), the deaths of two young stockmen from his stations in Western Australia, the inflated valuation of Victoria River Downs at $24 million only two years after he'd bought it for half as much, the stock market crash of 1987 and other factors eventually saw the value of shares in the publicly listed Sherwin Pastoral Company fall to the point where, at the end of the 1980s, it became an increasingly tempting takeover target.

Not that Sherwin was going to go down without a fight. It took two years, but in October 1989, Robert Holmes à Court's Heytesbury Pastoral, which already owned fattening properties in Queensland and Western Australia, managed to acquire control of Sherwin Pastoral. The $120 million price tag the new owners paid included taking on $30-million-dollars' worth of the previous owner's debts. The Big Run was valued at $22 million.

Holmes à Court's vision for Heytesbury and the Big Run will never be fully known, for in September 1990, only months after the deal for Sherwin Pastoral was finalised, he died of a heart attack, aged only 53. His untimely demise might have spelt disaster for his companies. However, it soon emerged that unlike other 1980s entrepreneurs who paid exorbitant amounts for mediocre assets, Holmes à Court had invested prudently and with an eye to quality. The result was a legacy that the Holmes à Court family successfully managed beyond the growth phase he led into one of consolidation.

Two qualities have emerged at the Big Run. First, the haphazard approach of days gone by was replaced by problem resolution at all levels of management. Thus while the BTEC program put cost pressures on many stations, some of which went under as a result, the

Big Run's new manager, Perc Crumblin, with the backing of senior Heytesbury management, tested 128 000 head in one year and turned off 28 000 head. It was probably the first time in the station's history that anything like an accurate headcount had been taken and that all, or nearly all, of the herd was mustered, yarded and processed.

Second, the Big Run started operating with what could be called a 'small is beautiful' approach. As envisaged as far back as 1949, the Big Run was divided into four stations: Victoria River Downs, Moolooloo, Pigeon Hole and Mt Sanford. Each station became an independent entity in terms of operation and costs. From the days when the Big Run covered 41 000 square kilometres, Victoria River Downs became a fraction of that: 2824 square kilometres. However, it carried 24 000 head of cattle, more per square kilometre than it had ever done before. It even managed to make a bit of money.

Coupled with the completion of the BTEC program and the introduction of heat-tolerant, tick-resistant Brahman cattle over the last 30 years, the station has become part of the northern Australian cattle industry's belated realisation of its potential. New export markets opened as Asian economies have advanced. Northern Australia has gone from remote and forgotten, to becoming a major contributor to the Australian economy, as hundreds of thousands of cattle have found their way to the nearby tables of Asia and the Middle East. It was a long road to get there and even today there are still unexpected reverses, such as the crisis over live exports to Indonesia, which broke shortly after I visited the station, in June 2011.

The public road I took to reach Victoria River Downs recalled the great pioneer of much of northern Australia, Nat Buchanan. From the Stuart Highway, through Top Springs, and on to the homestead of the old 'Centre Camp', the Buchanan Highway sounded like a fitting tribute to the man but was in reality an unsealed road, which in places was only two wheel tracks meandering through the Mitchell grass.

The homestead itself was quite a surprise for a newcomer like me. After kilometres of empty bushland, suddenly the scrub abruptly stopped and before me was a wide area dotted with houses, a landing area, from which half a dozen helicopters operated, and well-tended lawns that surrounded exotic trees and gardens.

As I drove in, there were plenty of reminders of days gone by, such as the bomb shelter and the Victoria River Downs post office that recalled the time when the station was so big it was given its own postcode: 0852. The hospital no longer operated, the flying doctor being available in emergencies, while Katherine is 400 kilometres away by mostly sealed road.

In the background the sound of a diesel generator provided the eternal outback station theme music, and because this was the dry season, it was joined by the titch-titch of water sprinklers that kept the lawns a vivid green.

The manager of Victoria River Downs, Rusty Richter, was beside the station store and recreation building when I pulled up. He wasn't particularly tall but he was remarkably solid. Rusty was as tanned as you'd expect for someone working the land in the Top End, and as dusty and dirt-stained as hands-on management will make you.

He directed me to the main house while he finished a few chores. There his wife, Julie, explained where the guest quarters were and offered me a cuppa. At the same time, Julie was juggling looking after her toddler son, who had a leg in a cast, and directing tradesmen, who were putting the finishing touches on renovations to the main house, which overlooked the Wickham River, 6 kilometres upstream from its confluence with the Victoria River.

Sitting under the revolving fans on the wide shady verandah, I admired the fresh white paint that accentuated the colonial-style architecture. Surrounded by bougainvillea, frangipani, mango and fig trees, I felt as if I had stepped back into an era where a jacketed servant might appear at any moment with a gin and tonic. Instead workmen were drilling and sawing, staff were coming and going on various errands, and the intensity of a modern cattle station was unmistakable. Where once the station had a staff of more than 100, now there were just 14 or 15: the manager and his wife, a head stockman, seven in the stock camp, a cook, grader driver, boreman and girl Friday.

Julie eventually joined me while we waited for Rusty to knock off for the day. She and her husband were both surprisingly young, in their early thirties, but their connections with the Big Run and Heytesbury went back more than a decade. Julie and Rusty had been at the Big Run off and on since 1999. They started in the stock camp, then went to Helen Springs. In 2006 Rusty became manager of the adjacent Pigeon Hole Station. In late 2010, he became manager of the Big Run, now more usually known as Victoria River Downs.

Julie wasn't particularly worried about raising her two-year-old son Nathan and eight-month-old daughter Hayley so far from medical attention. How he managed to break his leg was a bit of a mystery, but Julie well remembered the drive to Katherine to go to the clinic, then from there to Darwin. He was in traction for three days and spent five nights in hospital, his mother by his side.

'Injuries come with the territory,' she explained. 'We had one fellow who was a sleepwalker. He took a dive off his bed and dislocated his shoulder. We got called at 10 p.m. He was in terrible pain. We put him on a table in the kitchen and rang the district medical officer. The options were to drive into Katherine or try to reduce it. We gave him a shot of morphine and tried to put it in after three hours. On another occasion John Brosnan [a station hand] was pulling out Noogoora Burr at a bore when he was bitten by a brown snake.'

As the conversation moved on to the historic graves on Victoria River Downs, which dated back to the early 1900s, Rusty turned up and joined the conversation. There were 15 marked graves in the station's cemetery, but it was thought there were 25 in all. Some deaths were from malaria, others from accidents. There were three or four grave sites elsewhere on the property, stockmen buried where they had died.

Russell described the station as a mixture of basalt and red lime-stone ridges, fertile flats and volcanic soils. Its pastures included Mitchell and Flinders grass and black spear or sorghum. The rainfall was 700 millimetres per year, most of which fell from October to the end of April.

In a normal season the station had a wet and dry. October to March was the wet, although there could be rain in June and July. During the wet season, the Wickham was too high to cross, but an all-weather track through Jaspers Gorge to Timber Creek could still be used by light vehicles.

During the wet it wasn't possible to move cattle, and the tracks on the station also become impassable, so the stock camp shut down from late November or December until mid-March.

'The best of VRD country always ends up with rain,' Rusty said. 'It's been unreal this year, although the last two were below average.'

Stock are managed by keeping breeders separate from heifers and steers while sale cattle access the better country. The property turned off 6000 head per year. From once being open range, the property is now fully fenced, with repairs caused by wet season floods beginning as soon as the roads are passable.

Waters come from the Wickham and Victoria rivers. There are also ten bores, which yield water that stock happily drink and isn't too hard on the equipment that brings it to the surface and distrib-utes it. A bore runner checks the bores twice a week, covering half the property in a day.

Where once the original owners of the country lived and worked around the station, they have since established a community at Yarralin. In the mid-1960s, when the Aboriginal stockmen on Wave Hill walked off in support of an equal-pay decision (as detailed in the following chapter) the stockmen on Victoria River Downs intended to do the same, but a telegram to their union representatives announc-ing their intentions was torn up, instead of being sent.

Heytesbury Pastoral bought VRD just as land-rights claims were being negotiated with several groups in the district. Robert Holmes à Court told *The Bulletin* in 1989 he wanted to achieve a resolution that not only provided land rights, but addressed the fundamental social problems of the community. It was a view supported by his wife, Janet, in her public comments.

However, despite their best efforts, while the land-rights claims were satisfactorily resolved, the communities have struggled to deal with the social consequences of entrenched unemployment and welfare dependence.

For its part, the station facilitates access to significant sites within its boundaries, as Rusty put it, 'As long as people shut the gates.' There are some sites the public is kept away from due to their inaccessibility and the cost in time if station workers were required to rescue stranded sightseers.

It turns out that now one of the property's biggest challenges are weeds. There was a time when they could have been taken care of easily but now woody weeds, the Noogoora Burr and Baleria have spread. Control involves spelling paddocks and patch burning. The process means a 100-square-kilometre paddock can be lost for a year; however, once burned, it is good for the next three.

If not kept in check, dingoes are also a problem, attacking and killing calves, while wallabies cause erosion. There are still quite a few donkeys, although not the 20000 of years gone by.

Almost all the cattle from the station go to Indonesia, which imposes a 350-kilogram weight restriction on stock entering the country so they can be fattened on Indonesian feedlots before going to slaughter. Some cattle also go to meatworks in New South Wales and South Australia.

Rusty was in no doubt about why the station is now viable, whereas in the past it had sent some owners broke and left others glad to be rid of it at any price.

'Managing a property like this is about being more efficient,' he said. 'We used to have 100 Aboriginal staff. Ten or fifteen years ago, the stock camp numbered 12 to 14. Now it's seven. We use machinery to be more efficient, helicopters on a large scale. The costs are high but helicopter hours are the lowest, compared to diesel and wages that are the highest.'

The next day's jobs included fixing tyres and the endless repairs to fencing. For the uninitiated, fence repairs involve driving in posts and splicing, straining and tying off barbed wire while trying not to get sliced up by the barbs. Having done my share of fencing back in the Hunter Valley, I declined the opportunity to shed blood.

Over in the machinery shed, Rusty and head stockman A.J., a former central Queenslander, were busy fixing tyres for the station's grader. Neither of them was a tyre mechanic but it was just another of the many jobs managers and senior staff perform when there's no one else on hand. After a considerable struggle, the tyres were done and loaded onto the trailer. I was loaded into the front of the station ute between Rusty, who was driving, and A.J.

We headed off down a station track to find the grader and install the repaired tyres. While Rusty answered my questions, he constantly cast his attention around the vehicle. Passing stock he always slowed and assessed. He and A.J. shared comments on what they saw: 'That bullock is looking shelly [in poorer condition than he looks]. Those are all spayed heifers. There should be weaners out on this flat about now. They should have buried that pipe.'

The rough road made it impossible to take notes, so while hanging on over the bumps I tried to concentrate on his answers, so I could write them up later.

A typical year on VRD begins after the wet season with basic maintenance, especially repairing fences and creek crossings.

'There can be hundreds, possibly thousands, of breaks in fences before you can start mustering,' Rusty explained.

On the first muster weaners are taken off their mothers. Ideally, the mothers are already pregnant. Having raised their calves over the wet, as the dry takes hold and feed tails off, they are better off not having to feed one calf while gestating another. This, of course, is based on the breeders having a calf every year. During the first muster, weaners are branded and inoculated and mothers preg-tested.

After the weaners are sorted out, Rusty decides on which heifers will be added to his new breeders. Non-breeding heifers are spayed. In mid-year he musters again to take cattle for sale. Then in November he musters a third time and separates weaners again.

'During the wet, we virtually shut down,' he said. 'Julie and I stay at the property. We might keep a couple on to work on a few jobs around the place.'

As we drove down the track, he explained how some sections of road might be drivable in the wet but not others. He pointed to a patch of black soil and said, 'If you hit a patch like this one, you will sink. There's lots of washouts. Plus you don't want to cut up your roads.'

I asked him whether he struggles to get people to work in such a remote location.

'It's not hard getting staff, it's hard getting good staff,' he said. 'It's not like [the TV show] *McLeod's Daughters*. That's been good because it gets people to leave the city but we've had girls come out here and they're shocked by the reality.'

When considering applicants Rusty checks their references but also looks to see if they have played any team sports. Working in a stock camp means being part of a team. In fact, I'd already heard staff referred to as crew, and seen them behave with the same coordinated purpose I'd experienced while racing yachts. In both cases, the best crews rarely need to be told what to do. They already know.

Rusty also finds it hard to keep a good stock camp together when the station closes down for the wet. Some people are prepared to wait for work to start up in the next season, but others find alternative employment and don't want to leave it. He also regards the cattle industry as one where older staff, and long-term staff, are becoming increasingly rare.

'Young people now are looking to move up,' he said. 'They want to take the next opportunity. We've got one staff member who has been with Heytesbury eight years. Our oldest employee is our grader driver, he's 50. But look at me. I'm 32 and I know I don't want to be knocked around by cranky cattle when I'm 50.'

VRD was the first station where I'd experienced Brahman cattle firsthand. I'd read that they were intelligent and athletic, which meant they could be difficult to handle. If they decided they didn't like you, they'd hold a grudge.

'I love them,' Rusty said. 'They're cattle with a brain. They're inquisitive. You can take weaners that have never seen a human being in their lives, and they'll be in the yards one day and by afternoon they're coming up, sniffing at you.'

He's had bulls that have been missed in paddocks, that might not have seen a human for years, behave in the same way. VRD has run Brahmans for the last 20 years and hasn't been tempted by 'fads' such as Charolais crosses.

'As for Angus,' Rusty said of the beef that was fashionable in burger chains at the time, 'they'd die.'

The station brings in bulls to maintain vigour in the herd. Russell acknowledged that there had been attempts to breed bulls in the past, but they hadn't been done properly.

There were currently six or seven cattle yards on the property but Rusty wanted more so cattle didn't have to walk too far when they were being mustered. All the mustering was done by the one stock camp, while contractors assisted with fencing, preg-testing and spaying.

One of the key roles on the property was that of the chopper pilots, and the station had the pick of them as Helimuster, a major Territory aerial mustering company, was based at the station. Most Helimuster staff were already experienced with stock before they started flying, with good reason.

'You don't want cattle coming in heated up, calves mis-mothered [unable to find their mothers, therefore at risk of starving],' Rusty said. 'You don't necessarily want someone with lots of hours. They have to know cattle. They can't go in at 100 miles an hour.'

Even with a chopper, some land can't be mustered by air, particularly along the rivers and in the timbered country. On the ground, the station uses a mixture of motorbikes and horses. Helmets are compulsory.

'It's company policy,' Rusty said, 'a sackable offence. Everyone also has to say where there are going and when they'll be back. They've all got shoulder patches with UHF radios. Even if I go somewhere, I tell Julie what I'm up to, in case something goes wrong.'

Heytesbury is an equal-opportunity employer but Rusty reckoned that there are still gender dynamics that have to be managed.

'When you've got two women in a stock camp, they'll team up,' he said, 'but when you've got three, two team up and leave the third isolated. However, if it's all blokes, it can get a bit feral, especially in stock camps.'

After getting a quick lesson in how to put tyres on a grader and why you shouldn't do it in clean clothes, we headed back to the homestead.

Along the way, Rusty explained the areas where travellers could see the modern Victoria River Downs firsthand. Coming from Top Springs on the Buchanan Highway, it starts at a grid just after a sign that says 'Yard 36'. From there, you're on VRD for about 70 or 80 kilometres. The highway is the only public access.

'Tourists have to remember,' he said, 'we're a working cattle station. If they go off and get lost, we've got to look for them. Then we're a man down, which puts us behind.'

Back at my vehicle, getting ready to hit the road (and stop putting Rusty behind), I asked if there was prestige attached to managing a station as famous as the Big Run. Rusty simply said, 'It's a great place to raise kids.'

Leaving VRD, it struck me that there was a time when managers of the place might have thought differently. They demanded and were paid large salaries to compensate them for the hardships, isolation and challenges of running what was once the biggest cattle station and one of the wildest in the world. Since then, the wilderness has been tamed, the station developed to the point where it no longer sends its owners broke. What was most striking about Victoria River Downs, and other giant properties, was that the effort had taken more than 100 years. The place used to be called the Big Run, but its success turned out to be more about the long run.

Top: 'A Reminiscence of Drought in Central Australia'; wood engraving by Alfred Martin Ebsworth, 1886. (Image: State Library of Victoria)

Bottom: Dead cattle, photographed during a journey to Brunette Downs Station by James Suttor White in 1936. (Image: Northern Territory Library)

During floods on Brunette Downs in the 1970s, a helicopter was used to push stock towards dry land. The calves close to exhaustion were rescued by the boats. (Image: Ern McQuillan, National Library of Australia)

At Brunette Downs: a loader, road train and utility – the workhorses of modern times, although horses are still used on many outback stations.
(All images by the author unless otherwise indicated)

Opposite page: Mustering using helicopter and horses on Lake Nash Station. The wide treeless plains of Mitchell grass are typical of the Barkly Tableland. (Pilot Erin Gibson)

Top: Mechanic Reece Walker blowing dust from a truck tyre, Lake Nash.

Bottom: Feeding weaners on Alexandria Station with hay cut on the Barkly Tableland property.

Top: Ashley (left) and Kate Gray processing calves on Wave Hill Station, where women are treated exactly the same as men. Kate was the stock-camp cook but was helping out for the day.

Bottom: Part of the herd of 3000 Brahman cattle yarded for pregnancy-testing, part of an initiative to improve herd fertility on Wave Hill.

Top: Stockman Senna Lawson demonstrating agility in the yards, Wave Hill, a handy skill when feisty cattle are experiencing human contact for the first time.

Bottom: Droving weaners to accustom them to being handled, Wave Hill. Emma-Rose Knight (left), Yolanda Rushton and Billy Dakin (son of the station's manager).

Top: Wave Hill's homestead complex, an oasis amid the Top End grasslands. (Pilot Zeb Leslie)

Bottom: A head of 1500 Brahmans walking into the yards for pregnancy-testing, Wave Hill. (Pilot Zeb Leslie)

Top: Floodwaters lap the decaying timber yards at Old Andado Station, a relic of bygone days surrounded by New Crown Station, the second-largest cattle property in the world.

Bottom: An overshot dam constructed by hand more than a century ago on the Georgina River, Headingly Station. The careful orientation of each stone to resist the pressure of a flood is clearly visible.

Top: Helicopter mustering herefords on agistment at a block adjacent to New Crown. (Pilot Danny Rickard)

Bottom: A dam on the block adjacent to New Crown, flooded by rains from Cyclone Yasi. A temporary stock camp is located on the bend in the road. Colson's Pinnacle can be seen in the distance. (Pilot Danny Rickard)

Top: The Georgina River, top left of picture, in flood near Adria Downs Station in 2009. In places, the river was 60 kilometres across, wider than the Amazon.

Bottom: A dust storm rolling in from the Simpson Desert over the Muncoonie Lakes, Adria Downs. The lakes are watered by the Georgina River's floodwaters, with nourishing vegetation springing up as the floods subside.

Top: A bomb shelter on Commonwealth Hill Station, the largest sheep station in the world. The station is located entirely within the Woomera Rocket Range.

Bottom: Yards on Commonwealth Hill constructed using wire and locally sourced timber.

Top: Some of Commonwealth Hill's 50 000 sheep in the yards after shearing.
(Image: Charlie Bourne)

Bottom: Commonwealth Hill's eight-stand shearing shed. Like all of the buildings on the station, it has been built to last.

Top: Commonwealth Hill manager Simon Robinson setting a trap on the dingo fence. The rag in front of his fingers is soaked in strychnine to hasten the dingo's demise and reduce its suffering.

Bottom: Dogger Bob Wright repairing a hole in the 5400-kilometre dingo fence, Commonwealth Hill. Bob patrolled a section 240-kilometres long once a week.

Faces of the outback: Johnny Rankine, road-train driver, Alexandria; Scotty, snake-bite survivor, Commonwealth Hill; Jack Henry, jackaroo, Brunette Downs

B. J. Vankuyk, bore mechanic, Brunette Downs; Andrea McHardy, pilot, Commonwealth Hill; Chris Scobell, chef, Wave Hill

Jonesy, bore runner, Lake Nash; Pam Gobbert, head stockman, stud camp, Alexandria; manager Don Costello, mustering restless cleanskins, near New Crown.

This page: Signage and gateways to some of the largest stations in the world, spread across Queensland, the Northern Territory and South Australia.

Overleaf: A road train kicks up dust on the Barkly Tableland station Brunette Downs at dawn. (Image: Scott Bridle, scottbridle.com)

TVH

6. A TALE OF TWO COUNTRIES

Wave Hill Station

13 500 square kilometres

In the 1880s, with the money earnt droving other people's cattle in the Northern Territory, Nat Buchanan finally managed to take up leases on country he'd explored west of the Overland Telegraph Line. Even as he was delivering 20 000 cattle to Glencoe, he had a mob of his own cattle on the Gulf Track bound for a property he was forming with his brothers-in-law, the Gordons – Wave Hill, in the Victoria River district.

Once again he blazed the trail to the property, in the process helping stock one of the largest properties in the world, Victoria River Downs. From there he took 4000 head to the Ord River, in Western Australia, pioneering a 450-kilometre direct route from Katherine. Just as he'd crossed Queensland with a mixture of stock routes and exploring trips, he'd now crossed the Northern Territory (and nearly two-thirds of Australia).

Wave Hill was to be Buchanan's base of operations for more than a decade, despite it being extremely remote. Nat was prepared for most of the challenges, but there was one he never saw coming. In 1883, as the station was being established, Buchanan's attorney, William Kilgour, arranged for him to go into a financial partnership with his older brother, William. Kilgour probably did this with the best intentions, and the belief that the two brothers could trust each other. It was not to be.

William, the eldest of the Buchanan boys, had stayed on the family's original property and managed it while the younger Buchanans had been out seeking their fortunes. He'd only ventured as far as the Australian goldfields, where he noticed a remarkable similarity to the geology around his own district. He went back home and eventually struck it big. William was now doing most of his farming from behind a desk, but with his backing, Nat had enough capital to deal with the difficulties of Wave Hill's distance from markets and the frequent spearing of cattle by its Indigenous inhabitants. Despite its drawbacks, the area's quality grazing land made it one of the best cattle stations in the world. It still does.

In 1886, Wave Hill had to send cattle prodigious distances, first to Katherine, across to Queensland, then on to markets in Brisbane and Sydney. It was a terribly long way to drove cattle, but apart from the odd gold strike in the Northern Territory and Western Australia, with the subsequent influxes of hungry miners, there was nowhere else they could go.

In 1886, Buchanan contemplated the possibilities of a new stock route that would cut almost 650 kilometres off the trip to Queensland. The direct line from Wave Hill to the Overland Telegraph at Powell Creek was blocked by a belt of almost impenetrable scrub, referred to by some as hedgewood. Unfortunately, the hedge was 160 kilometres thick and had thwarted every attempt by explorers to find a path through it. Typical of the man, Buchanan was returning from Queensland (probably by the Barkly stock route) with 100 horses when he decided he'd had enough of the long detour.

At Powell Creek he met his old exploring mate, Sam Croker, who'd been rounding up stray cattle, and the pair decided to not only pioneer a stock route through the hedgewood, but to do it with stock in tow. Croker had befriended local people who knew a way through, based on an ancient trading route (see Chapter 5). They told Crocker there was water about 80 kilometres ahead and agreed to show the drovers the way through the hedgewood to the waterhole they called

'Murranji'. When they reached it without mishap, the grateful drovers rewarded their guides with plenty of tucker.

The guides then said there was another waterhole about as far again to the west. Accepting the offer of more tucker, they again showed Buchanan and Croker where it was. Eventually they came to what's now known as Yellow Waterholes. From there, Buchanan knew it was only 50 kilometres west by north to the Armstrong River, a tributary of the Victoria River that formed the stock route from Wave Hill to Katherine.

The Murranji Track was soon to become one of the most famous stock routes in northern Australia, in part because it was a great shortcut but also because it could be a white-knuckle journey for drovers. The Murranji and Yellow Waterholes weren't permanent. The long dry stages between them meant that disaster was ever-present for those who risked the journey.

Nat then pioneered another stock route to Western Australia, almost down to Perth, the last piece in a jigsaw of stock routes that reached right across the continent, an achievement unparalleled in Australia's history. Despite this, in 1894 Wave Hill was deep in debt. Much of the money was owed to Buchanan's wealthy brother. To get it back, William put the station up for auction. Whether he had a right to do so is questionable. Just as suspect was the result of the auction: the successful bidder was William. Nat Buchanan lost his property to a brother who'd never set foot on the place. In the whole time William owned Wave Hill, he never visited the property. Two years later, cattle prices rose and a port facility was opened at nearby Wyndham, giving cheaper access to the southern markets. In 1894 Wave Hill cost William Buchanan £15000. It was sold in 1912 to English company Vesteys for £200000.

Nat Buchanan and his enduring love Kate lived for a while at their son Gordon's property near Halls Creek. He dabbled in mining and managed Ord River Station for a while.

Despite the succession of disappointments he'd endured in trying to gain his own foothold on the land, Buchanan still enjoyed legendary status across the north of Australia. Many of the stations and districts that were now successfully raising cattle owed their genesis to him. In 1896, the *Northern Territory Times* described him as:

> [a]n unassuming explorer who has a far better claim to renown than most of the crowd who have posed of later years as Australian explorers. He must be now seventy years of age and he is possibly too old to stand many severe bush crises, but in his best day nothing was too rough for him . . . Hundreds of bush yarns are current about 'Old Bluey', as stockmen familiarly call him, but in none of them have we ever traced anything but the most flattering recognition of the good work done by Buchanan in the pioneering days of the Far North.

He was also known among Aboriginal people as 'Paraway', a corruption of his answer 'Far away' to their questions about where he was going next. It's perhaps fitting that his respect for Aboriginal people, in particular in his relations with the inhabitants of Wave Hill, ensured that they were still on their country, working as stockmen, when in the 1960s Wave Hill became the flashpoint that lead to the Aboriginal land-rights movement. Many other properties he pioneered still have their sacred sites, places men like Buchanan recognised and took care not to disturb.

In 1899, Buchanan's health started to fail him. He and Kate finally left the Kimberley and moved back to the milder climate of New South Wales. He bought Kenmuir, 10 hectares of land near Tamworth, where he grew lucerne to help make ends meet. It was a humble ending for a man *The Bulletin* described as having helped settle more new country than any other man in Australia. His legacy spanned the continent. One of the greatest bushmen the outback had ever known died on 23 September 1901.

Meanwhile, back at Wave Hill, the trials and tribulations of Vesteys had begun. Alongside Bovril at adjacent Victoria River Downs, the English company ended up becoming one of the two largest land-holders in the Northern Territory for a period of more than 50 years (see Chapter 5). Both found the experience difficult and for much of the time unrewarding. However, a feature that set Vesteys apart from other companies appears to have been its labour relations, particu-larly in its employment of the original owners of the country. Other stations may not have had exemplary records in this regard, but Vesteys appeared to be notorious.

In 1936, the *Northern Standard* (published by the North Austral-ian Workers' Union) carried a report under the title 'Wave Hill Stock Camp. Blacks Preferred To Whites. You Can Treat Them Rough'. It detailed a complaint the union had received that a head stockman on the station had refused to employ a white cook, saying, 'Leave the [expletive deleted in original text] where they are. A blackfellow will do me; you can stick it into them.'

The report continued:

His idea, the complainant was led to believe, is that white cooks spoil the blacks. Certainly the man in question will not spoil them with kindness, for he is a regular black nigger driver and one can hear a perpetual roaring of abuse of natives from morning to night. Whatever the man's abilities are as a stockman he certainly is not a fit and proper person to hold an Aboriginal licence or to be in charge of natives.

While the report may have involved a rogue employee, it wasn't an isolated incident. Only two years later, the *Northern Standard* carried another report that suggested the problems went deeper. Bad food was again the root of the problem but it had got to the point that, 'There was so much trouble that stockmen, jackeroos and half-castes were about to leave in a body, but the management very shrewdly transferred the men to other stations.'

I was surprised to discover the discontent that led to the Wave Hill Walk-off in 1966 may have been brewing a generation earlier. The second report further detailed labour relations at the station:

> The reputation of this station is such that many station workers refuse to take employment at any of Vesteys' stations, and it has become necessary to bring jackeroos from the south to fill the positions. These men come under agreement, but they also are dissatisfied with the conditions, and there has been nothing but trouble since the last batch arrived some weeks ago. One of the newcomers, alleged to know nothing about stock work, was placed in charge of one of the camps, but even the blackfellows rebelled at this and told the boss that 'this fella too much humbug', and said they would not work with him.

This while the Great Depression still gripped the country, and up to 100 people were camped around nearby Victoria River Downs, hoping for work.

If the problems really were that bad, Vesteys were able to keep them out of sight later that year, when the Federal Minister for the Interior, Jack McEwen, visited Wave Hill. All the special correspondent for the *Sydney Morning Herald* noticed was that 'the station has an excellent postal service, combined with bank and money order office'. The report was titled Minister's 'Party at Wave Hill. Bird Life Seen'.

A decade later, if anything, conditions were worse. In 1949, the *Northern Standard* claimed the station employed 20 whites and 250 Indigenous people, including 37 under the age of seven and another 37 under the age of ten. None was being schooled. No wages were paid to any of the Indigenous staff. Instead they were given a slice of bread and a piece of beef for every meal. The *Standard* also detailed what it described as a vicious practice:

> As there's a surplus of native labor at the station, some natives are worked for only six months and then a new team is started. This means

that for six months the native has to fend for himself when he is sent 'walkabout'. In those six months a white stockman would earn about £145 and, perhaps, be able to have a holiday. But the native is forced to live on lilyroots and bandicoots. Thus he is only too pleased to get his job back on the station to obtain a bit of white man tucker. So the vicious racket continues.

The poor conditions may have prompted the station's traditional owners to walk off the job around 1953. At the time the North Australian Workers' Union didn't have a field officer for the area and hadn't been advised of the strike action. Without any outside support, the strikers were eventually starved back to work.

The goings-on at Wave Hill couldn't stay hidden forever. By the mid-1960s developments with far-reaching consequences were spreading across the outback. The construction of all-weather 'beef roads' was revolutionising the transport of stock to markets.

At Wave Hill, the end of droving can be dated almost to the day. In *The Murranji Track* drover Mick Coombes explained that in 1967 he took the last mob of cattle from Wave Hill (and the second-last mob from any station) down the infamous Murranji. As had happened with many mobs before, the cattle rushed and he may have lost up to three-quarters of the stock in his care. Some were found up to 160 kilometres from where the rush started. He believed the incident prompted Vesteys to stop walking cattle to Queensland and switch to road trains.

The date may be right, but the motivation may not be. The beef road to Wave Hill was under construction in 1966 and completed in 1967. From then on, Wave Hill beef went by road.

An unexpected by-product of the beef roads was that they made it a lot easier for people, and ideas, to travel to the stations. And the latter were far less isolated from the eyes of the world. This just as major strides in attitudes towards Indigenous Australians were taking place. Civil rights activists, fired by developments in the United States, couldn't help noticing the glaring injustices in their own backyard. Indigenous leaders formed a national representative body, FCAATSI, as the nation prepared for a referendum in 1967 that would effectively recognise Indigenous Australians as citizens for the first time.

In March 1966, the unions and activists had a major win, when pastoral workers were awarded equal wages, regardless of their race, although stations employing Aboriginal workers were given two years to comply with the law.

Thus the push for equal rights and equal pay for traditional owners, coincided with the exact moment in history when the services of many of them were no longer required by outback stations. White stockmen were similarly affected. Some of the white drovers saw the writing on the wall around 1965 and moved on to other things, many leaving the cattle industry permanently.

For traditional owners, it wasn't so easy. In the case of Wave Hill, Nat Buchanan had managed to arrive at an accommodation (not without tensions and bloody incidents) that preserved the traditional owners' connections with their country, even as the cattle station was formed around them. They allowed cattle to graze their country while providing their labour and receiving station rations, cash payment or a combination of the two. However, even as early as 1949, the *Northern Standard* estimated there was only enough work for half the available workforce.

Generally, stations employing traditional owners paid them less than white stockmen, with the justification that they also provided for their families as well, and food was a component of the payment (or in some cases the only payment). While there were elements of exploitation in such relationships, there was another, unresolved issue that had managed to go unnoticed for decades: what would happen if the relationship between the cattle station and the traditional owners broke down?

The issue finally surfaced at Wave Hill Station in 1966. In the wake of the March wages decision, the traditional owners of Wave Hill, who identified themselves as Gurindji, were attempting to negotiate with the station's management, Vesteys, for better pay and conditions. They were supported by the North Australian Worker's Union and author Frank Hardy, who travelled to the region in June of that year. Predictably, Vesteys was extremely reluctant to do anything, at least until 1968, when equal pay would become compulsory.

In August, the negotiation reached a crisis point. At that point, the Gurindji decided they'd had enough, stopped work and walked off their camp at the homestead. One of the most significant moments in the history of Indigenous land rights was initially described as a strike, but it soon became apparent that there was much more at stake. At the time, many of the traditional owners may have been out of work already, or were about to be.

In any event, when the Gurindji walked off, they didn't actually leave the station. To do so would have seen them trespass on land that, according to their law, belonged to other traditional owners. So they set up camp 10 kilometres down the Victoria River from the Wave Hill homestead.

As the union endeavoured to continue negotiations, it also provided support for the 'striking' workers, in the form of food, clothing, makeshift shelters and transport. However, as time went on, it became increasingly apparent that the traditional owners never wanted to work for Vesteys again. The century-old relationship between the cattle station and the Gurindji was finished. What would happen next was anyone's guess.

Early in 1967, the traditional owners relocated to Wattie Creek, near Wave Hill Station's boundary with Limbunya Station, a site of cultural significance and an area partly covered by a Miners Right already held by three Gurindji. However, they still faced the problem that in common law they had only a tenuous right to be there. Nevertheless, one of the leaders of the walk-off, Vincent Lingiari, articulated the view of the traditional owners. It was quoted by Frank Hardy in his book *The Unlucky Australians*, 'I bin thinkin' this bin

Gurindji country,' Lingiari said. 'We bin here long time before them Vestey mob.'

His assertion was that he still thought of the land as belonging to the Gurindji. All Vesteys owned was the cattle. With the benefit of hindsight, it was an incredibly powerful statement of a simple fact: his people had enjoyed unbroken tenure of the land and nothing had yet occurred to change that. No treaties, no agreements, no formal notifications and no compensation. At best there was a blanket annexure made so far away and in a foreign language that no court today would countenance it for an instant. And indeed, Vesteys only leased the land, which in common law belonged to no man. It was still Crown Land, an ethereal concept of ownership only one step removed from *terra nullius*.

By April the Gurindji had articulated a plan to lease 1300 square kilometres of Wave Hill themselves, either to run their own cattle station or to remain there under the protection of a mining lease. They had begun establishing a permanent presence at what they now called 'Daguragu', with gardens, houses, sanitation and fencing. They erected a sign describing the area as the 'Gurindji Mining Lease and Cattle Station'.

Back at Wave Hill Station, the original Aboriginal camp was bull-dozed by station management to erase evidence of the conditions they'd been complaining about.

Hardy and local Aboriginal Welfare Officer Bill Jeffrey wrote a petition to the Governor-General, Lord Casey, on behalf of Vincent Lingiari, Pincher Manguari, Gerry Ngalgardji and Long-Johnny Kitgnaari, asking him to consider their 'desire to regain tenure of our tribal lands', specifically the return of the 1300 square kilometres they'd identified, on the basis that they would match the lease payments currently being paid for the land by Vesteys.

With regard to compensation for Vesteys, they pointed out that the company had been more than compensated over the previous 50 years by unpaid work by their fathers, and meagre wages subsequently. They told the Governor-General, 'Morally the land is ours.'

The Gurindji were in a relatively rare (but not unique) situation compared to other traditional owners. At that time many were living on Aboriginal reserves that comprised at least some of their country, or they could apply for Crown Land with which they had a traditional association. However, all the Gurindji lands were covered by pastoral leases.

The Gurindji were sent a response in June 1967, not from the Governor-General but from his secretary, who rejected the Gurindji's petition, pointing out that the Vesteys' lease still had until 2004 to run and while they had a right to enter leased land to hunt for traditional food sources and drink the water, they couldn't establish sole occupancy over any part of it. They also couldn't stay on the land they'd occupied under the terms of a Miners Right because it wasn't in a proclaimed mining area. While outlining the legal position in detail, the Governor-General's secretary avoided any reference to the moral dimension the Gurindji had raised.

However, the Gurindji weren't about to go away. Nor was the problem. The Gurindji were offered opportunities to resettle on other stations and on land reserved 'for the use and benefit of the Aborigines'. These offers were rejected because the country involved belonged to other groups of traditional owners.

While there were threats and intimidation from the Wave Hill management and local police, the Gurindji remained at Daguragu throughout 1967 and into 1968, while a groundswell of support for their claim and land rights generally spread throughout the wider community. The fact there was no concerted attempt to evict them may have had as much to do with the civil rights firestorm it might unleash as the fact that the logistics of doing so were beyond the resources of the Northern Territory administration.

It took a change of government, in November 1972, to change the political landscape. Gough Whitlam and the Labor Party had gone to the election with a policy to legislate in support of the land rights of traditional owners. Even then it took three years for the claim of the Gurindji to finally be recognised. It effectively involved Vesteys surrendering its Wave Hill lease and the government reissuing two leases, one to Vesteys for Wave Hill reduced in size to 13 500 square kilometres and a second lease to the Gurindji for 3300 square kilo-metres excised from the original station. The Gurindji land included the original Wave Hill homestead, which was subsequently moved to its present location.

On 16 August 1975, prime minister Gough Whitlam travelled to Daguragu to ceremonially return the land to the Gurindji. Under a makeshift awning, he poured a handful of dirt into Vincent Lingiari's hand and said, 'Vincent Lingiari, I solemnly hand to you these deeds as proof in Australian law that these lands belong to the Gurindji people, and I put into your hands part of the earth as a sign that this land will be the possession of you and your children forever.'

It was a significant moment in Australian history. However, it's doubtful the politicians and traditional owners really understood quite how hard it was to run a cattle station. The Gurindji had boasted in their petition to the Governor-General, 'We know how to work cattle better than any white man.' They may have been right, but as detailed throughout this book, there's a lot more than stock handling involved in making a cattle station work. And the big country had defeated some of the best, the brightest and the richest.

When visiting most of the stations in this book, it was my intention to do a bare minimum of research before arriving. The idea was to avoid the baggage of preconceptions that might colour my impres-sions. However, with a place as famous as Wave Hill, that wasn't possible.

As I turned off the Buntine Highway and drove the short distance to the modern homestead site, I was trying to maintain a veneer of professionalism despite the thrill of actually being there. To some people the house paddock might be no different to any other paddock in the Top End. Yet associations with some of the significant shifts in Australia's physical and social landscape could be traced to this country.

Despite this, I was feeling a little down after visiting the Big Run, not because I hadn't been well looked after, but from the firsthand experience of the efficiency in modern cattle station operations. It meant they were no longer a significant source of much-needed employment in the region. Driving through seemingly endless empty landscapes, it was hard not to wonder: What else was there?

Wave Hill was noticeably drier than Victoria River Downs, which adjoined it just to the north. Yet the Wave Hill homestead precinct was every bit as lush as VRD. Giant figs, bougainvillea and frangipani shaded the lawns of a central quadrangle, around which most of the accommodation, dining and recreational buildings were arranged.

Manager Greg Dakin and his wife, Allison, met me at the manager's house and we went through the slightly awkward introductions and exploration of what I actually wanted and what they were in a position to provide. For me, the process wasn't getting any easier but Greg and Allison were the kind of people I readily warm to. Greg was in his mid-thirties and had a friendly, easygoing manner that didn't disguise the focus and drive that typified every manager I'd met. Allison had all the frayed edges of a woman raising five young kids, but she had a focused intelligence that suggested there was more to her than being a housewife and mother.

When Greg understood I was happy to tag along and avoid getting in his way, while asking as many questions as I could, he was happy for me to accompany him on a drive to see how his stock camp was going marking calves. He relaxed further as he drove and realised I was genuinely interested in the station and its operations.

He described the place as a mixture of river flats and open rolling plains, grassy with belts of scrub that gave way to downs country and even a treeless plain more like the Barkly Tablelands than the Top End. When we reached the area he was talking about, sure enough, an unbroken expanse of Mitchell grass spread to the horizon. In the distance a road train was silhouetted against the sky, creeping along like a caterpillar with a plume of dust rising in its wake. There was also what he called desert (spinifex and scrub country). On the western boundary, along the Victoria River, there were gullies with sweet grasses.

The property runs mostly Brahmans, which it has done for the last two decades, but in the last five years Charolais bulls have been introduced for their high meat content, and due to market preference that's as much to do with fashion as the qualities of the breed. More recently, Droughtmasters have been brought in to increase fertility.

The station doesn't have much of a tick problem, having run tick-resistant Brahman cattle for so long. The Charolais carry more but Greg believed the ticks were more of a problem on the neighbouring property ('blackfella country' as he put it, or 'the bit they took off us', as one of his staff said), which was still running Shorthorns.

Wave Hill ran 50000 head and could carry more but surprisingly, after operating for more than a century, it was still not fully developed. Only the northern half of the two leases that comprised the station – Cattle Creek and Wave Hill – were being used.

'It is our plan to extend the usable area over the next few years,' Greg said. 'We will put in waters, fencing and build yards and roads. It has been attempted before but money is an issue. When times are good there's more opportunity. At the same time, there's room for efficiency improvements in our existing herd. At present we have a lower branding percentage [of calves] than we would like, so if we could lift that by even 10 per cent, with an operation this size, we're talking significant numbers.'

The station operates year-round with a staff of 17, supplying cattle for live export. The Buntine Highway, that passes through the property, is sealed, so during the wet, cattle ready for market are held in paddocks adjoining the road. If the contracts are there and road trains are allowed to use the road – 'they'll cut it up if it's too wet' – they're yarded up and sent on their way.

The property was owned by Western Grazing Company, whose portfolio includes the Channel Country property Tanbar; Rocklands,on the Queensland–Territory border; and Morestone, Oban and Magowra, in Queensland's Gulf Country. Western Grazing was a family company, established by Queensland dairy farmer Brian Oxenford, who bought Wave Hill from the financially battered Vesteys in 1992.

At the time, after nearly a decade of low cattle prices, a spike had allowed the English to exit the property with something approaching a decent return. The company is now owned by Brian's daughter, Pam Dearmer, after she bought out the other members of her family.

When it came to hiring staff, Greg reckoned that if they checked out all right and they were prepared to ring him, he'd give them a chance.

'We've got one fellow, he was a plumber,' he said. 'Couldn't ride a horse, didn't know what a cow was. No one else would give him a go but I did and he's one of the best in the camp. He started out a bore runner and now he's doing everything. He'd already showed he had the application to stick at an apprenticeship for lousy money and instead of going to work in the mines he wanted to work on a big cattle station for not much money. Another fellow is a retired dairy farmer who just wanted to work.'

I asked him if Wave Hill was an equal opportunity employer, as they'd say down south.

'We employ women,' he replied, cutting to the chase. 'I actually worked on a station where I was the only male. It had a female head stockman and an all-female crew. It wasn't planned that way but that's how it worked out. My approach is I pay women the same as the men but they're treated the same. They can't say I can't lift that or I can't do that. If they don't like it, they go.'

He also accepted that most young people won't stay long. They want to see the world and don't want to be working for the same boss for five or six years. That said, he explained, 'We like to get young people because we can form them. They're better than a lot of kids who've been raised on places like this because there are many things they won't do. They think it's beneath them.'

As we drove along he pointed out a strange-looking calf, a fluffy Charolais–Brahman cross. 'I don't know what's going on there,' Greg said, 'but I see that beast every time I go through here.'

It's sufficiently odd that he doubts that it's marketable. The live-export market can be quite particular about things like hide colour. Buyers used to only want white cattle but now they'll take some grey and brown. Cattle from Wave Hill go to Brunei, Malaysia, Thailand and the Middle East. They were also going to Indonesia, but shortly after my visit *Four Corners* screened its program that revealed animal cruelty in a handful of Indonesian abattoirs, including one beast with a Wave Hill ear tag. The federal minister for primary industry promptly banned live exports, only to resume it shortly after as the ramifications of his decision sank in, ultimately including the prospect of stations shooting large numbers of surplus cattle that had nowhere to go.

Greg grew up on family properties near Gympie in Queensland. When his mother died of cancer his father sold all the properties and retired.

'We were doing a bit of everything,' Greg explained. 'Lucerne, crops, wheat, a Droughtmaster stud. I was working for very little, thinking one day I would inherit some of it, but I ended up with nothing.'

Allison, who originally came from the Charleville district but had moved closer in when she met Greg, thought it was time to do something different.

'So we went to work on a property we thought was huge,' Greg said. 'I'd gone from 2000 acres [800 hectares] of intensive farming and thought 40000 acres [16200 hectares] was huge. I was a shitkicker, a station hand, and worked my way up. I became head stockman at Meteor Downs, then assistant manager of Brunette

Downs. I was then promoted to a manager of Carrum Station, near Julia Creek. We then moved into Townsville for six months, thinking to make a heap of money in the mines. And Allison was too ill to keep working while pregnant with our daughter Sarah. We originally meant to stay for six months but got jack of it. I then returned to station life as manager of Portland Downs, near Isisford. We realised when we came back how much the kids missed it.'

And now Greg was managing what to me was the most famous cattle station in the country, which he'd been doing since 2010. Was there any extra status in overseeing one of the biggest stations in Australia?

'I don't like to big-note, but yes,' Greg said. 'It is a step up. Managing one of these big places puts you at the top. I reckon within a day of getting the job the whole industry knew who I was, where I'd been, what I'd done, what disasters I'd got through or caused.

'Coming in, there's a learning curve. It doesn't take long to learn the layout and overlay experience of other places but in this business there's always something new. I tell my people, "You might know the way to do something, like muster a paddock, but you've got to be ready to adapt. Say the chopper breaks down, what are you going to do then?" You never know what it's going to be but you use your experience to find a way through.'

We pulled up at Camerons Yard, where 3000 Brahman cows and weaners were being held. The road train we'd seen earlier was at the ramp loading weaners bound for the paddocks that were nearer to the homestead and the sealed road. In the yards they were also weighed and grouped so they grew out to a consistent size for market. While they're held near the homestead they're mustered and handled frequently, to get them more used to being around people.

'It costs us a little more but it pays in ease of handling later,' Greg explained. 'We get orders specifically asking for Wave Hill cattle because they are so much easier to deal with.'

Over at the calf cradle, Greg wasn't wrong about women having to do the same work as the men. They were branding, castrating, dehorning and ear-marking calves. When one particularly athletic fella managed to turn himself backwards in the cradle, they were called upon to employ considerable strength to turn him back around. However, I noticed that when something like that happened, other members of the stock camp moved in to help, without having to be asked.

Driving back from the yards, along a different route, when I climbed into the ute after opening and closing yet another gate, I mentioned that figuring out how some of them worked was a bit of an intelligence test.

'Some of those old gates have killed stockmen in days gone by,' Greg said. 'They've got their fingers caught and didn't have the strength with one arm to lift the bar. They haven't had a knife to cut their fingers off, so they stayed there till they died.'

These days, such a thing was virtually impossible. As with each station I visited, the whereabouts of all staff are constantly monitored. If someone doesn't call, the search begins.

We weren't far from the homestead when we came upon a mob of weaners being poked along the road. I got out to take some photos and risked lying on the road while the stock walked quietly past and around me. The young Brahmans didn't seem at all concerned, although I sensed Greg was having kittens. Greg pointed out a young boy of about 12, droving the cattle along with two jillaroos. It was his son, Billy.

As the sun set and the cattle slowly walked along, the youngster looked to be in his element. He was supposed to be doing his schoolwork but instead was getting life experience you'd never find in books. As the stock drifted away from us, it was hard not to feel he had already gained something someone like me would always lack.

Back at the station, the staff who weren't out at the stock camp gathered for drinks at the social club before dinner, along with various contractors who were also about the property. They sat on a patio area overlooking the central quadrangle. Despite it looking immaculate, the gardener, Kate, apologised that she hadn't raked off the leaves over in one corner.

When the dinner bell started to chime, everyone headed into the dining building. Inside, the food was being laid out by a man who looked to be in his thirties, dressed in a buttoned-up white jacket and houndstooth-patterned trousers. He looked every inch a chef. Greg introduced him as 'Chris, the Wave Hill Poisoner'. Chris laughed, explained what was on the menu, then dashed off to his stoves.

The food looked fantastic. There was beef, of course, but a range of options and a choice of condiments. There were vegetables done several ways, including something that looked suspiciously like a ragout. Things had certainly changed since the Vesteys' days.

Breakfast was similarly impressive, apart from the fact that it was at 6 a.m. After stuffing myself on bacon, eggs, sausages, toast, coffee and juice, I washed up my utensils while staff who were heading out onto the property for the day made cut lunches and helped themselves to fresh fruit.

I went out and strolled around the homestead area, taking photos in the early light. Over by the road train, I met Curly who was, like all truckies named Curly, completely bald. He was getting ready to head out to the yards to pick up another load of weaners. The journey from the yards to the house could take him up to five hours each way. Sometimes it took longer when he had to detour to ensure he didn't bog on soft sections of road, especially when loaded with cattle. When empty, the three-trailer road train weighed 60 tonnes. Loaded, it weighed 120.

Not long after daylight, chopper pilot Zeb Leslie arrived to take me out for a fly. He was helping to muster cattle that had been turned out from the yards the previous night to graze in an adjacent paddock. Half of the 3000 cows had to be returned to the yards for the day to be preg-tested. The remaining 1500 would be tested the following day.

On the way out to the yards, Zeb gave me a tour of some of the property's features: verdant waterholes surrounded by paperbark trees, rugged flat-topped bluffs ringed by spectacular red-stone cliffs lit by the rising sun. And grass – endless seas of grass. My heart beat pace with the chopper's thudding blades. Here was the vision splendid. Buchanan's grass castle. Gurindji country. And my country, Australia. I felt privileged to have such an unforgettable view laid before my eyes.

Zeb had been a stockman before he decided to become a chopper pilot and undertook the costly lessons at his own expense. His experience showed now as he remained at altitude, putting gentle pressure on the 3000 white Brahmans below to move them towards the yards. He coordinated with the horsemen and a motorbike rider on the ground using two-way radio. There was none of the spectacular swooping and diving typically associated with aerial mustering. Instead he made slow passes along the flanks of the herd as it moved towards the yards, in a growing cloud of dust. When he thought the required number of cattle had passed through the gate into the holding paddock, he alerted the dust-shrouded ground crew, who closed it, dividing the herd.

Zeb then helped push the herd that was about to be preg-tested into the yards for the day. There was a bit of action when a couple of cows tried to break from the mob, but the ground crew spurred their horses in a flash to cut them off. The bright shirts many stockmen preferred made sense amid the dust and cattle. From the air and on the ground they made them highly visible. Of course, the glowing white cattle stood out like beacons.

Job done, Zeb dropped down to land near the yards. As we descended we noticed a dingo harassing a cow and young calf. If the dingo could run the cow for long enough, it would eventually become exhausted and become separated from the calf, leaving it vulnerable. Losses of calves to dingoes can be substantial on Wave Hill and the company invests a significant amount to control dog populations.

Over in the yards 1500 cows were now waiting to be preg-tested. Greg was washing up in preparation for a day ahead, which was going to be anything but pleasant. His crew were lining up cows in a race as he pulled on a glove that reached up to his shoulder. He then slid his arm into the first beast of many, to assess whether it was in calf or not. It was then released into the yard for pregnant cows. If it wasn't in calf it would have gone into another yard, for empty cows destined to be culled.

Now there were just 1499 to go. It was one of those moments that made a job that involved staring at a computer screen most days look attractive. It also typified the role of a manager: Greg was the most senior person on the place but the only one with the skills for this distinctly hands-on task. After a dozen cows had been put down the race and tested, the routine for the next however many hours had been established. It would go on for the next two or three days.

When I'd seen enough, Zeb flew me back to the station. He landed to refuel and we got talking. He was a resident at Kalkarindji, the township adjacent to Daguragu, where he ran a butchering business. It turned out he was leasing the land that was handed back to the community after the Wave Hill Walk-off. He asked me where I was going after I left the station. When I told him I planned to pop over to Kalkarindji to 'see what a success the hand-back has been', he caught my ironic tone.

'That's a good way of putting it,' he said with a laugh.

He told me about some of the problems he'd seen in the community. He had on occasion been confronted and threatened, sometimes by people who expected to be given meat for free. He had seen young men turn their backs on opportunities to pursue careers in sport and others who returned to a world of unemployment, welfare dependence, alcohol and violence. Despite being part of the community, there were many things he struggled to understand.

Our conversation digressed to the problems with young people generally. Even Zeb's two-year-old son had him scratching his head. 'When we were young we did as we were told,' he said, 'but when I tell him to clean up his toys he just refuses.'

After a while I asked Zeb how old he was. When he said he was 32, I couldn't resist saying, 'You know, Zeb, we're starting to sound like our fathers.'

He laughed heartily.

As luck would have it, I was back at the homestead before lunch, so took the opportunity for a chat with Chris, the Wave Hill Poisoner, in the mess building. While we talked, he made chicken satays.

Chris Scobell, 43 and a qualified chef, had worked in Cairns, on the Great Barrier Reef islands and at the Alice Springs casino. He was raised in Jindalee and apprenticed to Peter Hall, who operates a 40-seater BYO restaurant with set menus and a dynamic approach to food. He also did French patisserie for a year.

It all sounded a long way from piling food into hungry stockmen on Wave Hill.

'I worked in the Cairns International Hotel on the third floor of the basement,' he explained. Then he gestured to the kitchen window. 'Here, it's beautiful. The motive for coming is lifestyle. A chef's life is a chef's life. Now I get to spend more time with my kids, Maya, who's two, and Zachary, 14 years old. My wife, Kate, is the gardener.'

The move also meant taking a pay cut but it was balanced by substantial savings on expenses, such as daycare for 55 hours a week. There was also less pressure, although it was always busy.

After lunch, I went in search of Allison, manager Greg Dakin's wife. She was hanging out washing when I found her and was happy to chat. I sat on the back steps of her house, taking notes. When she finished at the clothesline, she suggested we move to a table and chairs some distance from the house and kids. I suspected answering questions was a small price to pay for a bit of a break.

She talked about the Wave Hill population as a community but was quite direct when it came to why it worked as well as it did. 'Basically, it's because there's zero tolerance for bullshit.'

That would do it. She also didn't consider the station as remote.

'I've lived worse,' she said. 'Before here, we were three hours from a small country town. Now we're only 40 kilometres from Kalkarindji. Kalkarindji has a store and everything. I don't think it's remote.'

We laughed about the fact that there weren't many people who would say proximity to a flyspeck outback town meant they weren't remote. Allison pointed out that things have changed. The place she was brought up on, in western Queensland, had a party line and no power during the day. Now stations had things like the Internet.

It made a big difference for her five children, who she described as, 'William (Billy), who you saw yesterday skipping school, aged 12; Victoria (Vicki or Sissy) a mad-keen artist, 11; Jaclyn who is musical and plays the violin, aged eight; Georgia (special George) aged five; and Sarah, two.'

All the school-aged children accessed the School of the Air with the help of Allison and a governess.

Allison did admit that remoteness manifested itself in less obvious ways.

'We have had some medical emergencies. Vicki had what we found out was appendicitis. One night she was incredibly sick. We spoke to the clinic [in Kalkarindji] which spoke to the doctor in Darwin. We had to get her to Kalkarindji because there were no lights on our strip, but we didn't want to drive through Green Can Hill [a section of road frequented by binge drinkers who littered the road with green VB beer cans] to get to Kalkarindji. So they said be there at eight in the morning. She was still in pain and they thought they should check for appendicitis, so we had to wait ten hours for the plane.

Fortunately there was a brilliant nurse in Kalkarindji, Tom. He quickly realised what was going on and gave her antibiotics. By the next morning in Darwin she was feeling a lot better. They thought she could go home but we insisted that she stay to get properly checked

out. It was a good thing we did because it's not like you can just pop
back. It was eventually found that her appendix had fused to her
bowel, requiring surgery.'

Vicki eventually made a full recovery and while her mum and I
talked, she was playing on a rope swing nearby, successfully avoiding her schoolwork. Allison referred to other incidents, including a
25-year-old woman who had a heart attack and a bore runner who
lost a couple of fingers, but overall she felt safer on the station than
she did in a city.

As we talked the air was full of birdsong. There were butcher birds
in the trees and brolgas out on the plain. Sitting in the shade, I felt
the station was an idyllic spot, particularly for those who made it the
centre of their world rather than somewhere on the fringe.

On the station Allison saw her role as supporting her partner,
Greg. She knew of some women who did their own thing but most
saw themselves as part of a team.

'Greg looks after the cattle,' she said. 'I help keep up with paperwork. It is a role. I'm actually quite private but have to involve myself
anyway. You can't not participate. Some of the young ones need extra
attention. And like it or not, managers on these places have a lot of
power. The previous manager was a lot stricter than Greg. And I've
seen some who make kids' lives hell. So I have to be a mother to
some but I do have other interests. I'm currently studying for a law
degree part-time.' I'd thought there was more to Allison than raising
kids. Mind you, I couldn't imagine there'd be much need for a lawyer
at Wave Hill, at least not these days.

'I don't plan to work as a solicitor,' she explained, 'but being only
40 kilometres from Kalkarindji there would be plenty of work around
court sessions when the travelling magistrate visits. There is usually a long list when they come and I'm thinking I could do the client
interviews and other bits and pieces.'

For the moment, Wave Hill seemed to be her future. She and Greg
didn't own property or other assets, but the situation suited them.

'It's a great place to raise kids,' she said. 'It's wherever they're happy, that's the main thing.'

Early the next morning, after leaving the station, I drove over to Kalkarindji. Along the way I looked for the National Trust-listed heritage trail that marked the route of the Walk-off from the original homestead. If there were any signs, I either missed them or they had long since disappeared.

There was no missing Green Can Hill, 5 kilometres out of Kalkarindji. While still on the open road, large signs reduced the speed limit to 40 km/h. Other signs warned: 'Watch Out For People'. At the top of a rise there was a large vandalised sign that indicated that beyond that point was an alcohol- and pornography-free zone, part of the federal government's Northern Territory intervention, a drastic attempt to deal with the catastrophic social problems that afflicted the Territory's Indigenous population. The ground all around the sign was littered with beer cans. Nearby were the ashes of old camp fires. The bent and twisted sign had the words 'fight racism' scrawled across it.

Kalkarindji, population 350, turned out to be a sharp contrast to the order of the nearby cattle station. It was a standard-issue outback ghetto where taxpayer-funded alcoholism was destroying the lives of generations of people. The store was covered in steel mesh and the town was divided along racial lines between dilapidated government housing strewn with litter and the well-kept properties of the community's service providers.

A sign indicated there was a place of historical significance nearby but it wasn't clear exactly where. A man outside the shop helped me with directions. It turned out to have nothing to do with the Wave Hill Walk-off. It was a monument to a stockman from New South Wales. However, the view from the monument site did provide a good look at the tiered hill, which gave the station its name. Depressingly, it turned out to be the western flank of what is now called Green Can Hill.

The vision of the Gurindji leadership clearly hadn't been realised. The idea of a cattle station owned and operated by traditional owners hadn't eventuated. No minerals of commercial value were found. Instead, with employment opportunities on surrounding cattle stations rapidly shrinking, the Gurindji found themselves dependent on 'sit-down money' and were soon on the slippery slope to generational welfare dependence with the social and economic consequences that inevitably follow. The idealistic notion that preservation of cultural identity on traditional lands would create some kind of utopian lifestyle had disintegrated into a reality of boredom, alcoholism, disease, suicide, imprisonment and reduced life expectancy.

There's no doubt the objectives of the land-rights movement never included the creation of a soul-destroying outback underclass. Musicians Kev Carmody and Paul Kelly had described the Gurindji's land rights campaign in their song 'From Little Things Big Things Grow'. Unfortunately, what has grown is a calamity on a terrible scale.

It occurred to me, as I wandered the streets of Kalkarindji, that if the Gurindji could turn back time, they would still be right to leave Wave Hill as they did in 1966. Without their own lands, they were trapped in a dependency from which they had to escape if they were to become full citizens of Australia. In that sense, it was inevitable that land rights became part of their emancipation. It was what happened after that where things had gone terribly wrong.

Today, anyone who has compassion for their fellow Australians, regardless of race, colour or creed, can't help but be heartbroken by the entrenched misery of outback communities. Real solutions have been few and far between. Yet as lawyer, activist and community elder Noel Pearson stated in an interview on ABC's *Four Corners* in 2011, the future of remote communities may depend on radical welfare reform, communities taking greater responsibility for driving education programs and many of their young people leaving the communities to seek employment and careers elsewhere. That is probably what the best and brightest from some communities have been doing for some time. As such, the success stories disappear into mainstream Australia, while the continuing problem is painfully obvious.

Having written about Daisy Bates and the policy of easing the road to extinction with 'the dying pillow' in my book *Outback Heroes*, and about assimilation and reconciliation with John Moriarty in his book *Saltwater Fella*, it was hard not to feel like things were coming full circle. Welfare was the new dying pillow.

Ultimately, the Wave Hill Walk-off was about achieving equality. Some fifty years on, real equality is still elusive. Yet without any prompting, Wave Hill's manager Greg Dakin had explained how he treated everyone equally, and would give them a go. It's tempting to think that with highly capable people like him the great outback stations could still make real contributions to solving the problems of remote Indigenous communities.

When they've become finishing schools for Indigenous chopper pilots and station managers, and when there is no more Green Can Hill, we'll know we're making progress. For Wave Hill, there's another chapter in its remarkable history yet to be written.

TOO TYB

7. RED GIANT

Crown Point Station
22 000 square kilometres

One of the characteristics of travelling alone is that, even within a short time, your real self starts to emerge. Soon you're doing what you want, when you want, at your pace. It can be surprising, even confronting, and probably explains why most of us prefer the company of others. There's less chance we'll meet ourselves.

I was up at 3.30 a.m., driving from the Top End to the south-eastern corner of the Northern Territory. It meant travelling in darkness along the very section of road where Peter Falconio disappeared. But I was keen to reach the next station, Crown Point.

The risk of death at the hands of another traveller wasn't as great as the likelihood of colliding with kangaroos or wandering cattle. So while it was dark I poked along at 90 kilometres an hour, even though the LandCruiser has a solid bullbar covered in spotlights that lit the road ahead like it was day.

Eventually, I caught up with a road train, which gave me the comfort of some company on the journey and 120 tonnes of truck and general loading between me and whatever might be ahead.

'Road train southbound, are you on channel?' I said on my UHF radio.

'Yeah, buddy?' a voice came back.

'You okay with me tagging behind?' I asked, so he wouldn't think I was stalking him.

'No worries,' he said.

There are plenty of people who deride truck drivers, but all across the outback, with my radio on Channel 40, I'd heard plenty of colourful language but also the consideration professional drivers have for each and other road users. It was only when the odd grey nomad filled the channel with banalities that they got testy. That wasn't a problem at the moment, for the grey nomads were all parked in the roadside rest areas, trying to sleep in RVs and caravans that glowed ghostly white in the passing lights of the big rig as it rumbled by. I settled in, comforted by the line of red lights ahead of me and the glow of the LandCruiser's dashboard instruments. I tuned the AM radio to the ABC's overnight program and let Trevor Chappell (an owl who has hosted the program for years) talk me down the Stuart Highway.

As I drove I thought about home. Our heifers would be sleeping in the field near the house. Puss would be coming in about now and settling on the bed so that she could pretend she'd been there all night. My wife would be sleeping soundly, perhaps with a hand outstretched to the place where I should have been. I wondered if she could feel me reaching out to her in her dreams. My logical self said no, but the romantic in me thought otherwise.

Feeling the fondness that absence brings, I drove on, into what for me was the best part of being in the outback: first light. The first hint was a gradual definition of the great sweep of the eastern horizon as the uniform blackness gave way to the sky's darkest shade of gray. Above it, inky blackness turned to the deepest blue while the stars still shone out like diamonds. As features in the landscape gradually took shape, the horizon became a line of orange that eventually brightened into gold and yellow and slowly filled the sky, extinguishing all the stars except Venus. The light grew until trees, road and dirt changed from the shades of night to the colours of day. Sunrise was still some time away but the day had already begun. I accelerated past the road train, pulled back into my lane and gave him a wave of thanks. He flashed his lights in acknowledgement. It wasn't yet 6 a.m. and he'd already done his good deed for the day.

All through the daylight hours I drove, then into a sunset where the changing colours of the morning reversed themselves, and I returned to darkness. South of Alice Springs I'd been daunted by the roughness of the direct route south and turned back to take the long way round to Crown Point via the Stuart Highway and Kulgera. That added 150 kilometres of driving but cut the amount of dirt road by 80 kilometres.

Crown Point was certainly going to be worth the drive. When I'd first contacted its owners and managers, Don and Colleen Costello, they'd been surprised to discover that by my estimate, they weren't the largest family-owned cattle station in the world. Adria Downs, owned by the Brook family and combined with Alton Downs, was slightly larger than the station I was initially interested in, 10 787-square-kilometre Andado. However, Colleen then explained that they had only recently purchased Andado and it was now combined with New Crown Station, along with the first station they'd owned in the area, Lilla Creek. Andado had aroused my interest because at its size it qualified as big country all on its own. However, the three properties combined, and now called Crown Point, covered 22 000 square kilometres. It was the second largest cattle station in the world, after Anna Creek, not far to the south, and the largest privately owned cattle station in the world by, well, a country mile.

The establishment of all three stations was closely linked to the development of key infrastructure in Central Australia, in particular the Overland Telegraph and the Ghan railway line. The rate of establishment also reflected the slow pace of those developments.

New Crown came first, following the construction of the Overland Telegraph from Adelaide to Darwin, in 1872. It was one of a string of stations that sprang up along the line, in part due to the access to communications and the opportunities to supply meat to the operators, but also because the telegraph followed a line of permanent waters. In the case of New Crown, which was first known as Crown Point (then Old and New Crown Point, then just New Crown), it was situated on the lower reaches of the infrequently flowing Finke River, 30 kilometres north of the Charlotte Waters Telegraph Station. It enjoyed another connection with the Overland Telegraph, as it was managed in its early years by Alexander Ross, eldest son of grazier and explorer John Ross, who surveyed almost the entire route for the telegraph before construction commenced.

As early as 1891, Alexander was giving evidence before a Pastoral Commission, dispelling the growing impression of Central Australia as the dead heart of the country. While criticising the South Australian government's expenditure in the outback, describing the wells sunk on the stock routes as 'perfectly useless', he said he believed water would be found at greater depths (which was proved correct some 30 years later). He also believed that the only thing stopping the country east and west of the station from being settled was the lack of water.

At that time, New Crown covered 11 564 square kilometres, encompassing parts of Lilla Creek and Andado, and was carrying 7000 to 8000 head, not far off its capacity today.

The discovery of gold at Arltunga, north of the station, in 1902, caused a small rush to the area that provided a local outlet for beef, although it was nothing like the grand scale that had seen other cattlemen, Jim Tyson and Sidney Kidman among them, make vast fortunes from hungry miners. It didn't help that the region, like most of Australia, was in the grip of one of the worst droughts in recorded history. The killing of prospector William Lange on Crown Point Station in 1903, by a local known only as Frank, also emphasised the untamed nature of the country.

Four years later the drought was easing in other areas but its effects were still being felt at Crown Point. In 1907, the manager of the station, Mr Taylor, sent a telegram to the minister controlling the Northern Territory, informing him that the Indigenous people

120 kilometres north-west of the homestead were starving because the drought had wiped out their traditional food. The station was feeding them as best it could despite itself struggling for survival.

While the station may have been hit hard by the drought, it still managed to get through relatively intact. Some years later, Dr Herbert Basedow answered a criticism in Melbourne's *Argus* that the centre was poor pastoral country and 'almost useless sand' by citing New Crown's situation at the end of 'one of the worst droughts on record': 'The run held 8000 cattle, 1400 horses, 800 goats, 100 camels, 100 donkeys, in addition to thousands of travelling herds, and the stock running wild.'

Basedow continued, 'The secret of successful squatting in arid Australia is the "opening up" of wells and subterranean water supplies. By doing this the manager of Crown Point Station [he used the names for the station interchangeably] has in the course of a few years, and under adverse conditions increased the capacity of the run from 3000 and hopes in the near future to raise it to 12000... Some of the finest station country of arid Australia lies between Lake Eyre and the Barkly Tablelands.'

The figures on stocking rates were a bit inflated but he made a good point. A year later, in 1922, the quality and capacity of the country was again being talked up as a Commonwealth government enquiry looked at the viability of constructing a railway line from Oodnadatta to Alice Springs, and ultimately to Darwin.

At New Crown Point Station (as reports of the time called it) the Commonwealth Public Works Committee met with Thomas Pearce, the manager and a shareholder (with Sidney Kidman and others) of the Crown Pastoral Company, which owned New Crown, Bond Springs and Allandale stations. Pearce told the bureaucrats that while the property was currently carrying 8000 head it was capable of carrying 15000. He said the property was suited to running sheep except that it lacked fencing, and the cost of shepherds meant the wool company wouldn't pay.

Pearce also believed that the country needed more people who were prepared to live on their holdings and develop them. He believed many capitalists living in the cities tended to spend more money on themselves than they did on improving the water supplies on their stations, which would ultimately be of more benefit to the country. He suggested the government should put down bores and wells on pastoral leases, then hand the leases over to intending tenants, who would then be in a position to pay higher rents while not having to bear the considerable expense of sinking the bores.

The government did go about the business of sinking bores, but mainly to supply water to the Ghan railway, upon which construction started in 1926. During that year, it was noted that, as had been predicted by Alexander Ross 35 years earlier, good water was found at greater depth than bores had previously been drilled, in this case 117 metres. The water rose to 30 metres from the surface and pumping it at 1700 litres an hour only lowered the level by 3 metres. The bore was drilled on what was referred to as the 'Andado pastoral lease', *Andado* meaning stone knife in the local Arrernte language.

There had been several attempts to establish a station at Andado prior to that time. Leases were first issued in 1880 but the land wasn't settled until 1908 when two men, Robert Sharpe and David Mayfield, took up the Andado lease. Several bores were sunk during that time by George McDill, who eventually took over Andado with his brother Robert and Henry Roper in 1914.

The McDills and Roper built the first house on the property, a basic mud hut, which they upgraded when George married in 1922. At the same time, the McDills and Roper started running sheep on the property, and despite a severe drought in the late 1920s, they eventually had a flock of 1300 sheep and a herd of 420 cattle.

The completion of the Ghan railway in 1929 was welcomed by many outback stations along the route, as freight costs dropped dramatically. However, it was also the beginning of a railway journey that was to become famous for disruptions, derailments and disasters.

The railway's name was a contraction of the Afghan Express, an ironic reference made by a railway worker to the cameleers who were the backbone of outback transport and who could still outpace the Ghan when it experienced difficulties, which was often the case. The modern service, which retains the name but not the reputation, follows a different route and has justly become one of the great railway journeys of the world.

Andado was destined for a week of fame in 1939, when it was involved in an expedition led by Cecil Madigan that became the first to traverse the centre of the Simpson Desert, which was named after the washing machine magnate who sponsored the expedition.

It was a mark of how tough the region was that the desert adjacent to Andado hadn't been crossed up to that date. Explorer Charles Sturt was the first to be thwarted by it in his attempt to reach Australia's geographical centre back in 1844. He wrote in his *Narrative of an Expedition Into Central Australia:*

> From the summit of a sandy undulation close upon our right, we saw that the ridges extended northwards in parallel lines beyond the range of vision and appeared as if interminable. To the eastward and westward they succeeded each other like the waves of the sea. The sand was of a deep red colour, and a bright narrow line of it marked the top of each ridge . . . familiar as we had been to such, my companion involuntarily uttered an exclamation of amazement when he first glanced his eye over it. 'Good heavens,' said he, 'did ever man see such country!'

Madigan was a former member of Douglas Mawson's Australian Antarctic Expedition who had traded trekking the snowy wastes of Antarctica for crossing the dead heart of Australia, as he titled his subsequent book. His party included Jack Bejah, son of legendary cameleer Bejah Dervish, and soon-to-be-famous Birdsville mailman, the late Tom Kruse. The expedition used Andado Station as the starting point for what Madigan expected to be a 400-kilometre crossing that would be waterless for most of the way.

To get to the station, Kruse had to get his truck over two high sandhills, which he managed by jamming 7.5-millimetre water pipes between his truck's double rear wheels to give him traction.

Madigan described Andado as it was in 1939:

> Here we found a typical Central Australian cattle station homestead, a corrugated iron house nicely white-washed, some gum trees, well-built stockyards, and a well and windmill nearby, with the usual blacks' camp in the offing, all walled in between two high red sandridges that stretched as far as the eye could see. Everything looked very arid and there was no feed to be seen round the station.

No sooner than the expedition unloaded its gear, the sand started burying it. They set up camp near the homestead, sleeping on the ground with the sand swirling around and over them. Madigan noted that with all the chickens and goats wandering around, it wasn't just sand. In the morning a tame magpie woke them, pecking their faces in hopes of an early breakfast.

The expedition transmitted live radio broadcasts during its successful crossing, which brought the remote corner of the Northern Territory and Queensland to national attention for the first time in almost a century.

The McDills eventually sold Andado in 1942, and it was resold several times before it was bought by the Andado Pastoral Company, a partnership between H. Overton and Molly and Malcolm Clark, in 1955. The Clarks had been at Andado since 1949, with Malcolm working as overseer. The Clarks bought out Overton in 1969, by which time the old homestead site had been abandoned and a new residence built 30 kilometres closer to the railway line and telegraph. Molly turned the old place into a museum in 1972, and it soon became an attraction for increasing numbers of tourists adventuring

across the Simpson Desert from Birdsville on tracks originally bull-
dozed during mineral exploration in the area.

After Molly lost both her husband, to a heart attack, and her son,
whose road train he was driving was hit by a train, in 1978, she continued to run the station. However, her difficulties were compounded
by the Brucellosis and Tuberculosis Testing (BTEC) program, which
required the entire Andado herd to be culled. The original Ghan
line also closed in 1980, as diesel engines meant the line no longer
needed to rely on water supplies and could be moved further west.
As a result, Molly was forced to sell Andado in 1984 for a fraction of
what it was worth. In 1987 she eventually had a 45-square-kilometre
lease excised from the original, and returned to Old Andado, running
the museum until 2006, when declining health forced her to relocate
to Alice Springs.

By the time I reached the homestead at Andado, I was beyond exhaustion. I'd been travelling for seventeen-and-a-half hours, and while
opening a couple of gates on the way in to the property, I was sure
Johnny Rankine's headless stockman from Alexandria Station was
about to touch my elbow and ask me for a smoke. Finally, the lights
of Andado twinkled in the distance, and not a moment too soon.

Don and Colleen Costello came out to meet me. Colleen was as
friendly as she'd been on the phone, a real salt-of-the-earth woman
in her early fifties. Her parents had named her well, as she retained
a twinkle of her Irish heritage despite being outback-born and bred.
Don, 49, struck me as being more reserved but so quietly observant
that I doubted he ever missed much.

They both made an immediate impression; they'd kept a roast dinner hot for me in the oven. I could have kissed them.

In the kitchen they introduced me to both Raquel, a hairdresser
from Alice Springs who was going out with their son, Peter, and a
labrador named Cooper (named after the Channel Country river)

who, as Don put it, 'is here on agistment'. Their own dog had been taken by a dingo not long before. They'd heard a noise in the night but could see nothing until morning, when they found what was left of the body.

While I ate, Don and Colleen talked about the station, even though I wasn't in much shape to take it all in. They told me there was a telegraph station at the site of Old Crown Station, which was now on Lilla Creek. And Lilla Creek could also claim to be in the centre of Australia as there was a location on it that was the balance point of the whole of the country. It was a lot to take in.

All three properties were owned in partnership with Viv Oldfield, a Central Australian cattleman and businessman whose family associations with the region, from Alice Springs to the Birdsville Track, went back generations.

Don and Colleen also had long connections to the area. They were both raised in the Red Centre, Don originally in Alice Springs. He didn't know if he was related to John Costello, the great pioneer of the Queensland Channel Country and Lake Nash Station, but in the outback, where nearly everyone was connected, it was more than likely. Colleen (née Fogerty) was raised at Lucy Creek Station, north-east of the Alice. Her great uncle was Ted Colson, credited as being the first European to cross the southern section of the Simpson Desert with an Indigenous guide in the 1930s.

The couple had owned Lilla Creek for 27 years, and New Crown and Andado since 2007. Daughter Tanya, 26, lived at Lilla Creek with her husband, Ben, (the overseer) and young daughter. Their son, Peter, 24, ran a roadworks camp and helped with mustering. Raquel, his partner, was based at Andado, often on her own, but considered it better in some ways than living out of a trailer with her boyfriend. She spent her days tending the gardens, keeping house and at that time exterminating mice that were in plague proportions due to the bounty that followed floods earlier that year.

The stations were in the midst of a great season. Early in 2011, after devastating much of Queensland's coastal regions, Cyclone Yasi degenerated into a complex low-pressure system after moving inland. It reached all the way to Central Australia, where the remnants dumped 156 millimetres over a 48-hour period. The homestead at Andado was on a wide plain and once the ground became waterlogged, the rain had nowhere to go, except up. As it rose, there was water all through the place and Colleen said they went to bed with 150 millimetres of water lapping around them.

There was still plenty of water to be seen the following morning, when Colleen drove me over to the homestead at Old Andado. We had to detour around a large blue lake covered in swans, pink-eared ducks, herons, ibis and pelicans. Beyond that, the lines of sandhills started, and where water had been trapped between them there were smaller lakes. Topping the dune that Tom Kruse once struggled over, the Old Andado homestead appeared on the flats below, at the edge of another deep-blue lake that sparkled in the sun.

The homestead was just as Molly Clark left it, complete with many of her possessions, from cooking utensils to a pianola, a rusty Super Snipe car and the remains of a D2 bulldozer. Some buildings, such as the butchering shed, were makeshift affairs with thatched rooves, the support posts bent at precarious angles. The homestead was usually staffed by volunteer caretakers from the Friends of Old Andado (who also operated a website, oldandado.com). When no one was there, accommodation was available based on an honesty system of putting money in a tin.

Old Andado was an extraordinary time capsule that vividly evoked the lifestyle of an earlier outback era, where an overlay of little luxuries couldn't hide the makeshift nature of the buildings themselves and the sheer isolation of their location. The homestead was constructed of rough-hewn posts and sheets of tin, some of them held on with fencing wire. The gaps between the walls and roof, and around window and door frames, gave credence to claims of dust storms in times past covering the homestead's surfaces, centimetres deep.

On the way back to the new homestead, Colleen described her role on the station. In essence, she is a business partner and personnel manager. The three stations operate with minimal staff so a large part of her job is to make sure everyone is happy.

'I basically live out of a bag,' she said, 'doing everything from running bores to mustering, whatever is needed, even bronco branding – that was a while ago, though. In the early days at Lilla Creek, we still used to cut out bullocks on horseback.'

Between them, the three stations carry in the region of 20 000 head. Lilla Creek is fully developed with fences and waters, New Crown is 60 per cent developed and Andado is half done. The key things they have focused on with the new stations are improving waters to help the carrying capacity and fencing paddocks to make mustering easier.

Between all three properties, 5000 to 6000 head of cattle are turned off each year. They run Hereford and Angus at New Crown and Lilla Creek, which are far enough south to be tick-free, and Droughtmasters at Andado. Unsurprisingly, fertility rates also reflect the level of development on each of the stations. Fully developed Lilla Creek has a 78 per cent fertility rate, New Crown has a 68 per cent fertility rate, while Andado's fertility is over 40 per cent.

Several of the challenges in developing Andado are unique to the region. Putting up fences makes it easier to manage stock but they are harder to maintain due to feral camels, donkeys and horses, and the shifting sand.

'When we first arrived at Andado,' Colleen said, 'we shot out 2000 feral camels, which might seem like a lot, but the population in Central Australia is doubling every eight years. Before the rains came there were 1800 stringing out across the property and at times we found large numbers had perished, piled around dry waterholes. At another station they got so desperate they were eating the innards of other camels that had died.'

The camel problem was acute at Andado, which is on the edge of the Simpson Desert, but even at Lilla Creek fences had been smashed.

Meanwhile, in the sandhill country, the shifting sand frequently buries those fences not knocked over by the camels, again allowing cattle to stray. Normally, they don't go far from established waters but after rains they can travel considerable distances. When the ephemeral waters dry up, and if they can't make it back to the permanent waters, they perish.

The properties don't get channel floods like those on the other side of the Simpson Desert, but there is some floodout country where the Finke River spreads out before its waters disappear into the desert sands. The rest of the property is tableland with sweet grasses, including some Mitchell grass. There is beautiful swamp country around Indinda swamp and Old Andado. While Andado is in a very low rainfall area, it has the advantage that the country is highly responsive to any rain it gets.

Said Colleen, 'Fifteen millimetres at the right time makes a difference. If it falls at the right time in a reasonable year, the growth that comes up can last two years without another drop. It will make no difference to your bottom line. After that you will have to make a few decisions.'

By that she meant reduction of stock numbers. Fortunately, with road trains it is possible to avoid stock perishing as the feed runs out.

Tourists still travel through the properties on the public road from Kulgera to Old Andado. The road then loops around to a stand of waddi trees in Mac Clarke reserve, north of the homestead, before returning to Alice Springs along a rough but scenic route that takes in the starkly beautiful eastern MacDonnell Ranges. Another road leads down to Mt Dare, a setting-off point for four-wheel-drive adventurers crossing the Simpson Desert to Birdsville.

In reality, few people pass through the remote property, although some have been found nosing around buildings, thinking they have a right to go anywhere they want simply because they are in a four-wheel drive and nothing has been locked up.

'As a general rule,' Colleen explained, 'we prefer people stay on the tracks and for anything else they should check with the property's management first.'

Despite the immense size of Crown Point, it operates year-round with a staff of only 12, which rises to 16 during mustering, including contractors. 'That means there's only one stock camp,' Colleen said, 'although Don is coming around to the idea that with such a large area he probably needs two.'

Back at the new Andado homestead, the plan had been to leave the vehicle we were in and take my LandCruiser and Colleen's bush-bashing ute over to the neighbouring station, where Don was mustering some of his cattle on agistment. When we couldn't get the ute going, we loaded all of Colleen's gear into the Truckasaurus and headed off together.

As we drove to New Crown homestead, the country looked nothing like what I'd imagined when I drove in the night before. Swathes of grass lay between ranks of red dunes dotted with spinifex. In places there were belts of gidgee and mulga. At the Finke River coolibahs and river red gums lined the banks and also grew in the dry riverbed.

'After the flood, when the river was going down,' Colleen told me, 'we had a woman come through here in a vehicle with three children under the age of five. She was going to drive straight through, thinking it was shallow right across but I insisted that we check it first. I got right to the far side before I found the river had cut a channel 6 feet [1.8 metres] deep. If she had driven into that . . . it doesn't bear thinking about.'

When I asked her whether she had a pilot's licence, to help her get around during floods, Colleen had a typical outback response.

'Nah, those planes are bad medicine,' she said. 'One drop can kill you.'

The paddock being mustered was north of the town of Finke, yet another outback welfare town located in the middle of nowhere. The road north formed part of the Finke Desert Racecourse and followed the old Ghan railway. It was the road I'd baulked at travelling down in Alice Springs the day before, and at the southern end it is still a heavily roaded corrugation, as opposed to a heavily corrugated road. After 40 tooth-loosening kilometres, we came to a track heading east.

The paddock turned out to be in the vicinity of Colson's Pinnacle. The peak is not as well known as the nearby Chambers Pillar, which is surprising considering it bears an uncanny resemblance to a woman's breast. We found the deserted stock camp and continued on in search of Don and his mustering crew. We managed to pick up a helicopter on the radio and moments later the pilot, Danny Rickard, landed beside us for a quick yarn before giving us directions. He then flew off while we continued on our way. For Colleen, it was a routine procedure, but when we got going again I pointed out that to an outsider it was one of those pinch-yourself experiences.

As we went bush in search of the musterers, I gingerly picked the LandCruiser's way around mulga stakes that could puncture my tyres in a moment and negotiated vertical drops where Cyclone Yasi's floodwaters had cut deep channels that could destroy the suspension. Eventually Colleen heard the cattle and the motorbikes in the distance and we pulled up to wait for them to come to us.

Another helicopter landed and pilot Rodney Mengel came over to say hello. Rodney was the burly, grey-bearded and jovial owner of Mengel's Heliservices and was there to assist with the mustering. He was also training a new pilot hoping to join his company. The new guy was flying around some distance away, looking for strays. With a chuckle Rodney said, 'He shouldn't get into any trouble. There's no cattle over there.'

Rodney said he had no problems getting pilots but was frequently disappointed by their work ethic, or lack of it. By way of example, he told of one fellow he'd agreed to give a try who then asked about pay and relocation expenses. 'I'm offering my helicopter and all the running costs while he gets experience, and that's not enough,' Rodney sighed. 'This fella I've got now is a bit different. He turned up one day after I made him the offer. He's keen and if he's any good, he'll go far.'

The mob was getting quite close and Rodney headed back to his chopper and took off. Shortly after, the first lines of cattle came stringing through the scrub. Mustering is one of those activities that most bush people don't consider to need much explanation. On smaller places where cattle are accustomed to being handled, it's a fairly routine operation. And in the paddocks at home I could just call my heifers Cassie (short for Casserole) and Barbie and they'd trot over expecting a biscuit of hay.

Not today. Quite a few of the beasts were unbranded and they were big, meaning they had not set eyes on people for some years, if ever. The only predictable thing about them was their eagerness to escape. Don pulled up in an incredibly battered ute and swapped places with Colleen. The idea was for me to have a chat while we drove along.

If I'd thought Don was very contained before, now his focus on the job at hand was intense. His mustering crew was a mixture of experienced hands and youngsters who'd been backpacking around Australia only a few months before. Don was constantly on the radio, especially to his inexperienced staff, coaching them on what to do.

The herd was volatility incarnate. One moment they were walking along quietly, the next a breakaway charged into the scrub, pursued by utes and motorcycles. It wasn't hard to understand how broken collarbones and impalement on protruding branches were common injuries among stockmen. At times, they needed to focus on several things at once – cattle, trees and creek washouts – while moving at speed.

At one point a cow that may have been injured earlier in the day tried to hide behind a tree and wouldn't move. The motorbikes nearby revved their engines with no effect. Don eventually decided to try to move the cow on foot. He left my car door open as he started walking towards her, but as he approached the animal saw him and charged. Don didn't run for it. In a cloud of dust and angry Hereford, he circled the tree for protection at a brisk pace. Only after the beast pulled up did he hot-foot it back to the car. It was a risky move but the cow had started walking again.

In breaks between high-speed manoeuvres, Don managed to talk, with somewhat divided attention.

'We get staff from all over, including backpackers,' he said, 'but I prefer tradesmen. They have a better work ethic and it's less about adventure. They can also do things when they're not doing cattle work, which can be a real bonus. A company called Outback Packer trains backpackers for station work but the boys don't like it when they've just got someone trained up and then they go.'

I mentioned a mate who had welding, truck, bobcat, forklift and other qualifications, and was also a diesel mechanic who was interested in working on an outback station. Don just looked at me deadpan and said, 'Give him my number.'

I asked if he used fixed-wing aircraft to muster.

'We only use choppers,' he said. 'I have a pilot's licence, to make it easier to get around, but I don't muster. I prefer to leave it to the specialists.'

I noted that most of the motorbike riders were wearing hats, rather than helmets.

'We provide helmets for motorcycle riders but don't insist they use them,' he said, admitting that he might soon have to. 'The main problem is they get hot and you can't hear the radio. The radio is on the shoulder pad, not in the helmet.'

There was no doubt about having to hear the radio. During mustering there is usually quite a lot of radio chatter (not always constructive), although for this crew it was very calm and specific. Each vehicle or rider had a position that was based on where they were in relation to the mob, with twelve o'clock being the direction the mob was heading, three o'clock the right flank, six o'clock the rear, and nine o'clock the left flank. So an instruction like 'watch those two at

four' meant the crew near the right rear of the mob had to watch for
a potential breakaway.

From time to time Don called a halt to give the mob a bit of a rest.
To my mind it gave them a chance to regroup for the next escape
attempt. As we travelled along, Don was getting increasingly edgy
and looked like he wanted to get back into his ute. Mustering was
clearly a combination of patience, timing and fearlessness.

'The worst accident we've had was my son-in-law Ben who had
a double break at the top and bottom of his leg when he came off a
motorbike,' Don said. 'He was out of action for six months.'

The sun was getting low when we finally reached the yards where the
cattle were to be held for the night. There the mob mustered by the
ground crew was joined by another mob mustered by the choppers.
Double the herd meant double the fun and there were breakaways
in all directions, with vehicles charging everywhere in pursuit or cutting them off. Even when the animals settled down, it was a tricky
business pushing cattle that had never seen stockyards through the
gates. Once it was done, 200 head crowded into the furthest corner
of the yard, as far as they could get from the people who had been
pursuing them all day.

The tension of mustering ebbed away as dust rose from the
yards, lit by the setting sun and framed by the backdrop of a dramatic table-topped hill ringed by cliffs of red stone. Across the plain
the grass called neverfail was changing from pale yellow to gold.
Central Australia could be a harsh and unforgiving place, but just
then it was beautiful.

'Andado and New Crown are so flat that the water just sits on
them,' Don told me. 'So you get blacksoil, the ground is fertile,
because the nutrient stays.'

It made the country perfect for fattening prime beef, and the yard
behind us was full of proof. The distance to markets meant the station

needed to turn off large bullocks, which meant the live-export market with its 350-kilogram limit wasn't an option. Instead, heavy bullocks weighing up to 700 kilograms and aged up to four years old were sent to an abattoir in Victoria.

It was surprising to discover there was a market for beef that wasn't tender yearling. Don explained, 'The meat from cattle that age is still tender; it's more a matter of how you handle them.'

Back at the stock camp, Colleen offered to return me to the comforts of the New Crown homestead, but I was interested to see what it was like to spend the night under the stars. She gave me a funny look, like until that moment I'd seemed a pretty sensible person, and left me to my fate.

It was just on dusk as everyone rolled into camp in their various utes. The bikes were left back at the yards, ready for the morning. No one needed to be told what to do as firewood was collected, the camp fire was kindled, and vehicles manoeuvred so their trays could be used as tables and the spotlights on their rollbars could illuminate the camp.

The rump of a beast that until recently had been fattening on Central Australian pasture was cut into steaks, which were soon sizzling on a hot plate. Wood was piled up for the night and the next morning. A bucket of water was put out so people could wash before dinner. A few beers were passed around and a billy was put on the fire to boil water for tea. Most of the stock crew carried their swags over to the fire and used them for seats while they ate dinner – steak and bread.

After their meal they had a few cups of tea and tuned a radio to listen to a game of football. They talked about cattle for a little while and then, at around eight o'clock, they started getting ready to turn in. The radio was turned off, even though the game was far from over. I was expecting them to roll their swags out around the fire but instead everyone drove their utes away or walked off in separate directions to find a quiet spot to sleep on their own. Some rolled out their swags on the trays of their utes so they wouldn't be bothered by the rodents that were everywhere due to the mouse plague.

By 8:15 p.m. all was quiet, but for the distant snoring of sleeping stockmen and the constant sound of scurrying rodents. Far above, the night sky was full of stars. Down below, the mice were close to matching them in number.

Not being as tired as the stock camp, I sat by the fire writing up my notes. With no one to notice, I decided to forgo the authentic stock camp experience and put up my vermin-proof tent fly so I could put my swag inside it. Sleep came easily, although in the early morning I was woken by a bull that came groaning and bellowing around the camp. After half an hour, it took its mournful noise beyond earshot, only for it to be replaced by the blood-curdling screams of a fox.

I woke again at 4 a.m. and was wide awake by 4.30. The temperature was near freezing. It was warm and snug in my swag but I got up and stoked the fire, rummaging quietly to make a cup of tea, expecting that the camp would be up before dawn. Not so. The eastern horizon was just turning from black to deep blue when they started to wake. By 5:30 a.m. they were up and about, emerging from their swags fully clothed. It turned out that two fellas in the stock camp didn't have swags: one had slept in a ute, or had tried to, while the other slept in his clothes on the ground.

Breakfast comprised sausages, bread and tea. Its preparation and consumption was a matter of a few minutes, by which time there was just enough light to see clearly. Having slept as long as possible, they'd timed their waking to perfection. The camp was away and over at the yards by dawn.

I started the morning with Don in his ute. The objective for today was to drove the cattle to a set of yards on Finke River Road, from where they could be trucked back to Lilla Creek.

When the gates of the yards were opened, the cattle were reluctant to leave what they now considered a safe place, especially as they

faced a collection of motorbikes and utilities. They eventually moved
out when a couple of motorcycles circled behind them.

Don's plan was to walk the cattle out onto the nearby flat and settle
them for a few minutes before starting to drove them. It seemed like
a good plan but the mob took it as yet another opportunity to make
breaks in several directions. Vehicles accelerated away in clouds of
dust to cut them off.

Don was back on the radio. While he had to give plenty of instructions to his less-experienced crew, people like New Crown manager
Victor Snelling needed no instruction at all. I noticed that when a
break headed for Don and Victor, they both reacted instinctively. Don
was extremely busy, constantly looking all around the vehicle as the
herd surged first one way, then another.

At one point a young bull came out of the herd, saw Don's ute,
turned around and went straight back in. Don said, 'Did you see that?
Yesterday, he hadn't seen a human being in his life, but he's already
learnt to pull up under pressure. Stock that have joined the herd, and
cleanskins, take a while to learn, but then they're good for life.'

While Don was watching the cattle, the cattle were watching him.
In a quiet moment I tried to get his photograph with the cattle behind
and asked him to turn towards the camera. As soon as he did, the
cattle beside the vehicle took off. Don must have seen my jaw drop
because he was already reacting before he'd turned back or I was
able to shout 'go'.

Gradually the herd started to settle and Don told his crew, 'Righto,
let's get 'em moving.'

Sure enough, the cattle were reasonably compliant as they started
the day's long walk. Don had another chance to answer my questions.

While the station operates year round, work only really gets started
once the severe summer heat starts to ease. At the moment there was
additional work as the newer properties (New Crown and Andado)
were still being organised. With such a big area involved, Don was
starting to plan for a second stock camp. One could take care of jobs

like branding while the other camp mustered. The rationale behind acquiring the new stations had a lot to do with the changing economics of operating cattle properties.

'The reality is that over the last 30 years beef prices have barely risen while production costs just keep going up and up,' Don said. 'So to break even, where you once might get by turning off 3000 or 4000 head, today you need to turn off 5000 or 6000. That's why we've expanded our properties. We had to, just to stay in the game.'

The station tried to do two musters a year but it wasn't always possible. Lilla Creek was usually easy to muster because it had trap yards at key watering points, so when stock came in to drink, which they had to do, they basically mustered themselves. However, when there was water all over the property, as there was after the floods early in 2011, trap yards weren't as effective. As for Andado and New Crown, there was a lot of investment required before they'd be as easy to manage as Lilla Creek.

The mob was walking quietly as we entered a belt of mulga.

'See how it's best to settle the mob before you start?' Don explained. 'If we'd headed straight into this, there'd be bedlam. We'd have no chance. You always have to think ahead. Stop trouble before it really starts. Then give relief rests.'

He pointed to some cattle nearby. 'See that?' he asked. 'Cattle only feed when they're relaxed.'

As the mob moved quietly on, Don ran me back to the yards to rendezvous with chopper pilot Danny Rickard. While we waited, Don fixed a pump that wasn't working properly, despite the fact that it wasn't his property and the last of his agisted stock were leaving it. It made no difference. It was a job that needed doing and since he was there, he did it.

When Danny landed, we took the doors off his R44 to make it easier to take photos, then got airborne. His task was to round up any strays that were still wandering the paddock but he did have time to take a quick tour of the spectacular landforms around the yards and the stock camp. Soon we were exploring the stratified remnants of what was once an ancient mountain range.

He flew to the edge of a cliff, then dropped into a near-vertical dive down its face. If he was trying to test my nerve, he was doing a good job. Near the rapidly approaching ground, he pulled out of the dive, cranked the machine over and raced away across the dunes in search of cattle.

'Nothing like pulling a few Gs to settle your breakfast,' I said over the intercom, trying to sound unfazed. Who was I kidding? You can't beat low-level chopper operations for a heady mixture of excitement and fear.

After executing a series of high-speed low-altitude runs with dunes looming on either side, in what felt like an outback version of the attack on the Death Star in *Star Wars*, Danny found ten more beasts, including cows and calves.

He manoeuvred them into a group, then gently pressed them in the direction of the main mob.

'The trick is not too much pressure,' Danny said. 'You really only need to do gentle loops.'

Gentle loops? I liked the sound of that.

When there were no more cattle to be found, being men of the world, Danny and I headed over to breast-shaped Colson's Pinnacle for a closer look. Climbers had erected a cairn, or in this case a nipple, on the summit. Danny circled so I could get photographs then set his course back to the stock camp to drop me off and refuel. Near camp we circled a waterhole still overflowing from Cyclone Yasi and tinged a dirty red by the desert soils. Danny then manoeuvred into a pinpoint landing close enough to several drums of aviation fuel for the fuel hose to easily reach his aircraft.

Leaving the station, I decided to take the Finke River Road, which I'd avoided two days earlier. Despite being rough as guts, it's one of the great outback drives, in places using the original cuttings and embankments of the first Ghan railway line. There were still old sleepers in the road base, and plenty of railway spikes in the dust, just to add to the c-c-corrugations.

At some of the old railway sidings and stations, there were signs for tourists, detailing the history of the line that had once helped bring life to the centre of Australia. I stopped to brew a coffee at one station, from which all signs of life had long since disappeared, never to return. For the tourists, the impression might be that Central Australia had an abandoned air, but as my billy boiled I knew that just to the south, it was a different story.

I had an enduring image of a mob of red-and-white cattle slowly making its way over lines of red dunes on their way to a distant cattle yard, guided by the Crown Point stock camp. There was still plenty of life on the biggest privately owned cattle station in the world, if you knew where to look. And when you found them, you discovered lives lived large.

8. HEARTBREAK CORNER
Adria Downs Station
11000 square kilometres

Of all the areas of big country in Australia, the Channel Country of western Queensland is one of the most remarkable. Three great river systems – the Georgina/Eyre Creek, the Diamantina and Cooper Creek – flow down from their northern watersheds in the Northern Territory and Queensland into the increasingly arid interior and on into South Australia. In an exceptional year, they will reach all the way to Lake Eyre, the sometime inland sea where an evaporation rate of 3 metres per year can leave it parched for decades at a time.

It is a quality of the three rivers that their flow isn't reliable. A good flood event occurs every three to seven years, but the period between flows can be far longer. How far downriver the floods reach is also unpredictable. The further north, the more reliable they are, while it usually takes big flood events in all three rivers to fill Lake Eyre. The result is an environment that has adjusted to a boom-and-bust cycle. The country lies dormant for years on end, exploding into abundance when the waters finally come down. A great pulse of life – vegetation, aquatic life, birds – rolls through the country like a second wave, following the raging waters.

It is another quality of the Channel Country that the floods roll down over country that is mostly flat. The blacksoil floodplains are many kilometres wide, allowing water to spread over thousands of square kilometres. The growth that occurs afterwards is miraculous. A dazzling array of plant species springs up – an estimated 250 varieties of grasses and herbage with an extraordinary capacity for putting condition on stock.

When searchers for the ill-fated Burke and Wills laid eyes on the Channel Country, their reports prompted the state of Queensland to apply to have its western border moved, in 1862, to encompass it. Soon after, pioneers such as John Costello were leasing large areas and establishing some of the great outback stations.

However, the challenges of distance and the unpredictable seasons meant it took exceptional people to survive, let alone prosper, particularly in the increasingly marginal regions towards the south of the Channel Country. Nevertheless, into the twentieth century, it was still possible for small players to get a foothold in station ownership, if they were good enough.

In 2008–09, while living for a year in Australia's most remote town, Birdsville, I came to know and love the Channel Country. I'd had the incredible good fortune to see it transformed at the end of almost a decade of drought by winter rains, followed by one of the biggest summer floods on record. The parched, seemingly lifeless land became almost incomprehensibly verdant. Lakes lay between almost every dune. As the water evaporated, grasses and spectacular displays of wildflowers emerged. The dunes themselves all but disappeared beneath a profusion of greenery.

I was also fortunate to befriend the owners and managers of the stations surrounding the town, in particular Adria Downs. The station's owners, David and Nell Brook, were regulars of our weekly tennis group. Manager Don Rayment was president of the Birdsville Social Club, while I was secretary.

There were several features that set Adria Downs and its adjacent properties apart. Unlike the stations to the north, it was family owned. It was also certified organic, one of several stations in the Channel Country (and now beyond) that market their beef under the banner of Organic Beef Exporters (OBE) throughout Asia and North America. I was particularly interested to find out more about how the station was established, and the man behind it, W. F. 'Bill' Brook, who was spoken of almost reverentially throughout the region.

His son, David, was general manager of Brook Proprietors, which operates Adria Downs and Kamaran Downs (in Queensland) and Cordillo Downs and Murnpeowie (in South Australia). David is unique among general managers in that his company headquarters remain in the small town where the business started, Birdsville, population about 75. He still has a hands-on management style, aerial mustering at the age of 60. He can talk as easily to a young stockman as he can a prime minister. He is sometimes listed among the hundred richest people in Queensland, yet he and I once spent hours chipping weeds out of dozens of horse yards out at the racetrack before the famous Birdsville Races. He was also the Chairman of the Stockman's Hall of Fame and had served for many years as Mayor of the Diamantina Shire.

There was always a lot going on in David's life, and when I managed to corner him to talk about his father, it was with a promise from me that I'd restrict my questioning to thirty minutes. However, David had other ideas. One of the things I'd learnt while writing books about the outback is that sometimes the best thing to do is stop asking questions, shut up and listen. In this case, after an hour and a half, I was rewarded with a detailed account of the pioneering vision, determination, effort and even family connections required to succeed in the area of Queensland sometimes described as Heartbreak Corner.

The first leases on what is today Adria Downs were taken up in 1876, when Patrick Drinan (an associate of the Costellos and Duracks), settled Annandale Station on the Georgina/Eyre Creek system. He sold it a year later, to two brothers named Collins, who sold it in 1881 to Edward Reinholdt. The first applicant for the actual Adria lease was Frederick George Smith, on 29 December 1881. It, too, was sold only a year later, to Alexander McDonald.

Annandale was eventually absorbed into Glengyle Station to the north. Blocks like Adria, which weren't on any river, often broke their occupants and ended up neglected or abandoned. Many of those further west, beyond the last of the Channel Country rivers, were never taken up, and eventually became what is now the Simpson Desert National Park. Gradually, however, several families established properties in the Channel Country.

'I suppose Dad out at Adria Downs and the Smiths [at Ethabuka, now a wildlife conservation area] and Charlie Rayment [father of Adria manager Don Rayment] at Kurran were ones who started out certainly not with what you'd call living areas,' David explained. 'Jack Clancy took up a property, Kamaran Downs, which was again a small block west of Bedourie, a dry block. They were there because they wanted to be in the cattle game. They were talented in their ability to understand the conditions. They were determined to make a go of it. Dad took every opportunity over the years to expand onto these dry areas, which he could see being made into something by spending money.'

Bill Brook was born in Adelaide on 21 January 1900. He lived in the suburb of Glen Osmond, in the Adelaide Hills, not far from the estate of Tom Barr Smith, whose forebears had helped Bowen Downs recover their cattle after Henry Readford stole 1000 head of them and droved them to South Australia (see Chapter 1).

As a schoolboy, Bill and other local kids used to go down to the gate of the estate where Barr Smith left every morning on his way to his office. The first boy there got to open the gate and if they turned up in the afternoon, they'd open the gate as well. Barr Smith would then give them a coin and thank them.

Bill's mother died when he was still quite young, around 11 or 12. Being the oldest child, he left home at around age 16 to look for a job. He went to see Tom Barr Smith and got work at Beltana Station, a large sheep-and-cattle property near Leigh Creek, in the northern area of the Flinders Ranges.

'Then he asked Mr Barr Smith: could he get a job at Cordillo Downs because he wanted to work with cattle,' David recalled. 'He knew that Barr Smith had some cattle at the Cadelga end of Cordillo.'

The young stockman didn't know it at the time, but he would eventually purchase the property, with his son, in 1981. David can identify the exact date his father started at Cordillo. He still has the station diary, which records: '18 February 1918, W. F. Brook started at 30 shillings a week.'

Bill worked at Cordillo for a couple of years. However, by 1920 he was based in Betoota, the small town just to the north of Cordillo that is now uninhabited. A woman wrote David a letter after his father died in 1984, saying that at that time Bill worked as a kangaroo shooter, and he was known for being meticulous in ensuring the skins weren't nicked.

Around that time Bill became a regular visitor to Birdsville (200 kilometres west of Betoota) and eventually made a living breaking in horses and supplying them to properties and to drovers travelling cattle down the Birdsville Track. He bought a house in Birdsville in 1931, which eventually expanded into an entire block of the town, and this remains the headquarters of the Brook Proprietors company.

In the 1930s, David's mother, Dorothy Gaffney, was already living in Birdsville. She was born in Adelaide in 1911 and lived for a period at Annandale Station, where her father was the manager for Sidney Kidman, who had bought it and Glengyle in 1904. As David explained, 'I think Dad might have had a bit of an eye for her when she was in her twenties or whatever. They eventually married in 1942.'

During the 1930s, Bill started to acquire a few cattle. In 1939 he took up his first lease, Adria, a small block of 70 square kilometres, 150 kilometres west of Birdsville, without any river frontage. It was followed by the Neringee Block, bounded by the Simpson Desert on the west and the Mickrapyra Block, which had river frontage, on the east. He then added the Primrose Block, a large block between Eyre Creek and the Diamantina, again without river frontage or flood-plains, and Baigombo.

As David recalled, 'Baigombo was one of those blocks that was waterless and not in demand. People really looked to get access to the rivers because there was mostly permanent water on the rivers and little need for infrastructure spending by way of dams, wells or bores or that sort of thing.

'Actually, [Dad] already had wells in this little narrow strip of coun-try, which is not very big at all. He had a well at Adria Downs, one at Neringee and one up at a place called Engine Well. So he had three permanent waters and I guess he had those there because there was no alternative. I mean, he didn't have a river so you've got to approach it a bit differently.'

Some years ago, stockman Freddie Sims told David about working for Bill soon after he took up Adria Downs. Adria didn't have much water at that time and when it started to get dry, the cattle would wander. Eventually they'd make their way to the Diamantina River, where it passed through Pandi Pandi or Clifton Hills Station.

Pandi's owner, Celse Morton, would start noticing them and say, 'Bill, I've seen some of your cattle in the river. I don't know what they're doing there. You'd better get them off.'

Freddie said they'd muster them up and walk them back out to Adria. However, if it was still dry, they'd be back again in a week or two. Then Bill would depend on them not being seen for a couple of weeks. Then they'd do it all again.

'There were no fences,' David said. 'So that would be a smart thing to do: put them somewhere where you're told to, but in the knowl-edge that unless you stood there and looked after them – I mean, if you're really going to make them stay somewhere, you'd have water and then you'd track ride [make sure none wandered off by following their tracks] them for a week to make sure they really settled down.

But if you didn't want them to stay there, you'd put them there and do as you were asked to do and not much else.'

Bill's cattle certainly weren't straying because he didn't know how to handle them. David mentioned that while horses were his dad's life, he also understood the ways of cattle.

Bill once said to him, 'When you take cattle to waters, make sure when you water them you actually take them into the water. Make sure that they cannot only see it, seeing it's no good, they've gotta smell it. So you've gotta have the breeze coming over the water so they know it's there.'

'He was 63 when I left school,' David said, 'so I didn't have a lot of time with him, but we used to draft on horseback, draft fats out. You might have a mob of 500 and have to get 80 out but the exactness that you'd look for those last three – you didn't want to have three left in the herd that were better than the three you'd taken out.'

Former stockman, now Simpson Desert Park Ranger Don Rowlands, also regarded Bill Brook's skills highly.

'Bill Brook was a magic man,' he told me in an interview in 2011. 'His men mustered in the day and while they were sleeping, he'd walk the cattle at night to where they were going. There aren't many whitefellas who can find their way around this country at night but he could do it.

'He had this grey horse. He'd sleep in the saddle and the horse would ride around the cattle. If some walked off, it would walk out to them.

'He looked after all his people. If you worked for him you were right. He had all blackfellas in his camp. At Christmas he'd take them into his store [in Birdsville], put cardboard boxes on the counter and say, "Take what you want. Fill 'em." Then he'd load the boxes into his Land Rover and deliver them down to the camp at the Fish Hole.'

In the mid-1950s, Bill finally managed to acquire some river frontage, the Mickrapyra Block, from S. Kidman and Co., Sidney Kidman having died in 1935. The Kidman executives may have thought Bill needed the block more than them. In addition, while it was part of Glengyle, it was a long way from the station's main homestead and so far down Eyre Creek that its carrying capacity, in an undeveloped state, was much less than other areas of Glengyle further to the north. At Glengyle, the Georgina/Eyre Creek system ran nearly every year. At Mickrapyra, it was lucky if it ran every four years.

'Once Dad got it,' David said, 'he realised that it's pretty useless without water. So he set about doing wells and bores.'

In 1955 he had a man named Roy Ruwolt bring in a drilling rig and was successful with two bores.

David explained: 'One, Ruwolt's, is a very good bore and it's just to the south-east of what is known as Goonamillerie Waterhole. He was able to find good rainwater there at about 33 feet [10 metres] at 1000 gallons [4500 litres] an hour, and that became a major watering point, a major yard. It was pretty much dead smack in the middle of that Mickrapyra block and that was about 1956–57.

'He did another one about 10 or 15 kilometres to the north-east, also successful, and that was called Kings Bore, after his offsider [Kevin King]. And that was also a good bore, the water quality not quite so good, but we drank it okay, 600 or 700 gallons [2270 or 2649 litres] an hour at about 20 metres deep, or thereabouts. Those two bores were really the foundation of the block.'

In 1957 Bill also sank what became the Coochee Bore in the southwest corner of the Baigombo block. It went down 900 metres, and took two years to drill. Len Evans was the driller. When he didn't get water at 3000 feet, the contract had to be renegotiated, which meant Bill had to commit to paying more and going further. It was a gamble, but about 20 metres further down, they finally hit good water.

Len Evans wasn't so lucky. After drilling for two years, he went to Birdsville to tell Bill he'd got water, along with his co-driller, Long John Taylor, and Henry Butler, who had co-starred with Tom Kruse in the 1954 documentary *Back of Beyond*. At the time, Bill was in Adelaide, where his wife was in hospital. Len sent him a telegram with the good news about the bore, spent a day or two in town, then headed back out to the station. On his way out he camped at Listore Creek, near the bore. That night, he died in his sleep.

Bill then got hold of some earthmoving equipment, dug a drain from the bore down ListoreCreek and ran the water from it 29 kilometres to water a third of the Baigombo and Primrose blocks. Later on, in the 1970s, David replaced the drain with a pipeline. In those days there was no poly pipe, and 6-metre lengths of 100-millimetre PVC were used, rubber-jointed every 6 metres for 11 kilometres.

That worked well until a big flood washed parts of it away. David is now planning to get the redistribution system going again, redoing the pipeline in polythene. First, though, he'll have to cool the water that comes up at 99 degrees Celsius to 70 degrees so it won't melt the pipes.

Up till the early 1960s cattle from Adria were all sent to market down the stock routes – either down to the railhead at Marree for South Australia (650 kilometres south) or 200 kilometres towards Quilpie for Queensland. Cattle walked as far as Betoota, to the east, and were then loaded on trucks. As beef roads were built in the 1960s, trucks were eventually able to get as far as Clifton Hills and Roseberth, then to Birdsville and finally to the station itself.

'We built our first trucking yard on Adria about the mid-1960s,' David said, 'and that was at Nappanerica, which is just near Big Red [a large sandhill on Adria that tourists from Birdsville can visit to watch the sunset]. The yard is still there. That was our one and only yard for some time. Then to the east the trucks could get past Roseberth to Birdsville and Adria, and they'd come around through Monkira, Cluny, Glengyle. We built another yard at the Four Mile, which it was called because it was 4 miles [6 kilometres] from Carcoory [an abandoned homestead], up the creek there.'

David and Bill thought they were pretty well off with two trucking yards but as time went on a problem emerged. They tended to bring large mobs of cattle to the yards to truck, because if they were going to truck 200 to 400 head, they'd bring 400 to 600, for spares or in case they needed a few extra.

'Along with those there'd be the last two or three days of mustering,' David said. 'So there would be cows and calves, et cetera. You often ended up with 1000 or more by the time you got to that yard because the areas are big and you might have started the muster 100 kilometres back, collecting as you go.'

The cattle that were left behind at the yards generally didn't get taken back to their place of origin. They might be walked back for half a day or a day and then be let go, on the assumption they'd find their way back to where they came from. Often that wasn't the case. They stayed near the yards and the areas around them ended up being overgrazed. It wasn't long before it became obvious that they needed more yards.

However, knowing what was needed, and having the money to pay for it, didn't always coincide.

As David put it, 'Dad would always push for doing something because – money, there wasn't much money, and his bankers wouldn't say he was very diligent in meeting the conditions of loans, I don't think – he was always looking ahead.'

Sometimes, though, vision wasn't enough. David described a time when it was very dry. It was about 1965 or 1966, and they had only about 1000 cattle left after the drought had worn them down. They needed to pay back some money but simply didn't have it. Eventually they were instructed by Dalgety's, one of their major lenders at the time, to muster all the cattle and truck them off to settle the debt.

Bill said, 'Well, we won't have any left if we do that.'

And they said, 'Well, that's how it is. You're running late paying your bills, so you've gotta do that.'

They sent the trucks up and said, 'Righto, Bill, the trucks are coming on this date, and you will load them.'

'So blow me down if the trucks came up,' David recalled. 'It was late in the year, a time when you'd normally hope for a storm and you'd be wanting to hold them and keep them. Some trucks got to Birdsville, some got out to the yard and some got stuck along the way in the rain, quite a bit of rain. Dalgety's still wanted the cattle trucked.'

Bill said to the truckies, 'Look, I know you're here with instructions to load these cattle, but if you truck them you won't get any future business from me because I won't have any cattle.'

He said, 'I'll pay you half the cost of the freight if you turn around and go back empty.'

It was an extraordinary proposal. Nevertheless, the truckies got together and had a meeting to discuss it. Eventually, against the instructions they had from the agents, they decided they'd go back empty.

'I think that was a bit of a lucky turning point,' David said, 'one of those decisions he made, to offer half the money with a prospect for the truckies of getting business for the next number of years which was better than the whole of the money and no business. So that happened and then we built back up again.'

While Bill was gradually accumulating land at Adria, Bill's brother-in-law was acquiring land across the Queensland border in South Australia. In the early 1930s, he took up the mostly dry Alton Downs, to the south of Adria. Initially it was a block of about 1200 square kilometres that adjoined the giant Clifton Hills, at the time one of the biggest stations in the world at 25 000 square kilometres and encompassing the sometimes-bone dry, sometimes brimming Goyders Lagoon, fed by the Diamantina and Georgina/Eyre Creek systems.

South-west of Clifton Hills and south-east of Alton Downs, on the edge of the extraordinary floodout country of Goyders Lagoon, David's mother also owned a small block called Narromine/Booreree.

Quite why she owned it, wasn't clear: 'perhaps she thought it was a good thing'. For some time it wasn't used because it was isolated from Alton Downs. It was one of a number of small South Australian blocks that changed hands from time to time but it wasn't particularly useful to anyone due to its size, remoteness or lack of water. When David's mother died, in 1957 Narromine/Bararie reverted to David's father.

In the mid-1960s, Bill's brother-in-law, Jack Gaffney, applied to the Lands Department of South Australia for a strip of country that would give Alton Downs access to the more reliable waters of the Diamantina River. Some of the Diamantina's waterholes were permanent as the river flowed more frequently than Eyre Creek.

As David put it, 'About when he got [the strip of country he asked for] was in that period 1955 to 1971, when Eyre Creek didn't run. So he would have been getting a bit frustrated. The Lands Department resumed a piece of Clifton Hills, extending into what is known as Andrewilla Waterhole. It added about 1500 square kilometres of country to Alton Downs. Good country, not well watered, though. Apart from the access into the Diamantina in the areas of Lovers Nook, Ten-Mile Waterhole, the Eleanor Channel of the Diamantina, Andrewilla Waterhole and Mungananni Waterhole on the main channel of the Diamantina (which is more access to water than access to country), it was a fairly thin strip, but it probably more than doubled the size of Alton Downs. It's now about 3500 square kilometres.'

David's father also arranged for the Narromine/Bararie lease to be folded into the expanded Alton Downs lease, mainly for convenience because it couldn't operate by itself. Theoretically, the property was then able to run 3000 head of cattle.

In 1967 or 1968, Jack Gaffney transferred the central homestead from Old Alton Downs (about 15 kilometres south of the Queensland border, on the western side of Eyre Creek) and built a new homestead on the eastern end of Andrewilla Waterhole, which is an offshoot of the Diamantina at the bottom end of Pandi Pandi Station. It was a lovely homestead with staff quarters and a workshop, but he only lived there another year. He died of a heart attack in Adelaide soon after building the place.

Jack's brother Bob then managed the property but in 1974 one of the largest floods on record in the Diamantina came roaring down. It stayed high at Andrewilla for some time, particularly where a channel of the Diamantina ran around a sandhill. Eventually the wave action caused the sandhill to collapse. About 100 metres of it fell into the river, which then cut a new channel. The homestead was in its path. Not only was the house swept away, there was a channel 3 or 4 metres deep where it once stood.

David recalled, 'So that left a pretty big hole in the operational ability, the bank account, and just about everything else because he'd spent a lot of money developing the homestead, new fencing and all of the things that you have to do. Normally when you acquire a block like that, when it's basically taken off someone else by the government in their reallocation, the new owner is required to replace all the fencing.'

Bob Gaffney eventually built another homestead, on a much more modest scale. The key issue of finding and distributing waters remained. During periods of drought, the property had to be destocked, obviating the need for a permanent presence at the homestead for years at a time. Eventually ownership and management of Alton Downs became a combination of the Gaffney family and the Brook family, with management operating from the Adria homestead.

As the Adria/Alton aggregation grew, so did the competing demands on money for development. David recalled doing work with a man named Angus Rolton, back in the early days, on wells out at Adria Downs, Nulneringee and Herbert Hut.

'We actually put windmills and tanks on them. And they were quite expensive to get people to do those sorts of things. Dams, Dad put in a lot of dams, major dams like the Four Mile, The Gap, Baigombo,

Twin Tanks, Boulder, David's Dam, Nappanerica, any number. I think we've got about 30 now. We continue to invest in them.'

While the combined station was growing in size, it still covered mostly marginal country. However, in 1981, Bill and David negotiated with Kidmans to buy the 3900-square-kilometre Annandale Block, which adjoins Adria to the north and extends up to the Muncoonie Lakes area.

David's manager, Don Rayment, still can't understand why Kidmans sold what is prime floodout country, an oasis in the middle of the desert dunes. Lesser floods that sometimes didn't break out of the Eyre Creek's channels on Glengyle did spread out when they reached the two Muncoonie Lakes, bringing up rich cattle-fattening pasture, while Glengyle got nothing. Don said some of Kidmans' managers referred to Annandale as 'Brookie's Gain'.

When I mentioned that to David, he just smiled.

'It was in a similar way to this other one [the Mickrapyra block],' he explained. 'It was a bit remote from their operations and they had probably better country further up the river and on a number of other properties that they held. And Annandale itself, I and probably Dad as well, eyed it off for a long time or endeavoured to see about purchasing it. And John Ayers Senior was the one who offered it at that time.'

The key may have been David's family connection to the block, which went back even further than the Kidmans' connection. Glengyle was the second property Kidman bought in Queensland (Carandotta, at the top of the Channel Country, being the first). The manager at the time was John Gaffney.

'John Gaffney married my grandmother,' David said. 'It would have been the early 1900s, so it was John and Dorothy Ella Gaffney. She was Dorothy Ella Smith, and my mother, who was the second-born of their children, her second name was Annandale, and that was a reflection of the fact that that was where they lived.'

'I'm further told that, when Glengyle originally came on the market, just the major, the better part of Glengyle shall we say, it was my grandfather that let Sidney Kidman know it was on the market and suggested it might be a good property for him to buy. That information comes from a lady, Eileen Clancy, who in her memoirs suggested that. She may well know that because her grandfather, George Gaffney, was John Gaffney's brother and George Gaffney bought the Bedourie Hotel and that bit of land there. The Bedourie Hotel, it was part of a Kidman lease, and he had a very close connection with Kidman as his bookkeeper and other things. So they no doubt had contact with Kidman and he may well have said to him, "Well, look, you should buy this property if it ever comes up," and I think that's what happened.

'So John Ayers Senior, who is now deceased, he probably would have known the history of its usage and I say to myself perhaps he felt it would be in good hands because – it's a business interest in it obviously in the cattle side – but there is a long historic interest going back a hundred or more years in the lease itself.

'It's really the heartbeat of the property now because we are a little bit further upstream, the floods that do come irregularly get there more often, and they get further down.'

The Annandale Block has since been developed into an area where Adria is able to fatten cattle. When Bill and David acquired it, there was only one bore. Soon, another artesian bore was put down in the area of Eyre Creek, in the north-east of the Muncoonie Lakes. More than a 100 kilometres of pipelines were then extended in five different directions to reduce pressure on the river frontage and lakes. The lakes were fenced so the numbers of cattle accessing them could be regulated, which also relieved the pressure on other areas that had been heavily grazed in the past.

David believed his company had many reasons for developing the area, while Kidman had other areas that were a higher priority.

As he put it, 'The work we've done there – building yards, fences, paddocks, the bore, pipelines – I think Kidmans would recognise that they would never have done all that. No one would have ever seen the best of it.'

The new block also changed the way Brook Proprietors operated. In recent years, a new station complex has been built, on the banks of Eyre Creek, although Don and Judy, who both hail from further north, reckon it's still the Georgina.

'Dad started with the homestead in Birdsville and it remained there for most of the time because there was no suitable place in the deserty parts of Adria to do it,' David said. 'But now that we've got access to that great Channel Country fattening area, it works very well for us. Of course since that time, we've moved to certify the properties as organic and it's just the perfect garden for organic cattle. It enables us to structure delivery, supply chain, around the floodplains and selectively use the whole property. It's great for cattle fattening, it's a great environmental spot.'

While the Annandale Block was a gain, plenty of challenges remained. About that time cattle properties across Australia faced the challenge of eradicating brucellosis and tuberculosis, under what was known the BTEC scheme, as both diseases existed in pockets throughout the whole country. Some station owners didn't survive the process. Others tackled the challenge and used it as an opportunity to modernise even further.

On Adria, BTEC meant destocking entirely. It was a tough time but the extra cash that came from selling all the stock at once was used to build more stock yards and further develop the station's infrastructure.

David explained, 'We could see by then that, from the early testing we had to do to determine if there was any prevalence of these diseases, this was going to be a new thing for us, shall we say.

'In those days we didn't have any yard complexes, any races. They were all just 50 yards [45.7 metres] by 50 yards, or 60 [50.2 metres] by 60 bronco yards. All the work was done on horseback. There was no need to put cattle up races to take blood or do anything like that. If it had to have been done, it would have been done with the broncoing method, which would have been to individually rope and pull up to a central point each beast, which would have been very time-consuming.'

While it was clear they needed new modern yards, they had to be numerous and spread across the property to prevent concentrations of cattle that could lead to overgrazing. To get to the yards, they needed roads.

David rolled off the construction program from memory: 'On Adria we would have built the yard at Baigombo and then I think the next one was at Yambalo. We would have done one at Twin Tanks. On this other side, down at the bottom end, at Nappanerica, the next one we built was at Blue Bush because the first yard we constructed at Nappanerica was only really suitable for trucking to Adelaide because the sandhills in between Nappanerica and here [Birdsville], we couldn't get over them. So that yard serviced South Australia and the Four Mile Yard serviced Queensland.

'To use the Nappanerica yard for Queensland we made a road down into South Australia to what is called Lovers Nook and Karathunka because we really didn't have the machinery to build roads over the sand hills. There it joined the old Inside Road back to Birdsville but that was a 96-kilometre trip for what is about a 25 kilometre straight-out road. We used that for ten years or so.

'In the interim, though, we built the yard at Blue Bush, which was in the early 1980s, which is about 20 kilometres out of Birdsville, and that then serviced the Queensland side.'

Today, Adria and Alton have 22 yards. Apart from the western parts of the station, where trucks still can't get over the very big sandhills, most of the cattle graze within a day-and-a-half's muster of a yard.

'So when we're looking to sell them they're basically on their natural feed to within two or three days of being trucked,' David said.

'So they're gaining weight instead of being walked long distances, instead of losing weight.'

They're also mustered in small lots and let go again in their own surroundings. Cattle to be sold are selected and taken out. For the remainder of the mob, the calves can be put through, separated, branded and back with their mothers within an hour or two, sometimes only minutes, reducing the stress on both.

'It's all for a more efficient operation,' David explained. 'It saves costs in that respect. It keeps the condition on cattle and is very convenient. There is an added cost in that the trucks are probably in some cases going another 100 kilometres to reach a yard but that is counterbalanced by the time it would take to otherwise walk the cattle with a stock camp. Today, it's often five or six people – head stockman, three or four or five others – walking them for that time. They'd walk 10, 15, 20 kilometres a day, depending on where the yards were. So it's an extra 100 kilometres for the truck but you save a week's time. We're also able to have calves available for branding and sorting out at a much earlier age. At the same time, in some areas the older calves can be weaned off and removed to another paddock or something, which again aids management down the track.'

In recent times, the station has also adapted its strategies with the distribution of water, again to spread cattle more evenly over the property. The focus has shifted to smaller dams that might only last three or four months but which take the pressure off major waters.

'As I look around now,' David reflected, 'there is a lot less pressure being applied to the country. Not necessarily many more cattle but the cattle are able to be sold at an earlier age because they get fatter quicker, because they're getting better feed and they're not overgrazed.

'Before they might be merely fat but then the outside waters go dry and they come back to the major waters and [the country there has] only been marginal, enough to grow them but not enough to fatten them, so there's a tendency to keep those for another year. The age of the cattle that we turn off has probably halved in the last

20 years and it's better everywhere, even on something like a dam. If you haven't got those bigger bullocks or heavier ones going down the bank, the dams don't silt up as quickly. The heavier beast, as they walk into water, they tend to push the soil down the banks.'

Younger cattle are also desirable as modern markets believe younger beef is superior. The specifications for most domestic markets are animals that don't have all their permanent teeth, so they're less than a couple of years old.

'Not that there's any problem on this type of feed with the older bullocks,' David said. 'The older they are, probably the more taste, but you don't want antiques.'

While much of David's focus was on the details of how Adria was developed, he also talked about the pressures of the 1970s, when beef prices fell to catastrophic levels, and the 1980s, when prices rose but interest rates soared. And while he had his hands full developing Adria, with the encouragement and advice of his father, David bought Kamaran Downs in the 1970s, and Cordillo Downs in the 1980s.

'Dad was pretty alert to seeing opportunities,' David said, 'really from Adria Downs to there. I think we were one of the first or second or third people in the district to get a plane, to develop the waters, to put pipelines in. He wouldn't have known that we got Murnpeowie [in 1988] so we've got a bit of a chain of insurances around.

'Kidmans did that and did it very successfully, and we had to do it on all these places – Murnpeowie, Cordillo Downs, Adria and Kamaran. They were all in their native state, second-rate, shall we say, compared to a good place or a better place. The acquisitions have been fairly strategic. There's thought in them all, strategic a) you can grow, but b) a security side to give you that flexibility. Then comes the development of them with bores and dams to improve the on-property security.'

There was still much to be done. With regard to Alton Downs, he said, 'I really am proposing that as soon as possible we will get the proper water supplies in and get the proper housing so that we can do there something similar to what we've done out at Adria Downs in building up an independent, good-quality station with the right accommodation to attract and keep staff.

'We've drilled for underground water, for shallow underground water, sub-artesian, without much success. The sub-artesian and some soakage water around tends to be fairly brackish.

'The artesian water, that would be possible, but it's at a depth of about 1400 metres. So it's at least a $400 000 investment. And that is without getting the systems to cool it, the pipelines to distribute it. The numbers haven't come up yet where that's an economic alternative, although it would be a very good alternative, but we haven't tackled that yet.'

With this in mind, he described the current situation with the management of the two stations as 'not necessarily a long-term arrangement'. Considering it's been operating in this way since the 1970s or '80s, it's an insight into the outback definition of 'long term'.

'All of this has really happened in 100 years,' David reflected. 'We've made big gains in 140 years of settlement, when you look at Europe and everywhere else. And in an area where it's difficult to make gains when you've got costs like freight against you, and seasonal conditions, because sometimes you have to mark time for a few years. The bigger gains – the opportunity to get money to do the development – really don't come as regularly as you'd like. You get a good season or two and reinvest all that pretty much in the land.

'Ever since Dad started, everything we've earnt has been reinvested,' he said. 'Over the years, there's been no real block of flats in the city or anything else. It's all in improvements. Today, $250 000 in poly pipe, $200 000 bore at Muncoonie. Bulls: we're gonna end up today with a $25 000 bill for five, six, seven bulls. Another one tomorrow for the same. Often it's money you really don't have but you can't not do it. We've got to have good-quality stock. You can get by without good-quality stock but you get by better with good quality.

'Now that we've developed up this market for organic beef, which is admired as one of the highest-quality grass-fed products out of Australia, we've got to keep the standard in the livestock, the meat, the management of the properties, the development, the environmental care. There's a whole range of things. You'd like to think, if the meat eats well, no one will ask any other questions, but to sell organic beef to the really discerning major customers, they want to see the whole operation. They want to know what's happening on the property. They want to come and have a look and make sure there is nothing being done which is negative.

'It's all part of trying to bring the management, the transporting, the slaughter, packing, delivery, the communications with customers, up to a pretty good standard. We've just had customers here from Malaysia, customers from America. This year we had them from Taiwan and Japan. It's all about demonstrating the product, its environment, people, the whole box and dice. It's not just about what you necessarily see on the supermarket shelf. It only gets on the supermarket shelf if the owner of the supermarket chooses to put it there.'

When we finally wrapped things up, I wasn't too concerned that a visit to the property was difficult because it was virtually flooded in, thanks to the waters left by the remnants of Cyclone Yasi months before. Thanks to David I already knew more about the place than I'd have thought possible.

As it happened, after talking to David, I wandered over to the machinery shed to catch up with mechanic Padraic O'Neill. Padraic and his then partner Olivia had come to Birdsville several years before to work on Cordillo Downs. When it was discovered Padraic was a diesel mechanic, he was brought in to work at the Birdsville Auto, also owned by the Brook family. I got to known him when we did a couple of desert rescues together. When their visas expired they returned to Ireland, where the economic downturn meant poor job prospects. David Brook sponsored the newlyweds, and newborn Patrick, to return to Australia.

Padraic was about to head out on one of the station's flood roads to fix a broken-down vehicle. It was just an afternoon job and he was happy for me to tag along. As we deviated around several lakes, diverted down small tracks and tackled the climbs over giant red dunes, I realised I'd have got lost or stuck attempting to travel this way myself.

Padraic was from Westmeath, Killucan village, an hour west of Dublin. He was now 32. His wife, Olivia, who as a qualified accountant helped keep the Brook Proprietors' books, was 30, while little Patrick was six months old. Padraic and Olivia had loved the outback from the time they started at Cordillo. They eventually sent eight of their friends there as well. Only one didn't work out.

For Padraic, the floods meant just getting to work was an adventure.

'At the moment, sometimes I fly into the desert, then get into a boat to reach the job,' he said. 'There's not many places like this. I'm currently based in Birdsville, supporting Adria and Cordillo: all their vehicles, solar, pumps. I started in March 2011 but I'm behind due to the wear and tear and difficulty of access because of the wet season. I wish I'd started three years ago. I'm looking forward to catching up and then maybe spending time with cattle.'

After crossing another dune we encountered grader driver Bob Crombie. Bob pulled up and Padraic introduced us. Bob had just recovered from a life-threatening head injury caused when two fighting bulls smashed open a gate, which hit him and nearly crushed his skull. He was saved by the combined efforts of the station's staff, the nurses from the Birdsville Clinic and even the son of the Birdsville baker who drove the ambulance to the scene, over treacherous flooded roads.

Padraic and I eventually located the vehicle he was looking for, a battered Suzuki ute near the Half Finish Yards. He soon got it started, worked out there was a problem with a relay and started wiring around it. While he worked, manager Don Rayment pulled up with his daughter Bec in tow.

Don was as weather-beaten and gruff as they get but with a big heart. The last time I'd seen him, I'd driven back to Birdsville to lend a hand at the bronco-branding championships. Don didn't speak to me all weekend, until the end, when he asked, 'Are you glad to be home?'

It was an unexpected question but I answered, yes, I was.

With the Zuke running, the fanbelt set up a squeaking that threatened to send its driver deaf. So Padraic set about retensioning it using a crowbar. While I handed him tools and took photos, Don growled, 'I've got 50 other things to do and I'm holding up a bonnet! We're three months behind due to the wet, and we were three months behind before that!'

To stop him grumbling, I asked whether the rains had been widespread. It turned out Adria was into the third good season in a row, and this season was the best. They'd had two floods in the Georgina in one year. In one eight-week period, they'd had more than 300 millimetres on the outside country. That in a region with an annual average of only 150 millimetres.

'It's hardly been seen in the last 100 years,' Don said. 'There's been the 1950s and the 1970s and now this. It's rained from the tip of the Cape York Peninsula to Tasmania this year. The Georgina is still running. We're still having a good flood.'

Despite all the water, the feed was slow in coming due to winter.

We talked about Bob Crombie's accident, which had nearly killed him. They didn't know whether he'd been shutting the gate or if it was already shut, because it was wrecked after the bull hit it. What Don was sure about was how good a grader driver Bob was. He could do 20 kilometres a day, sometimes doing five to eight cuts, or passes, with the grader's blade.

'He only pulls up for a bit of tea and cake, then off he goes again,' Don said.

When the ute was driveable, Don's daughter got in to take it back to the homestead. Don headed off to where his stock camp were mustering. There was so much water on the property's roads they were back to walking cattle to the Four Mile Yard, on the eastern side of Adria, then trucking them from there.

I headed back in with Padraic, and he talked about the initiative you need to be an outback mechanic.

'The hard thing out here is there are no parts,' he said. 'It takes two weeks to get something mailed, or a month. So you fix things on site. You repair or bypass things.'

While the country and the lifestyle were major parts of the attraction of living on one of the most remote stations in Australia, the other factor was management.

'Don is a great manager,' he said. 'I think if he left, most of the staff would walk off with him. When I came to work in Australia, I considered offers from mines but David made me a better offer.'

And it wasn't just the money. I suspected it was part of the culture of the place.

Back in Birdsville, Don Rowlands had told me of Bill Brook's vision: 'He said, way back in the sixties, "One day Birdsville is going to be a mecca for tourists." Years later, he was right on the money. He was one of only a few men who looked at this country and had a real vision of what it could be.'

Another of Bill's qualities was his ability to pass his vision on to his son. David and Adria's manager, Don, still shared that vision, and were making it a reality.

9. THE HAPPIEST STATION

Headingly Station
10032 square kilometres

Rolling south from Camooweal, the historic crossroads of the stock routes that arrived from the north and west and continued on to the south and east, I had come to realise that for my purposes it was still remarkably central. I'd dropped into the town's Drovers Camp several times during my travels. Returning from yet another trip further out, I'd enjoyed Liz and Col Flood's hospitality overnight, then spent the next morning trimming grass with a whipper snipper and doing various other chores to get the place ready for the next annual drovers' reunion. I'd also avoided taking tourists around the exhibits in the museum.

'You'd be great at it,' encouraged the old drovers who normally did the deed, limping around on bent or busted-up legs.

Having heard them relating stories about their former lives, animating even the most insignificant-looking exhibits, I knew I wasn't a drover's little finger. They were the masters.

From there, it wasn't far to the next station on my list, AACo's Headingly, 170 kilometres south. The road was another passage into the past. While staying on the higher ground, away from the softer country along the Georgina River, the modern road closely follows the stock route that had once seen hundreds of thousands of cattle grazing along and fattening on some of the sweetest grasses anywhere in the country. The land was gently undulating, with wide expanses of stunning yellow grass broken by the occasional belt of gidgee. Off to the right, the line of the Georgina was marked by coolabahs, those fabled trees under which swagmen have been known to camp. I'd experienced enough of the outback to know that if you were camped by a billabong, you'd almost certainly do it in the shade of a coolabah, because they're specialists in surviving an occasional inundation. Wherever there's a coolabah, it floods.

Cattle coming across the Barkly and intending to head south often took a shortcut before reaching Camooweal, travelling over Lake Nash before striking the Georgina lower down. If the river was in flood, they might have no choice but to keep to the west bank until they found a safe place to cross, or got ahead of the water rolling slowly down through the land. Many crossed at Headingly.

Even after I had visited so many stations, Headingly still had the ability to surprise. It is pretty much a regulation cattle property at the top of the Channel Country, yet even before I arrived I was struck by the culture of the place.

It started with manager Steve Hagan. I'd rung him the night before, expecting that he'd been forewarned of my visit and imminent arrival.

'Haven't heard a thing about it,' he said, as he listened to me describe my project. 'Come anyway.'

Steve's easygoing manner on the phone was repeated in the flesh. I'd timed things so I arrived late in the afternoon, and found him at the stockyards near the homestead. He was a younger, better-looking version of Paul Hogan. While he brushed down a horse, he proved easy to talk to as I started asking questions about the property.

As he talked two jillaroos drove up in a truck loaded with horses. They turned towards the loading ramp so quickly you could hear the horses slipping in the back over the sound of grinding gears. They then started manoeuvring to get close to the ramp.

'This is about to go to shit,' Steve said as he looked on. 'You can tell by the smiles.'

However, before the situation turned unpleasant, Steve went over and supervised the unloading. He showed the young women what to do, made sure the horses were unloaded unharmed, and betrayed no annoyance that he should have to get involved.

While he did that, I looked around at the rest of staff, going about the last jobs of another long day – brushing horses, feeding stock in the yards, putting away equipment. That's when it struck me. It was late, they were tired, but they were still in a good mood. Everyone around me was actually happy. It may have been a subtle thing, but they were enjoying what they were doing.

With the horses safely off the truck, Steve came back over and took up where he'd left off.

'We run mostly Santa Gertrudis but we're changing to the Barkly composite [a mix of breeds specially tailored to the Barkly region by AACo] and SC [Senapol Charolais]. We run 20000 breeders and 15000 steers. All up we have around 50000 head.

'The cattle here are very fertile,' he said. 'We have 90 per cent fertility and even in the drought of '08 it was 80 per cent. That said, we trucked off 47000 in '08.'

He reckoned the property was about 80 per cent developed. The eastern side is grasslands with good water and bores. On the western side the gidgee goes for miles but the water from the bores is so salty the cattle won't drink it. The station had dug bores up to 300 metres deep, at a cost of hundreds of thousands of dollars, looking for clean water. So far only one bore had succeeded.

In areas where the water is good, cattle always graze within a 4-kilometre radius of water. If the station could be fully developed, it would be able to carry up to 60 000 head, matching adjacent Lake Nash but with only 10 000 square kilometres compared to its 16000. As things now stand, in the undeveloped country, musters still uncover cattle grazing up to 10 kilometres from water.

'At Headingly we're on the edge of the consistent wet seasons,' Steve said. 'The Barkly gets different weather. We still get a lot of water. We might not get a drop of rain but you can't cross the river for two months and we have to do bore runs in the chopper. Big runs of water can be useful. The water that came down last summer is still trickling at Carandotta [a property that is now amalgamated into Headingly].

'In a dry year I'd prefer to be here. It doesn't need a lot of rain. It's sweeter country. In 2008 we had to feed and supplement but for the last two years we haven't even had to put out lick blocks. We're on the border of the Channel Country and the Barkly. We're either northern Channel Country or southern Barkly.'

The country might be sweet, but the experience of developing Headingly has had its fair share of bitterness. As with neighbouring Lake Nash, it ruined the first people who tried to develop it. Early attempts to develop properties along the Georgina River, in the 1860s, were thwarted by the predations of dingoes, the distance from markets, and a serious economic downturn in the middle of the decade.

Ten years later, run-hunters again took an interest in western Queensland. In 1875 the station brand, 7TY, was first registered to William Taylor of Sandford Sawmills in Brisbane. Leases were then acquired by pioneering pastoralists Oscar De Satgé, James Milson and other partners around 1881. They formed what they called 'Carandotta' out of the stations known as Lower Headingly, Springfield, Carandotta, St Ronans, Bannockburn and Upper Roxborough. They and others also formed the Carandotta Pastoral Company, with working capital of £250 000.

The aggregation amounted to as much as 1 214 070 hectares (3 000 000 acres). De Satgé, who was born in England but was of Catalan and French heritage, and his partners, invested heavily in developing the property and stocking it with 100 000 to 150 000 sheep (sources vary) and 10 000 cattle.

Nevertheless, the place remained something of a frontier. According to Michael Costello, manager of neighbouring Lake Nash at about the same time, cattle were still being speared by local inhabitants during the 1880s. He wrote in *The Life of John Costello* (using language this writer in no way endorses):

A strange thing happened on Headingly, a station which was formed about the same time as Lake Nash. The blacks would, from time to time, make raids on the cattle, helping themselves to beef. Their system was to sneak closely to the stock, then fling a spear, striking one, but the first blow was seldom, or never, instantly fatal, and had to be followed up by other attacks, sometimes the animal receiving numerous wounds before finally succumbing. One day a stockman, riding out, came on a remarkable scene, a dead bullock with a dead black fellow impaled on the long, spear-like horn. They had both been dead several days, and the bullock showed signs of numerous spear wounds, and its body held a number of broken spear shafts. The position was simple enough to explain. The tracks of natives were printable close around. The animal had been fatally injured, and this particular nigger, more daring than his fellows, approached to very close quarters to administer the final *coup-de-grace*. Then the maddened beast, first standing at bay, made a last, fierce rush, driving his long, pike-like horn clean through the bold warrior and, at the same time falling forward, pinned the black fellow to the earth, where both expired together. The rest of the tribe, evidently struck with superstitious fear and horror, rushed far away from the scene of the tragedy, and never returned, either for meat, or to bury their dead companion.

The cattle were not the only targets of the first inhabitants of the country. Loopholes can still be seen in the old homestead of Wolgra (also Walgra) station, now part of Headingly, through which settlers would fire on any potential attackers.

However, the greatest threat to the station was the climate. As nearly every station in this book had found, the drought that gripped

Australia in the 1890s and into the new century fell heavily on even the best-developed properties. Over a three-year period, from 1891 – only 300 millimetres of rain were recorded at the property, which is less than it usually gets in a year. Headingly may have lost 18000 head in four days. Some sources suggest the entire Carandotta operation may have lost as many as 90000 sheep and 10000 cattle. The Carandotta Pastoral Company went to the wall and the properties were taken over by the bank of New South Wales.

De Satgé had gone into the partnership in Carandotta in 1881 with £70000 from the sale of other stations he'd successfully developed. When he died, in 1906, his estate was valued at £443.

The bank's attempts to recoup its losses saw the Carandotta aggregation broken up. In 1903 cattle king Sidney Kidman acquired Carandotta itself for the bargain price of £20000. It was the first property he bought in Queensland, and was soon followed by a number of others, particularly in the Channel Country. Kidman built a chain of stations through which he could move cattle to markets from his stations further afield, such as Victoria River Downs in the Northern Territory. He sold part of Carandotta in 1910 for £9500 and the remainder in 1916 for £86000, for a total capital gain of £75000 in 13 years.

In the 1920s, Carandotta was still running 50000 head of sheep and had a 12-stand woolshed, which is still standing but long since abandoned. While Carandotta hasn't run sheep for many years, neighbouring properties carried some sheep as recently as 1986.

Headingly itself appears to have gone unoccupied until 1908, when the bank found a buyer in Messrs. Philp, Leahy, and Co, who stocked it with 5000 head of cattle, according to the *Winton Herald* of 19 October. It was then purchased by AACo in 1916 and has been held by the venerable company ever since.

Headingly became the nucleus of the present-day station, with Wolgra added in 1965 and Carandotta in 1985. Wolgra had been bought by Bovril in 1940 to provide agistment for travelling cattle and to breed horses for mustering on Victoria River Downs (see Chapter 5).

Smaller blocks had also been added over the years, bringing the station's current total area to 1 003 251 hectares, divided into 47 paddocks averaging 20 800 hectares, with an additional 14 holding paddocks. The property basically functions as a breeding operation, supplying cattle for AACo's 1824 domestic beef brand (1824 being the year the company was founded). The station has a staff of 18, including a manager, head stockman, a stock camp of six, two bore runners, a mechanic, grader driver, road-train driver, handyman, bookkeeper, gardener, cook and fixed wing pilot.

With the work of the day over, everyone headed over to the homestead. At the recreation building, Steve shouted me a beer and introduced me to a blur of names, faces and jobs. Most of the skilled jobs were held by older staff, while the stock camp was a mixture of younger men and women. The discussion of my project soon developed into a discussion of who had worked where, which stations were better than others and the various disasters they'd experienced.

One of the girls, Harriet, was actually on holidays from uni, where she was doing an arts degree, but while visiting her sister she'd ended up working alongside her. She didn't mind. Both came from an agricultural background in Victoria and she was finding work on a big station a great experience.

Again I was struck by the fact that the gathering comprised pretty much the whole staff and they were all keen to get together at the end of the day to swap stories. Two beers into the conversation, though, people start leaving to clean up for dinner.

As cook Rachel Bagshaw later told me, the raw young jackaroos and jillaroos had driven her crazy until she got them trained in kitchen etiquette. Rachel, only 23 but having grown up on stations in the region, encapsulated the rules: 'They have to be on time, clean and tidy, wash up and leave their boots outside.'

Sure enough, when I made my way to the meals building, I was the last there and everyone was getting ready to eat. They were making cups of tea and milling around while Rachel set out the food. Nobody went near the service area until Rachel quietly said, 'Righto.' Then it was something like an extremely orderly shark attack. A line formed instantly, everyone with a plate in hand. The first in line served themselves, quickly piling up food, then moved out of the way of the hungry mass behind.

Once dinner and dessert had been demolished, everyone washed their plates and headed off, mostly to bed. It wasn't yet eight o'clock but the area around the homestead was soon quiet, but for the pervasive sound of the diesel generator that's ubiquitous on outback stations.

I headed over to the home of mechanic Ian Kelly and his partner, Lisa, the station's bookkeeper and manager's assistant.

Ian was the embodiment of the outback can-do attitude. The 45-year-old was virtually self-taught in his chosen trade. He was originally from Marysville, in country Victoria, where he'd first worked in a sawmill. He eventually met Lisa and moved to Queensland where he became a truck driver. After five years on the coast, one day Lisa saw an AACo ad for outback workers and suggested they apply.

'It was a spur-of-the-moment thing to go to the Northern Territory,' she said. 'We moved in a week with a box trailer.'

Ian got a job as a gardener, Lisa as a cook, her initial vocation, at Rockhampton Downs, on the Barkly (AACo sold the property, which it had owned since 1948, in 2009). Ian tended the grounds for some time before taking on the mechanic's role, almost by osmosis.

'They had a good mechanic,' Ian said, 'then three mechanics in a month. I'd worked for eight to nine years as a gardener, and the manager's wife had taught me how to do Kubota motors. I just went from there. I have no formal qualifications but I'm now doing a remote-learning Certificate Three in Engineering and Mechanical Trades.'

I doubted it covered everything within his area of responsibility. He repaired whipper snippers to graders, and everything in between.

The only thing he didn't fix was the road train, which was the domain of its driver, Greg Vinson.

'I just have a go,' Ian said. 'The first big job I did was at Rocky, a grader's gearbox. I rebuilt the gearbox. They got an old feller out from Mt Isa to help me. He sat in the corner snoring. Out here, there's all sorts of different things: in the stock camp a bloke couldn't change gears and I found it was a rock caught in the gearstick. An old bloke broke down 75 Ks out. He was out of fuel, he thought. It was just that there was no pressure in the prime tank.'

Ian and Lisa moved to Headingly in October 2004. Lisa, who'd been cooking for 20 years and had tired of it, transitioned to administration, essentially filling the role many manager's wives take on, especially since Steve was divorced. She now has a Certificate Three in Business Administration.

'When Steve is away I hold the fort,' she said. 'When he was away for four months, everything was left to the head stockman and me.'

That said, there were some things Lisa preferred to leave to the boss.

'It's not my job to pull people into line,' she said. 'That's Steve's job. If I know there is a problem, I'll tell Steve. For a lot of staff it's their first time away from home and they do need some help. Some of them like to confide in someone older. I can handle that all right. Some of them, if they get injured, still say, "I want my mum."'

One thing she did do, which was common to a lot of stations, was encourage younger staff to consider a career on the land and help them undertake additional training. As elsewhere, a lot of young people come for a year or two, then move on. Retaining good staff is something of a holy grail.

Ian had no doubts about the reasons he and Lisa have been at Headingly for the last eight years.

'We're happy here,' he said. 'After four or five weeks away we can't wait to get home. We like the lifestyle and the freedom. There's no worries about people knocking stuff off. You either like it here or you don't, and we have a good boss.

'You need hobbies out here. I've got a four-wheeler and shoot pigs and dingoes. Once a year we go for a big shop and have got to get away.'

Lisa seconded all of that and added that she liked the opportunities the company gave its staff to develop their skills, in her case ranging from Rural Business Management to First Aid and Drug and Alcohol Testing.

The following morning Steve had my day well organised. He wanted to show me around a bit then suggested I meet up with the road train to take some weaners to another paddock. He took me into the main house where he'd made up a small dossier on the station.

Among the maps and condensed histories was a list of the mobs that had been driven through Headingly for the year 1950. Between mid-April and the end of November (the droving season) 98 mobs, ranging in size from 600 fat bullocks to 2122 cows and calves, had passed. Most mobs were of more than 1300 bullocks. They included a mob of 1417 bullocks being taken from Bedford Downs to the railhead at Dajarra by legendary drover Edna Zigenbine that passed on 1 November. Altogether in 1950 there were more than 100 000 head walking, endlessly walking, past the station.

'My father used to drove cattle across the property up until 1965,' Steve added. 'There's supposed to be a phone hanging in a tree on the other side of the river, which they used to use to call across.'

Steve was a real son of the outback. He grew up at Brunchilly Station, on the western side of the Barkly Tableland, which his father managed for 30 years, after the construction of the beef roads in the mid-1960s brought his droving days to an abrupt halt. On his mother's side his family were from Muckaty Station, which was about 100 kilometres away. Steve went to an Adelaide boarding school from 1980 until 1984, then returned to Brunchilly to work for his father breaking horses. He became a jackaroo on Avon Downs under

Jeff Wagstaff, then ran a stock camp at Brunette Downs from 1987. He spent five years there as assistant manager (a role generally considered a breeding ground for AACo managers) then went to Avon and managed it in 1996. In 2002 he became manager at Headingly.

'I had a go at being married,' he said. 'It didn't work out but not because of being in the bush. There were other reasons. I now have a girlfriend who works in the mines at Mt Isa. Her parents used to own Bowen Downs some years ago.'

In addition to his good humour, Steve also had abundant energy. As he sat and showed me things, he couldn't stop fidgeting, wanting to be on the go. Soon enough, we jumped into his four-wheel-drive ute and drove down a rough track that bounced over the flood plain and gutters to the main channel of the Georgina.

It was worth the bouncy ride. Steve had said he wanted to show me an old overshot dam that was mostly intact. I'd kind of gone, 'Yeah, whatever', thinking I'd seen what he was talking about before. When I saw what he was talking about, my jaw dropped. Someone had collected thousands upon thousands of white rocks, then angled them all in the same direction, cleverly overlapped so that they protected each other from being washed away. The dam was a couple of metres high, and the genius behind the construction, that had only been washed out at one end, was that it had withstood the massive Georgina floods for more than 100 years. Steve thought it may have been built using Chinese labour.

The idea of the dam was that it would trap enough water behind it to carry stock through dry spells. The reality was that until the advent of bores, used to tap the more reliable artesian water below ground, dry spells left even the overshot dams empty. Nevertheless, it explained how Oscar De Satgé and his partners spent some of the £250 000 they'd invested in Headingly and Carandotta.

As we drove back, we talked about public access to the river and the station's agreement with the local Waluwarra people.

'The locals have access to the property,' Steve said, 'they camp on the river, which is no drama. They come out chasing roos but they leave stock alone.'

The station had fenced off some sensitive areas to protect them from stock. However, in some places they'd found it was better not to fence sites because it advertised the fact that something was there.

Back at the station the Truckasaurus decided to complicate my plans by refusing to start. This despite my having had the vehicle serviced before every outback trip I made. Steve, who was far more mechanically minded than I, a distinction enjoyed by a great many people, couldn't find anything wrong. The thing just refused to turn over. He eventually got me going by hitching a snatch-strap to his ute and roll-starting me, after which Trucka purred like a 2-tonne kitten.

I was now falling behind for the scheduled rendezvous with the road train, and hightailed it south along the public road that connects Camooweal with the town of Urandangi, which sits near the centre of Headingly. It's yet another outback welfare town, and a refuelling point for tourists coming across from Alice Springs on the Plenty Highway (which also travels through Headingly). However, it wasn't as blighted as those in the Northern Territory. I didn't spend enough time there to find out why but on previous trips through the town I'd found the locals friendly and sociable. On one trip I'd stopped at the pub to buy diesel and after a yarn with the proprietor, who filled me up, she also gave me a postcard of the town in flood and a bottle of the pub's red wine. Headingly staff also seemed to have a good relationship with the place they referred to as 'the Dange'.

Past the town two roads in the gidgee diverged, and I wanted to make sure I chose the one the road train had travelled by. To make sure, I called on the station's VHF channel to see if the driver, Greg Vinson, could hear me. He repeated the directions, and I realised I was on what I'd thought was the right road. Not long after I discovered I needn't have worried. A cloud of dust rose in the distance, thrown up by the three trailers of his road train. A short time later I caught up to him where he'd pulled up to give directions to another road-train driver, a contractor from a road transport company, RTA.

They were talking about an accident that had happened the day before, involving a truck on the Plenty Highway. The heavy vehicle laden with cattle had been forced off the road by a tourist and had rolled on its side, killing a significant number of cattle.

Outback people know that the usual procedure when approaching a road train on an unsealed road is to slow right down or stop and give the road train the whole road.

If you're smart, you pull over to the windward side of the road so you don't get a dust bath. One of the reasons for stopping is so you avoid having your windshield chipped or broken by a stone thrown up from the road train's many wheels. The other reason is that in many places the ground on the sides of the narrow roads is too soft to support the road train's weight.

Greg wasn't your typical truckie. He'll hate me for saying it but he reminded me of Paddington Bear. He was round-faced and friendly, but he also had a similar hat! He was one of the best blokes I met during my several trips outback, which is saying something. He looked to be in his thirties, although due to bouncing in the road train my attempt to take notes recorded his age as something like 8N. Greg was also another long-term Headingly employee. The father of three had been there since 2005.

'We came with a five-year plan, which we now have taken out to ten years,' he said. 'We've got a house in Charters Towers that's rented out. This place suits us now.'

The weaners were yarded up in Moontah Paddock, where a team of contract musterers assisted with loading them. Even the contractors were in a good mood. The five of them were a close-knit team of a husband and wife, two young jillaroos and a young jackaroo. They all clearly knew what they were doing. Everyone was too busy to talk much so I helped push cattle up the race. I thought it wiser not to follow them into the drafting pen to coax recalcitrant stock along. I couldn't imagine how anyone would explain to an insurance company how a writer came to be in such a place when he got hit by a charging beast. I also kept well back from the iron rails of the race, having seen the results of stray hooves flying out to break or badly bruise a leg.

'You sometimes get caught by cattle,' Greg said. 'I got kicked once; it caught me through the rails of the race, fair on the end of the percy. That folded me up all right.'

The weaners were loaded 40 to a deck on the six decks of the station's road train, a Mac Titan with a 600-horsepower Caterpillar motor. Once they were loaded, Greg posed for a few pictures, then we were on our way.

Greg was originally from Hughenden, where he did his local schooling before spending two years at Brisbane. He started driving trucks in Townsville on a range of jobs, including carrying station supplies. He used to load wool for a neighbouring property but in 1986 they stopped running sheep because of the cost of labour and falling prices as a result of the wool-stockpile debacle. Most of his driving for Headingly was done on the station.

'I cart about 18 000 head a year to yards, then back out to the paddocks,' he said. 'I've also done trips to Longreach, Roma, Toowoomba and South Galway. Last year I did 137 000 kilometres, all on Headingly, except for one trip to Avon Downs and one trip to town [Mt Isa]. I did 220 kilometres one day and never left the station.'

In 2008 he did quite a few trips to save cattle that were in danger of perishing due to the drought that affected the entire region.

'We didn't put stock up the ramp to the top deck because they were too weak,' he said. 'By the end there were only 3000 head left on the property.'

As the landscape slid slowly past, I asked Greg whether he had to keep his speed down to avoid throwing the stock around.

'On dirt we're doing 60 km/h and even slower,' he said. 'It's about preservation and keeping your gear in good order. The trailers are 31 years old. They're pretty tough and hold up well. They were made to last. But tyres get shredded. The stones are small and sharp and pierce tyres. Cheap brands fall apart. You have to get good quality to get the life.'

Slower speeds also mean a saving in fuel, although the cost of running the road train still works out at about $3 per kilometre. Our trip with 240 weaners cost the equivalent of an entire beast, just in moving them from one paddock to another.

With the road train travelling so slowly, even relatively short trips can take considerable time. While there may not be transport inspectors lurking so far from major centres, Greg has done training in fatigue management, and to a degree polices himself.

He also has to contend with some unexpected obstacles. The river crossings can catch the unwary. Even when it's dry, as it was when we went over the Georgina, negotiating the crossing with a truckful of skittish weaners and a vehicle with a loaded weight of 120 tonnes calls for considerable skill.

When we were across Greg pulled up to check they were all right, then we rolled on past the Dange, which turned out to be the source of another unexpected hazard.

'One thing you have to watch out for on these roads is stray timber,' Greg said. 'Locals come out to load up with gidgee and sometimes it falls off on the way back to town. You can be driving through open country and come across a log in the middle of the road.'

When we started talking about his time at Headingly, something of a recurring theme emerged.

'Steve has been good to me,' Greg said. 'AA has been good to us. Because we've got kids we go to Mt Isa quite a lot. There are no other families here, no interaction, so we try to get them out a lot. The kids go to school but we like to keep them occupied and seeing different things all the time. But it's not isolated here. There's plenty of interesting things and you can talk to people. In the cities you don't know your neighbours.'

Greg talked a lot about his family. Two of his children are at boarding school while the third, his daughter, was being home-schooled. She sounded like quite a character. Greg told a number of stories about her, including the first time he took her, at about four years old, for a game of tennis.

She got onto the court and said, 'Okay, Daddy, we're gonna play tennis. Prepare to cry for Mummy.'

We made it back to the station for lunch, then headed back to Moontah for Greg to pick up another load. Back at the yards, the Truckasaurus still wouldn't start, so the contractors gave me another tow-start. It was pretty vexing, and I was starting to suspect my starter motor or a faulty relay. Unfortunately, Ian the mechanic had left for a holiday that morning, so he couldn't help me. I suspected he'd be able to find the problem in a blink. That said, not even Greg, who did all the work on his road train, could work out what was awry.

Back at the station yard, the stock camp was processing the weaners. Sam the pilot was operating the cradle, Joe and Anna were doing eartags, John was dehorning, Lucy was castrating, Troy was the leg man, Dominic was branding, and Harriet (who was visiting her sister Lucy) was sending them up the race and vaccinating. For the weaners, it was a stressful experience but the stock camp was well-drilled and each weaner was processed in as little as 30 seconds. The faster it could be done, the better it was for all concerned. The only delay was when I tried for a shot of the brand going on and they paused for a few seconds to help me.

While they were doing that, Pat the head stockman was keeping an eye on things nearby, while shoeing horses.

When everyone was about to knock off for the day, a road train pulled in with another load of weaners. Nobody left until they were all safely unloaded. Then they headed off for a beer and a shower, while Steve banged about closing gates and checking water troughs.

Over at the recreation building, Steve started chiding me.

'No trouble finding the road train this morning?' he asked.

I guessed he'd heard me on the radio, checking my directions.

'Nope,' I said.

'Didn't get lost?' he asked with a gleam in his eye.

'Surprising as it may seem, no.'

After dinner that night, I managed to corner the station's young pilot, Sam McKendry. He was a youthful-looking 20, but had already logged 400 hours flying time as of 24 June 2011.

'I'm a Brisbane boy,' he said. 'I started flying when I was 15. I always wanted to fly. I suppose I have a different goal to most pilots, who want to get into the airlines. I'm more interested in the RFDS or corporate jets.'

Sam had been at Headingly for three months, his first job on a station. He had his mustering endorsement but on the station he only moved cattle.

'The choppers muster,' he explained. 'The last but one pilot crashed at Austral, after he'd finished mustering, a cowboy stunt, and he was badly injured. The main thing I do is inspection. I fly the fence lines to see if any cattle are hanging on the fence or in a corner. If they're hanging away from water, they'll perish. I do bore runs, check troughs and pumps.'

When he isn't flying, he pretty much does everything the other staff do: bore work, cattle work, and helping in the yards, which has its moments.

'I've been hit by a cow,' he said. 'It was my first day, in the round yard, and a big heifer got me from behind, pushed me into the rails. You've got to watch those heifers, especially the really smoky [hot-tempered] ones.'

As was the case with other properties I'd visited, Sam heard about the station through friends who'd had good experiences there. He applied for a job but initially didn't get it.

'Eventually I got a call and Steve offered me a job,' he said. 'It's a great experience. I've met people and done things I wouldn't do in a city. The flying is different – low level, a different use of the plane. It becomes a tool.'

He was also discovering a different kind of work ethic, although he may not have known it.

'I've got a hobby,' Sam told me, 'building a T-rex chopper: radio-controlled. I'm not making any progress. I'm always busy. If I'm not busy, I'm trying to sleep. I've had the chopper for two months. At home it would take me only two nights to build it.'

The following morning, the Truckasaurus still wouldn't start. After breakfast it was dark but the station was buzzing with activity and 'Give the Hapless Writer a Tow-start' was just one of the jobs that got put on the To-do list before everyone headed out to their various jobs for the day.

After they got me going, the lights of the station vehicles disappeared in plumes of dust in the early morning light. As they went, I couldn't help but envy them. My first impression that Headingly was a great place to work hadn't been shaken.

A lot of that was due to manager Steve Hagan. He had a knack for getting the best out of people, though he may not have known he was doing it. I subsequently discovered from other managers that he had a similar effect at company gatherings for senior staff. Not only was he a born leader, he was also fun to be around.

I'd given him a couple of my books to thank him for having me, and in return he lent me a book that said quite a bit about him and his 'We'll-all-be-rooned' sense of humour: Phil O'Brien's *101 Adventures That Have Got Me Absolutely Nowhere*.

Steve had suggested I visit the woolshed for some extra photos, and maybe the old homestead with the defensive loopholes, but with the Truckasaurus uncharacteristically unreliable I hightailed it the 200 kilometres to Mt Isa to get it looked at. Being a Sunday, everything was shut, so rather than twiddle my thumbs all day, I drove another 650 kilometres to Longreach, as you do.

Next morning, after a couple of hours in the workshop, just before the mechanics started pulling the car to pieces, they decided to try cleaning the battery terminals. The thing started first kick.

Dirty terminals.

So obvious. And yet, not.

The one consolation was that by the time the car was fixed, while going absolutely nowhere I'd chuckled my way through most of the book Steve lent me.

If he had a motto, I suspect it was: Leave 'em laughing.

10. THE HOT SPOT

Commonwealth Hill Station
10 000 square kilometres

The running of the 1931 Melbourne Cup will always be remembered as Phar Lap's last race. It was the five-year-old's third Cup and he'd started all three as favourite, coming third in 1929 and first in 1930. In 1931, carrying a colossal 68 kilograms, he showed his class as the field turned into the final straight, the thunder of hooves joined by the roar of an immense crowd whose hopes soared on the possibility that the mighty champion would win again. Then hope turned to anger as the field ran away from one of the greatest horses of all time, leaving him in eighth place. The winning horse, White Nose, carrying 43 kilograms had led from the start, but was booed over the finish line.

For the owner of White Nose, pastoralist H.P. MacLachlan, the thrill of winning Australian racing's most prestigious prize was tempered by the fact that the Melbourne Cup had never been more of a poisoned chalice. The win was considered the most unpopular in the race's history. A couple of days later H.P. was philosophical at a lunch to celebrate the win, held at the Tattersalls Club in his home-town of Adelaide. He told the assembled members he thought they'd be happy the Cup had been won by a South Australian horse, even if none of them had backed it.

H.P. then made some comments that said as much about the man

as they did his victorious steed. He explained how he had backed
White Nose at three local meetings and had himself been disappointed every time. However, he said, 'I knew the horse was good.
I had the courage to take him over for the carnival, and my judgement was justified. I knew that White Nose was a stayer, and any
horse that is a good stayer always has a chance in a Melbourne Cup.'

The words 'courage', 'judgement' and 'stayer' were entirely appropriate for a pastoralist of H.P.'s calibre. Unlike sprinters like Fisher
and Lyons who, as detailed in Chapter 5, rapidly rose to great wealth
only to fall just as quickly when they overreached at Victoria River
Downs, MacLachlan and his family were a mixture of determination
and endurance.

H.P. had started out raising sheep in the starkly beautiful low-rainfall country around Yunta, 400 kilometres north of Adelaide, in the
early 1880s. It was an area that was lucky if it got 225 millimetres
a year, the kind of place where you needed courage and judgement,
and plenty of both, to stay one step ahead of disaster. In 1888, H.P.
founded Jumbuck Pastoral, which he steered through the financial
turmoil and terrible drought years from the mid-1890s to 1904,
while other landholders large and small went to the wall.

In the late 1920s, H.P. and his son, B.H., set about pioneering new
sheep country in South Australia's arid north. They did so with as
much care as H.P. chose his horses. They identified an area north-
west of Tarcoola, on the Trans-Australian railway line, as having
potential. However, there were two good reasons why the area hadn't
been developed by as late a stage as the 1920s. With an annual rainfall of only 175 millimetres, it was even drier country than they were
used to. Meanwhile, there was no shortage of dingoes, which made
short work of whatever sheep managed to find enough to drink.

The MacLachlans were undaunted. Before a single sheep set hoof
in the area, they made substantial investments in wells and bores to
ascertain where there was underground water and in what quan-
tities. Their expenditure of up to £16000 in the midst of the Great

Depression was rewarded with several discoveries; however, the water was found to be sub-artesian while its reliability was questionable. So at some sites water was pumped for up to two years while water levels were closely checked. Only when the water supply proved sufficiently reliable was the decision finally made to send sheep into the area.

It was around the same time as White Nose was repaying H.P.'s judgement that three adjoining stations – Mulgathing, Commonwealth Hill and Bulgunnia – were established, covering a combined area of 18 000 square kilometres.

With the water supply assured, the next priority was protecting that vast area from the predations of the ravenous dingoes. The plan was to surround all the properties with a fence that would exclude them. Such fences had been built before; however, most were funded by governments and had fallen into disrepair when maintenance fell behind. In places where rabbit-proof fences had been erected and were still effective, some pastoralists had increased the height of the fences to prevent dingoes getting over them, raising them to about 180 centimetres. By 1939, 250 kilometres of such fencing protected the sheep north of Tarcoola. Then good prices for wool during World War Two saw the fencing program accelerate.

After the war, the opportunity arose to join the various sections of fencing erected by pastoralists and governments in three states – South Australia, Queensland and New South Wales. The MacLachlan family, in particular B.H. (H.P. having died in 1939), was pivotal in the negotiations. When the South Australian Dog Fence Act was passed in 1946, a member of the MacLachlan family was appointed to that state's Dog Fence Board. There has been a MacLachlan on the board ever since.

The Dingo or Dog Fence now extends for 5400 square kilometres from the Great Australian Bight in South Australia, north to the corner of Commonwealth Hill, then east to the New South Wales border. It follows the SA–NSW border north to Camerons Corner, then doglegs east to follow the QLD–NSW border. It ends in the more closely settled Darling Downs. The fence is the longest man-made structure in the world, twice the length of the Great Wall of China. Unlike the Great Wall, it is still performing the function for which it was designed.

For the MacLachlan family, 20 years of careful investment and planning paid off in the boom years of the 1950s, when wool famously reached a price of £1 per pound (0.4 kilograms). The Tarcoola stations were by then fully stocked and shearing 100 000 merinos, with staff numbering in the hundreds.

The development of the stations continued, with up to 20 000 kilometres of internal fencing erected to form over 100 paddocks on the largest station, Commonwealth Hill, which by then was combined with Mobella to form what is now the world's largest sheep station, at just on 1 000 000 hectares.

It is only rivalled by Rawlinna, on the Nullarbor Plain, which was also established by Jumbuck Pastoral. Rawlinna, however, exists beyond the Dog Fence, an island in a sea of dingoes, built around a survey peg put in the ground in the 1960s by B.H.'s son Hugh.

While Jumbuck expanded and developed its properties during the boom years, the buoyant market wasn't to last. However, while markets fluctuated, Jumbuck survived the ups and downs, demonstrating that it was one of the real stayers in the industry. Then in the 1980s, the Australian Wool Board's attempt to establish a floor price for wool unravelled spectacularly, resulting in a stockpile that accumulated until it eventually grew to 4.7 million bales. When the floor-price scheme was abandoned in the early 1990s, wool prices crashed and many producers went broke or got out of the wool industry. Jumbuck Pastoral did neither. What was true of the stayer White Nose in 1931 remained true of the company 60 years later. It still is. Jumbuck Pastoral is now the largest wool producer in the country.

The road to Commonwealth Hill Station is unlike those to any of the other stations I had visited. Just after I turned off the Stuart Highway, 150 kilometres south of the opal town of Coober Pedy, signs explained that I was entering the Woomera Prohibited Area and public access wasn't permitted. The entire station is on a rocket range that was still in use, though not as frequently as it had been in the 1950s and sixties.

The unsealed deep-red road also provides access to the Challenger Gold Mine (which is on Commonwealth Hill's Mobella outstation) and the road was so regularly graded to allow the passage of mine vehicles that much of it was a metre lower than the surrounding countryside. At one point, I encountered a giant dump truck coming the other way, with pilot vehicles in front and following, the huge machine towering over the mulga scrub as it took up the whole road. I pulled over to let it pass.

It was late winter and the south-westerly that was ubiquitous in the outback at that time of the year was carrying threatening clouds up from the Great Australian Bight. Occasional sprays of rain turned the red dust on the LandCruiser into livid splotches.

The country was in good heart after three straight years of above-average rainfall that had come at the end of a decade of drought. In the sandy areas and occasional undulating rocky country, bullock bush, sandalwood scrub, saltbush and bluebush were thriving. Spear grass, mulga grass, white top and wire grass covered the ground. From time to time green-flashing flocks of budgerigars took flight from the roadside. In a couple of places, clumps of Sturt Desert pea, in spectacular red-and-black flower, grew wild by the road.

I counted myself fortunate to be allowed to visit the station. In the wake of the ban on live exports of cattle to Indonesia, which affected Jumbuck Pastoral's three cattle properties in the Kimberley region, the fourth generation of the MacLachlan family was understandably sensitive about having a writer visit their flagship property. However, to his credit, Callum MacLachlan (who, with his brother Jock, was co-managing director of Jumbuck) gave me a fair hearing, then gave me the green light.

The 100-kilometre road to Commonwealth Hill passed the company's other station, Bulgunnia, before crossing the Central Australian Railway. Some 40 kilometres onwards the first of Commonwealth Hill's buildings appeared, a large yellow-stone eight-stand shearing shed, built in typical South Australian style – solid and permanent. Beyond were the expansive shearers' quarters and beyond them the station itself. The most striking feature of the station complex was a large bomb shelter, an earthen mound with a tunnel through the centre of it, built for protection against falling missiles from Woomera. It was quite substantial, which in a way was both reassuring and disconcerting.

At the main house, I was welcomed by Gayle, manager Simon Robinson's mother-in-law. She and her husband, Alan, had been semi-retired, travelling around Australia but somehow ended up at Commonwealth Hill, Gayle filling in for the cook, Alan working in the garden. Gayle gave me a tour of the garden and explained that they were re-establishing it after the ravages of ten years of drought.

While we were talking, a jackaroo and two jillaroos came to stoke the fire of the homestead's boiler. Like the buildings, the boiler dated from the 1920s, when the station was established. The homestead was built in stone, again in the South Australian style – to last forever. Wide verandahs all around were enclosed with flyscreens.

One of the jillaroos, Tegan, was from Eltham in Victoria. Meagan and Steve were backpackers from Chicago, who had been at the station for only a week, and in Australia for not much longer. They'd been through a one-week training course with an employment company that introduced them to motorcycles, horses and stock handling. The course cost them $1000, which included guaranteed work. They were excited about working in the outback but admitted they had no experience of farm work and agreed they were a long way from Chicago in every sense.

I wandered off to take some photographs and eventually ran into station manager Simon Robinson and his dingo fence boundary rider, Bob Wright. Simon turned out to be one of the friendliest managers I came across. Tall, solidly built with a tanned face, he was a straight shooter, intelligent and very sociable. It took about ten seconds to break the ice and get the feeling that I could ask him anything. Like other managers, in the time I spent with him I never saw him with a To-Do list. He was never flustered, always totally organised, or at least appeared to be.

Simon and Bob had a problem. They thought at least three dingoes had got through the dog fence, where it had been damaged by camels. They'd since caught two but not before they'd caused losses of between 1500 to 2000 lambs, by Simon's estimate.

'I'm pretty sure that's right,' he told me when I expressed surprise that two dingoes could do that much harm. 'The fertility rate in the area where we caught them is down to 80 per cent. Everywhere else it's 100 per cent, so that's a pretty good indication of how many lambs I'm losing.'

It came as a shock to realise how few dingoes it might take to decimate the station's 55 000 merinos. As for the third dingo, Simon and Bob had seen its tracks but so far it had proved too cunning to get caught in a trap or take a bait.

As the daylight faded, Simon called it a day and took me back to the homestead, where we cracked a couple of beers and yarned on the verandah before the evening meal.

The station's pet dogs, stumpy tail red cattle dogs Scotty and Bindi, lay at our feet. Scotty was lucky to be alive after being bitten by a Mulga snake not long after Simon started managing the place, in early 2011.

'He was in a bad way,' Simon recalled. 'I didn't think he was going to make it. He was shaking violently, muscle spasms, frothing and being sick. He was in terrible pain. I was about to give him an injection of morphine to make it quick but I held off. He started to go quiet but I could still see he was really hurting. I put a mattress down where he sleeps and stayed with him. During the night I woke up and he was gone. He'd crawled off probably to find some water because he'd lost a terrible amount of fluids.

I started to think he might make it so I put him in the car to take him to the vet in Port Augusta [500 kilometres away]. By the time we reached the highway [100 kilometres away] he was trying to lift his head. Halfway down he was trying to stand up. In Port Augusta he was barking at people in the street. The vet kept him under observation for a week but he'd already pretty much recovered.'

Simon was originally from Adelaide, a city boy, but his grandfather had been a manager of a station near Burra and he'd always loved the bush. 'I can't bear being under a roof,' he said. 'I have to come in at night but if it's daylight, I want to be outside.'

He also has an older brother, who works for his uncle, Trevor White, manager of a property owned by Hugh MacLachlan's brother-in-law.

'When I was five, my brother, who was 17, used to come home with this hat, sunglasses, saddle and a ute, and I thought, "I want to be just like him."'

Simon had been with Jumbuck off and on since 1983, having started working at western Queensland's Retreat Station (which was held by the company until 2007) when he was 15. In between he spent time contracting, repairing windmills and fencing, and worked for ten months with Elders. As a result he's familiar with a surprising number of outback people, especially in south-western Queensland. He knew Lake Nash's Scott family through working at Thylungra, and the Rayment family, associated with Adria Downs.

He has been through drought and flood, on one occasion swimming through floodwaters to bring mail to Retreat Station. When he arrived, he handed some letters to Jumbuck's then managing director, Hugh MacLachlan (who handed over to Callum and Jock in 2009), with the words, 'Sorry they're wet.'

Along with his uncle Trevor, Simon counts Hugh MacLachlan as a major influence in his life and Richard Armour, who he worked for as an overseer on Mulgathing Station for seven years.

'I have the utmost respect for Hugh MacLachlan,' he said. 'He's like God. He never forgets anyone. He's an expert in everything. He was a great sportsman; he played polo for Australia. He can get down to grassroots level with his workers. He's a real, genuine bloke, very well respected, a gentleman. He can be hard but a good friend.

'He was the reason for me staying with Jumbuck. He cut me a lot of slack when I was having my ups and downs. People have bagged the MacLachlans, saying they're cheap, but they had big enough heart to stay in wool where a lot of others have fallen over. They had real grit all the way. They've got staff who know that all they earnt went back into their properties, all their properties. It's a case of you don't make it, you don't spend it. You don't spend what you don't earn.'

The family's commitment was repaid with loyalty from their staff. Two managers, Shane Miller and Harry Palmer, have been with the company since the mid-1970s. However, the changing nature of the management role was making it harder for older men. The days of managing a property from the verandah are long gone, as managers are increasingly hands-on, doing what their staff do, and often more.

On a sheep station the workload was even greater than on a cattle station. Simon compared Commonwealth Hill, with 160 paddocks averaging 80 square kilometres in size, all of them watered, to giant cattle station Anna Creek.

'It's only got about six paddocks,' he said, half jokingly. 'Those cattle boys have got it easy. They just wean 'em, watch 'em grow, then truck 'em out.'

It was now dinnertime but unlike other big stations there was no dinner bell and no separate dining room for staff. Everybody gathered around a large table in the kitchen of the main house at the designated time, 7 p.m. It was like a family meal and the intention was deliberate.

'It's a chance to catch up with everyone, find out how they're going, let them know what is happening,' Simon explained. There was no surprise when it came to the menu: roast lamb.

The dining room was pretty lively, with jackaroos, jillaroos, Bob the dogger, overseer Matthew Vick, pilot Andrea McHardy, Gayle, Simon and I. Simon's wife, Katie, and father, Alan, were away in Port Augusta, picking up a car. There was plenty of curiosity about what I was doing and what I'd done. After dinner, Simon and I returned to the verandah, to continue yarning while enjoying a glass or two of red.

One of the big challenges currently facing Commonwealth Hill was its internal fencing. The approximate 20 000 kilometres of it that were erected in the boom times of the 1950s were coming to the end of their life, but with a replacement cost of $1500 per kilometre for materials alone, the property's budget usually only stretched to ongoing maintenance rather than a replacement program.

Another big challenge was water. Surprisingly, it was this, rather than the availability of pasture in what was semi-desert, that limited the number of stock the property could carry. In a normal year there was enough feed for 90 000 to 100 000 sheep but water restricted the station to an upper limit of 60 000, a conservative number but a safe one.

'You have to be canny about your water,' Simon said. 'It's very limited from bores; it's quite a shallow aquifer. The place is pretty flat so there isn't a lot of catchment. If you find a hill, you put up a dam. We're trying to put in more dams, we want to put in more, but we're always trying to find country where we can dig a hole. Where we've got water and dams, we pipe out from there. If we find a good batch – not too salty – then we send it out to other areas.'

While the property carried more stock in the glory days of the 1950s, and water was pumped more freely to water them, for the last 30 years the station had become aware that it was gradually depleting a resource that was slow to replenish.

'Numbers were reducing in the 1980s,' Simon said. 'It was Hugh who realised it and said, "We're pumping too much." Now we will actually turn windmills off when they've pumped enough water so it isn't pouring out over the ground and being lost.'

In 2012 the station had 58 bores, 18 dams and a pipeline network to all of its 160 paddocks. It carried 55 000 sheep, turned off 16 000 per year and produced 1400 bales of wool.

As with every station I visited, Commonwealth Hill was always on the lookout for good staff. And they were hard to find. Simon explained that Matthew Vick, his current overseer at the main homestead (he had another overseer at Mobella outstation), was promoted at the age of 19 and was now only 20.

'Matthew basically got the job because he was prepared to stick it out,' Simon said. 'He's got a big heart, the heart of an old type person. It was a big step for him but he's quite good compared to what's out there. He thinks like someone from ten years ago. Young kids now are not as tough. We get backpackers from Denmark, Sweden, New Zealand et cetera, because the Aussies don't have much heart.'

While some properties cut back their activities during the heat of summer and/or the wet season, Commonwealth Hill operates year-round. The whole property is mustered in late December or January. In February, shearing is done by contractors. In March and April all sheep are back out on the property. Lamb marking is done in June/July.

For much of the time the sheep are spread over the entire property and with such large areas involved, mustering is a very different proposition compared to smaller properties.

'We usually concentrate them in an area using the plane, then drove them with the bikes,' Simon explained. 'It takes about half a day to muster a paddock. In reasonable years we can hold sheep in the yards for a few days but in dry years the sheep would starve. We have to get them in and out in 48 hours. In good times we can muster three or four paddocks and hold them all in one yard between crutching and marking. In bad years we can't do that but we can muster

by turning water off. When the sheep get thirsty they'll hang around
the troughs.'

Simon and I talked late into the night, and well into the red. When
I apologised for keeping him up after midnight, knowing he'd be up
at the crack of dawn, he replied that he was actually glad to have
someone new to talk to.

Breakfast was at a comparatively late 6.30 a.m. However, being in
South Australia's north-west, it was still dark.

The night before, Simon and I had worked out a plan for my
day. First up was a trip along the dingo fence with Bob the dogger.
After one of those big outback breakfasts that would make a heart
specialist cringe, I started helping Bob load his ute and rearrange the
passenger seat to accommodate an unexpected guest. Bob loaded
up chops, sausages, eggs, bread, potatoes and more – enough to last
him from Monday morning until Friday night or Saturday.

We headed out past the shearers' quarters and shearing shed. It
was a two-hour drive to the start of the dingo fence on the north-
east corner of the property. Along the way we passed a low rise that
turned out to be Commonwealth Hill. As hills go, it was only just
higher than the surrounding country.

Bob, in his mid-sixties, had been a New Zealand car dealer and
importer until changing economic circumstances and new technology sent him out of business in 2006. In his younger days he'd also
been a merino farmer, 'though in a very different way to the operation here'.

Late in life he was rediscovering how much he enjoyed working on
the land. He had just returned to work with Jumbuck after a previous three-month stint. 'It's more than a job,' he said, echoing others
I'd met who saw the outback as a lifestyle, rather than a workplace.

As we drove along the fenceline of the neighbouring property,
I made up for the disruption to Bob's normal routine by opening

and closing the gates between paddocks that appeared every 5 or 10 kilometres. The boundary fence was a six-strand sheep fence that was kept in reasonable repair. As Simon had said the night before, the internal fences were only maintained to the extent that time and money allowed.

When we arrived at the dingo fence, it was immediately clear that this was an entirely different proposition. It was approximately 1.6 metres high, some 50 per cent taller than the usual fencing on a cattle or sheep property. It was constructed using locally sourced timber posts and a mesh-like chicken wire but with a more open weave that had holes about the size of cricket balls to allow small animals to pass through while stopping foxes and dingoes. At ground level the mesh extended out from the fence for half a metre to discourage burrowing. Foxes could still dig their way under the fence but dingoes couldn't. However, they could get through the fence where a fox had made a hole. While the external boundary of Commonwealth Hill extended for approximately 550 kilometres, only the 240 kilometres of the northern and western sides were fenced in this way.

Bob's work began immediately. There was a hole right in the corner of the fence where it joined the neighbouring property. It was probably made by a kangaroo but was big enough for a dingo to get through easily. Bob bent the fence back into shape and used extra wire to reinforce the weak point where the hole had been.

Back in the ute he noted the work he had done and the location. Every repair to the fence was recorded so that reports could be compiled indicating how much work was being done and the areas where damage was concentrated, suggesting hot spots for dingo activity. As we drove on, Bob pointed out a small metal square with a number on it. It indicated the distance, in miles, from the corner of his section of the fence. It was a useful guide to determine his location in order to identify problem areas, or in case he needed to be rescued.

We didn't get far before Bob spotted another problem: there was a small hole where a fox had started to burrow under the fence.

He pulled up, took a shovel off the back of the ute and shovelled sand into the potential breach. Within the first couple of kilometres we stopped another half-dozen times. When rocks or thick pieces of wood were to hand, Bob used them to add solid material to his back-filling to further discourage vulpine excavations.

'We're not actually on the official dingo fence yet,' he explained in between shovelling stops. 'This used to be a dingo fence in an earlier era but it's still maintained for extra insurance. When the MacLachlans first set this place up, they ring-fenced it [meaning they put up dingo fence all around it].'

Three weeks had elapsed between the departure of the previous dogger and Bob's return, and it was extraordinary to see how many burrows foxes had dug in such a short time. It wasn't long before Bob and I worked out a routine. We took turns shovelling red sand into the holes. For bigger holes I shovelled while Bob put out a poisoned bait that worked on foxes and dingoes, appropriately called Doggone. Bob picked up and placed the baits using the point of a knife, so as to avoid physical contact with the dangerous poison.

'The station has always maintained its dingo fences,' Bob said. 'And the station patrols the fence weekly while contractors paid by the South Australian government only patrol every three weeks. The problem with that is you can check a fence in the morning and a dingo or camel could damage it in the afternoon. That means you could have dingoes getting through for the next three weeks.'

Bob drove along the fence at 20 to 30 kilometres an hour. While watching where he was driving, he was also checking the top wire of the fence for camel damage, the fence itself for any holes, the foot of the fence for burrows, and the posts for any breakages. In addition, he was on the lookout for any camels or dingoes that might be in the country alongside the fence. A rifle rested in a rack behind the seats. At times Bob also noted tracks of camels, dingoes and foxes walking along the fence.

Camels are considered the major problem in the maintenance of the dingo fence. There are estimated to be more than a million of them roaming the desert regions of Central Australia. When they come across the dingo fence, the large beasts don't regard it as an obstacle and will push over entire sections, which then lets dingoes through.

Some sections of the fence showed signs of a massive fire that had swept through the station in the mid-1970s. A run of good seasons had built up the fuel load enough for fire to spread. Some wooden posts had been charred but were still solid, while others had been replaced with steel posts.

Much of the fence was original, the materials that were used to construct it having survived 80 or 90 years. The mesh was actually made to H. P. MacLachlan's specification, and the initial order was so large that the manufacturers tooled up specifically for the one job. The mesh was now no longer available.

Pulling up to fill another fox burrow, Bob pointed out an additional feature of the fence. The mesh and wires of the fence were actually stapled to the posts. The idea was that when a camel hit the fence the staples would pull out, preventing damage to the supporting wires or the mesh.

We continued to shovel our way across the South Australian outback until Bob decided it was time for lunch. This he signalled by simply stopping where he happened to be. However, before we ate, he insisted we wash our hands.

'I've been handling poison and we've both been handling the shovel,' he said. 'So it's better to be safe than sorry.'

And he didn't mean a quick rinse. I held a water cask while he thoroughly washed his hands with soap and running water, then he did the same for me. Then we ate cheese and salad sandwiches that Gayle had prepared back at the homestead, washed down with sweet coffee from a thermos.

'It does get a bit lonely in the camps,' Bob said of the four nights he spent alone on his patrol. 'I do spend a bit of time staring into the flames of the fire and thinking about the things that have gone on in my life. But after a week out here I'm really thinking about getting back to have a shower. Sometimes I just camp anywhere but there are a few favourite spots, mostly places that offer some shelter from the wind.'

So far he hasn't had the unpleasant experience of a previous dogger, of waking while camped one night with the sense that something was not quite right. When he opened his eyes a large dingo was standing 3 metres from his swag, staring at him.

The original plan was for me to spend the morning with Bob, then in the early afternoon rendezvous with Simon, who was marking lambs in a nearby paddock. However, with all the foxholes we'd encountered we had made slow progress. It was now past one o'clock and there was no sign of Simon.

Not long after we got going again his vehicle appeared in the distance.

'There's something wrong with your radio,' he said to Bob when he pulled up. 'I've been trying to reach you for hours.'

A quick test revealed Bob's radio could neither send nor receive. Bob couldn't continue his patrol without it because he had to report in on it every night. It was an unbreakable rule. So Simon took on yet another of the tasks not specifically mentioned in a station manager's job description: troubleshooting communications problems.

While he checked the aerial and cable he asked how I'd been going.

'Real good,' I replied. 'Bob even let me have a go with the shovel.'

If there was one thing I'd learnt in the outback, they won't let you drive the road train, they won't let you fly the plane, they definitely won't let you drive the police car, but they will let you do some digging.

After half an hour or more of investigation, Simon discovered the radio problem to be the connection (or specifically a lack of it) between the cable and the antenna. It hadn't been installed properly and when the antenna flexed after hitting a branch, the cable was simply pulled out. Eventually Simon was forced to abandon his attempts at a repair and reorganised Bob's patrol. He would continue along the fence for the rest of the day, then head back to the station for the night, and Simon had more tools with which to do a repair.

As the day was getting on, Simon had left his stock camp to mark lambs while he headed to the north-west corner of the property to check waters. We continued along the inner dingo fence until we reached the dingo fence proper. Here the efforts to control dingoes were even more intense. As well as the fence, there were also traps at regular intervals, particularly in areas where dingo numbers were known to be high.

'Dingoes seem to favour particular areas,' Simon explained. 'There are avenues of particular terrain and vegetation that they use. So they tend to concentrate in some areas while in other places there are almost none.' Although he was not patrolling the fence, Simon stopped occasionally when something grabbed his attention. Despite travelling at about 80 kilometres an hour he'd suddenly slow down and pull off the road.

'You see here,' he'd say. 'These are dingo tracks. With this wind today they're definitely fresh. You won't even see our tyre tracks along here in a couple of hours.

'This north-west corner of South Australia is a real hot spot,' he said. 'At times, when they've been breeding up, they can be here in their hundreds. Times like now, when there are plenty of mice, they've got lots to eat, plus birds, lizards, you name it. When it gets tough they all end up starving. It's just terrible. They will eat each other. I didn't think they'd bother with foxes but I've seen them kill them as well.'

Simon pulled up to show me one of the traps. It was buried under a light covering of sand and surrounded by sticks and branches on three sides to prevent other animals from accidentally wandering into it. No meat was used in the trap because it would also attract eagles and large lizards. Instead, a small amount of dog droppings was used to trigger the dingo's territorial instincts.

Simon triggered the trap, which had been set three weeks before. In that time, dew and light rain had made the sand hard and the trap could barely close. Simon reset it, using his shoes to reopen the trap's jaws and a stick to set the trigger plate. When I asked why he didn't use his hands, he pointed at a piece of rag tied to one of the jaws. It was sprinkled with a tiny amount of strychnine. The idea was that when a dingo got its paw caught, it would lick the paw and the rag, hoping to get free. The poison acted quickly to make the animal's suffering as short as possible.

When the trap was set, a sheet of newspaper was laid over the top, snugged down, and given a light covering of sand. Simon then put a single stick across the front of the trap. 'The previous dogger thought it made the dingo step over the stick and directly onto the trap,' he said.

We continued along the fence, which in this section was on the boundary between Commonwealth Hill and the Tallaringa Conservation Park. Here, the dingo fence delineated the boundary not only between sheep and dingo country but between the opposed ideologies of eradication and conservation, human activity and nature in the raw. Situated at the north-west extremity of the South Australian dingo fence, Commonwealth Hill was literally a cornerstone of the attempt to separate the settled from the wild. Nature broke in wave after wave against it, held back by steel mesh and equally steely determination.

There has been considerable debate on the question of the environmental impact of culling dingos. It has been suggested that top predators like the dingo maintain balance in populations of other species and there is evidence that the reintroduction of wolves in the Yosemite National Park in the US (and it may be worth noting that dingoes are a species of wolf) has improved its ecological diversity.

On this subject a popular story doing the rounds of the Internet suggested Environment Minister Peter Garrett once proposed to NSW sheep farmers that instead of eradicating dingoes, their populations could be controlled through the capture, castration and release of male dingoes. This suggestion elicited a response from an old sheep farmer along the lines of: 'Son, you don't seem to understand. The dingoes aren't fucking our sheep, they're eating them.'

In fact, this story has also been attributed to former Queensland minister Russ Hinze, and before that to the US Forestry Service and a plan to castrate coyotes. What is true, however, is that this method is proposed by animal welfare groups. For example, on its website, Animals Australia states:

> Where there is a proven case of severe damage due to an overpopulation of introduced animals, Animals Australia advocates humane, non-lethal methods of population control such as fertility control which has the potential to be far more effective in reducing populations of introduced species. However, currently governments are unwilling to prioritise fertility control research on the basis of cost, and land managers generally require the 'quick fix' lethal methods rather than longer term and ongoing sound management techniques.

The problem seemed to be that even one sterile dingo could still slaughter hundreds of lambs. At Commonwealth Hill that meant that, without the dingo fence, there would be no sheep. And without buffer properties like Commonwealth Hill, the sheep industry in Australia would be an entirely different proposition. Far from the dingo fence, where sheep safely graze, it's easy to forget the constant struggle that is carried on unseen and unceasingly to provide that security. It was far from being a quick fix.

After turning through a gate, we left the dingo fence and headed south, bound for Garford Bore, the main water source for the north-west part of Commonwealth Hill. At the bore there were three windmills operating, while nearby there were several other bores and wells that had run dry. Remarkably, they were all within several hundred metres of each other.

We stopped at an ancient bore pump that looked like it should be in a museum. In fact, it was a workhorse that pumped water to a tank several kilometres to the south. Simon topped up the oil, pumped diesel into its tank and fired it up.

Near the windmills there was a small stone cottage. In days gone by a watchman kept the pumps operating, staying in contact with the main homestead over a telephone line strung through the bush. The cottage was now abandoned but a more lonely location could hardly be imagined.

As we continued on our way, Simon talked more about how water conservation on the property had evolved.

'When the MacLachlans first came here,' he said, 'they really were pioneers. The first thing they did was put down wells, then they pumped and pumped to see if the supply was reliable. They did that for a couple of years and the water level didn't seem to drop. It was only then that they started developing the place. They had no way of knowing that 40 or 50 years later there would be a problem. There's no way you can test for that long. Now we know they were pumping too much and we're much more careful.'

At Thunderbolt jump-up, Simon checked that the water pumping from Garford was coming through. A thin stream of water poured into the bottom of a large and largely empty tank. Simon noted that there were some sheep in the vicinity of the tank and the fenced area around it, which wasn't characteristic behaviour for that time of day. He suspected there was a dingo in the area.

'I'm pretty sure there's one but I haven't been seeing any bites,' he said. 'So he may be leaving the sheep alone.'

The tank was on an escarpment and from there Simon pointed out where he planned to site a dam. 'You see that hill with the gully behind it? If we got an inch of rain it would fill.'

Looking in the opposite direction we could just make out the Challenger Gold Mine. Since 2002 the mine, which employs over 270 people, has yielded some 750 000 ounces of gold. It is one of the richest and most productive mines in the country. Simon compared the goldmine to the days when wool produced a golden fleece that underpinned Australia's wealth. Then and now Commonwealth Hill has yielded great wealth.

As we looked, we also noticed red dust being kicked up as a fierce south-westerly front swept over the property. In 2009, Commonwealth Hill was identified as the source of a huge dust storm that engulfed much of eastern Australia. In fact, the station just happened to be the nearest identifiable point to the origin of the storm. However, at the time it was possible to drive on Commonwealth Hill's dirt roads and not kick up any dust because it had all blown away.

Leaving the escarpment we continued south as the red dust swirled over the vehicle and the temperature dropped. Sheep scrambled in all directions as we passed and Simon noted quietly to himself, 'They're all looking good and fat.'

We passed through a succession of gates and paddocks. The methods of securing the gates demonstrated the extraordinary creativity and variety that could be achieved with a few hooks and pieces of wire.

'We have sometimes thought about reducing the number of paddocks on the place,' Simon said. 'However, it actually works quite effectively the way it is. The paddocks operate to keep sheep at several waters. Without them they would congregate at only one.'

We pulled up again at Jumbuck shearing shed where the manager of Mobella outstation, Ben Hammond, was rearranging equipment in an ancient truck. Mobella was purchased after Commonwealth Hill and developed later but it was now managed jointly, with a crew at each homestead. While Ben and Simon caught up I checked out the shearing shed and shearers' quarters. The wind was making doors creak and windows rattle, giving both an eerie abandoned atmosphere.

When I got back to the vehicles Ben asked, 'Did you see the ghost?'

According to him the shearers' quarters were haunted. They certainly felt that way.

Near the quarters a separate cottage was available for station staff to stay in during shearing, but it was never used. They were usually too busy mustering sheep and bringing them in to actually stay at the sheds.

Back at the station Simon's wife, Katie, had returned from Port Augusta with her dad. At dinner the kitchen table was getting too crowded so the overflow spilt into the dining room proper. Again there was no hierarchy. People sat wherever they found a space.

Having worked his way up from the bottom, Simon, and his management style, had an egalitarian streak. It extended to technology as well. While some staff had satellite dishes and Internet in their houses, those that didn't were welcome to use the Internet in the main house. In the end, it was a small investment if it kept the sense of isolation at bay.

While we were at dinner, Bob gave me a short article he'd written for his friends back in New Zealand, trying to explain to them what life was like on a station like Commonwealth Hill. In it he detailed the activities of the Woomera rocket range, which had conducted some 4000 rocket launches over the years. Whenever a rocket was about to be tested, the stations it might land on were telephoned and everyone made for the bomb shelters.

Simon chipped in that he didn't think the shelters afforded much protection. On Mobella a 9-metre rocket had hit a sand dune and completely disappeared inside it. The rocket range scientists knew with reasonable certainty where it had landed but they never found a trace.

Simon also explained that predictions about where rockets were going to land were notoriously inaccurate. During rocket tests, the policy was that everyone within 40 kilometres of ground zero had to take shelter. On one occasion, a research team that was observing a test set up their post right on ground zero, reasoning that going on past predictions it was the one place the rocket would surely miss.

As people finished dinner and went on their way, I got talking to Simon's partner, Kate. She was originally from Brisbane but since 2004 had been living in the outback. Kate started as a jillaroo at Retreat Station, in western Queensland, where Simon was manager. At Commonwealth Hill her job title was housewife/domestic, which included operating computers and doing the bookkeeping. When the station was short of staff, it also involved mustering, marking lambs, pulling bores, driving cars and generally helping out.

'It helps that Simon and I had a business fixing windmills,' she said. 'Usually I deal with domestic issues such as cleaning, cooking, dealing with invoices and the office work.'

The isolation of Commonwealth Hill didn't bother her, although six months without going anywhere was about her limit.

'There have been a few times when Simon is working that I've been all alone, but they pass,' she said. 'I'm also studying for a diploma in animal management. I did vet nursing and I'm working towards a vet qualification.'

According to Kate, there are more positives than negatives to living in the remote outback: 'Being out here you can do what you want. There are no hassles, no schedules, you can take it as it comes. And it has a lot of rewards. Simon and I see each other for a couple of hours each night. I can always go out and work with him if I want to see him. I'd love to bring up kids in the bush; there's none of that crap you have to deal with in the cities out here.'

Early the next morning, the south-westerly was still blowing close to gale force, which meant pilot Andrea McHardy was unable to go mustering. As with nearly all outback pilots, she was incredibly young. The 21-year-old was raised in New Zealand on a property near Gisborne called Tangi Hau (meaning howling wind). Her father managed the 6500-hectare property that ran sheep, deer and cattle and whose biggest paddock would fit easily into the smallest on

Commonwealth Hill. Despite this the property carried more sheep: 65 000 on 6500 hectares compared to Commonwealth Hill's 55 000 on a million hectares. During the seven months she'd been at Commonwealth Hill, her parents had come to visit and her father had been 'shocked' at the size of the property.

Andrea had wanted to fly since childhood.

'When I was ten I saw the movie *Pearl Harbour* and I loved it,' she said. 'I decided then that I wanted to be a pilot.'

She got her pilot's licence in November 2009 and her commercial licence in February 2010. Commonwealth Hill was her first flying job. She explained that flying on outback stations was the fastest way to get your hours up. Ultimately she would probably get a job with an airline, although she suspected there was more job satisfaction in general aviation.

'When I arrived in Australia, I went to Barry Forster at Leongatha to do my low-level endorsement,' she said. 'He's one of three people in Australia who can do that. You need to do eight to ten hours at low level but I was able to use some hours from my lessons at home. He teaches you the turns, manoeuvres and how to "bomb" the stock. You fly at 10 feet with trees coming at you, practice engine failures at low level and turns.'

Andrea heard about the job at Commonwealth Hill through a friend who was already working there. Other than doing office work to pay for her flying lessons, it was her first proper job. She applied on a Monday and was offered the job the following Wednesday.

'I arrived here on 31 January,' she said. 'I loved it. It's a true Australian experience. It's not all easy, though. I like the comforts of civilisation. I was a bit shocked by the living conditions. I didn't know that there were places with woodfired boilers for hot water. I couldn't believe how flat it was. But the people are great and mustering is awesome. I like that type of flying where you're working low. It is dangerous but it's your choice.

'I've only had one serious incident, when I was bombing sheep

in 45-degree temperatures. In heat like that the plane doesn't handle the same way. I almost didn't make it out of the bomb; I almost
stalled it. It was a real wake-up call and a reminder not to ask the
impossible of your machine.

'Other than that I've had electrics that caused problems, a problem
with the starter motor and no radio. When you don't have a radio it's
surprising how well you can communicate with the ground. You can
use hand signals to show the ground crew where to go. When my
radio was broken I had one Danish fellow say, "I understand you better when you're not talking." When the previous dogger had a radio
problem, I flew out to find him then said, "Wave if you can hear me
but can't talk back." When he did that, I then said, "Wave again if
everything is okay." '

Not surprisingly, Andrea finds working stock is completely different to the way she used to do it in New Zealand. When she's in the
plane, she takes control of the people on the ground, directing them
to the sheep.

The day we spoke she was supposed to rendezvous with Ben from
Mobella outstation but he had already left the homestead when the
decision was made that she couldn't go mustering. The only way to
reach him was with the plane's radio when it was flying at altitude.
She offered to take me for a quick flight in her Cessna 172 while she
made the call.

Out at the airstrip, after doing her pre-flight checks she took off and
circled the homestead so I could take some photographs. Meanwhile,
her attempts to raise Ben were frustrated when the radio turned out
to be malfunctioning. The radio was transmitting and receiving but
Andrea couldn't hear anything through the headphones. Mice, which
were in plague proportions at the station, were the suspected reason.
She'd been putting poison baits in the plane and they were being
eaten but one seemed to have found its way to an electrical cable.

As Andrea circled and tried to get some response from the radio, I
tried not to think of what else the mice might have chewed.

We eventually landed and headed back to the station where Simon and Bob were still working on Bob's broken radio. By that stage they were removing it and installing a new one. The work was taking up Simon's time but without an auto-electrician within 500 kilometres it was just another of the problems he had to micro-manage. After that, the plane was probably next on his list.

I said my goodbyes and got out of his way as quickly as I could, then headed out along the road back to the Stuart Highway. Back on the sealed road, heading north to Coober Pedy, bound for Anna Creek, the last station on my list, I noted that while there was no public access to Commonwealth Hill, the terrain from the turn-off north was fairly indicative of the country the station covered.

It looked like hard country, and in many ways it was, but as a result of a judgement and staying power, sheep thrived there. The world's largest sheep station, working away in quiet isolation for more than 80 years, had survived everything the seasons, predators and volatile markets could throw at it. If nothing else, it was an unspoken testament to the generations of the MacLachlan family and those working for them, who seemed to have endurance in their DNA. In an age when people talk about vision but rarely see it, Commonwealth Hill was a tangible example of the real thing.

11. THE BIGGEST COUNTRY

Anna Creek Station

23 677 square kilometres

After leaving Commonwealth Hill Station, I decided to take a detour of a couple of hundred kilometres to drive through what is currently the world's biggest cattle station, Anna Creek. I wasn't able to access the station, but I still wanted to at least lay eyes on it as I travelled the public road from the opal town of Coober Pedy, 160 kilometres east, to William Creek.

There had once been a time, and not so long ago, when I would have regarded the country I drove through as desert. It was certainly low-rainfall country but good rains earlier in 2011 had brought up a variety of grasses that had since yellowed and were swaying gracefully in the ubiquitous winter south-westerly. A few creek crossings revealed large areas of green herbage. My overall impression was that the country was similar to Crown Point (see Chapter 7) and Adria Downs (Chapter 8). There were areas of rolling downs and others of dunes, most of which were yellow rather than the more ancient-looking red.

Anna Creek's history reaches back to the first explorers to traverse the arid north of South Australia. On his epic journey across Australia and back, the indefatigable John McDouall Stuart first named Mt Anna on his journey north to the vicinity of Darwin on 15 November 1859, and Anna Creek on his way south to Adelaide on 19 July 1862. He gave no indication of the identity of the Anna he was honouring.

Trees along the creek may have been used for poles when the Overland Telegraph was being constructed in the late 1860s and early 1870s. Pastoral leases were made available in the area shortly after. A manager and one of the partners in Anna Creek and Strangways Springs Stations, Thomas Hogarth, had settled in the area in 1872. However, he may not have held Anna Creek from the beginning. In 1882 the estate of Edwin Swinden advertised the first publicly announced sale of the Anna Creek leasehold, covering 800 square kilometres.

While many of the stations I had visited struggled throughout their history with their remoteness from markets and the difficulties of transport, Anna Creek had the good fortune to have what was known as the Peake Railway, the Port Augusta to Government Gums Railway or the Great Northern Railway, built near the homestead in 1887. The line reached Oodnadatta in 1891, where it terminated until it was extended to Alice Springs in the 1920s. Its passenger service eventually became famous as the Ghan.

In 1888, the premier of South Australia inspected the line. At the time the country around Anna Creek was in the grip of the driest season in ten years. The northern stock routes were closed, while work on the line proceeded with the 'invaluable' assistance of camel trains and their 'Afghan' cameleers.

Camels, which were first introduced to Australia in the 1840s, may have already been going feral by that time. In 1894, an Afghan 60 kilometres from Anna Creek Station was attacked by a mob of them. He was seriously injured and spent three days without food or water until he was found by a boundary rider and taken to a neighbouring station. But his troubles weren't over. While he was recuperating, a snake slithered onto his bed. He was too badly injured to do anything about it and lay in terror until it was discovered and killed by the station cook.

Interviewed in 1911, 61-year-old manager Thomas Hogarth gave an extensive description of the struggles and pioneering efforts in his early years at Anna Creek. He described himself as a 'thorough bushman' who was driving bullocks at age four and working as a shepherd when he was 12. At the time of the interview, his stations covered 15 539 square kilometres.

'It is 39 years since I went to the Strangways and Anna Creek country,' he told the *Adelaide Advertiser*, 'and in the early days of our undertaking we had to battle against many more disadvantages than would have to be faced if we were only now taking up the country, because the railway did not go beyond Burra then. Now, the Oodnadatta line takes everything within a comparatively short distance of the stations.'

Initially the property ran sheep, with some 3000 cattle and 600 horses. The stations were in low-rainfall country, with an annual average of only 125 millimetres. Some years it got far less, some years it got none at all. The best country on the station could carry 13 sheep per square kilometre, with up to 50 000 being shorn on the property in some years. In other years hot, dry winds could scorch the place bare, and Hogarth referred to one occasion when he lost 9000 lambs as a result.

'It has been a matter of hard and persistent work for the whole of the 39 years,' Hogarth said. 'We have spent over £100 000 on the property. That portion of the runs used for sheep comprises an area 1500 square miles [3900 square kilometres] in extent, and it cost us £10 250 to erect a dog-proof-fence around it . . . The sheep are depastured in paddocks varying in size from 10 square miles [26 square kilometres] to 100 square miles [260 square kilometres], and the cost of the fences was another heavy item, because everything had to be carted. No one would attempt to keep sheep in that country except in dog-proof-fenced paddocks, because dingoes are as numerous as sheep, and quite recently we have discovered foxes on the property.'

His effort in dingo-proofing his sheep predated the dingo fence by some 70 years (as detailed in Chapter 10). While safe from dingoes, Anna Creek was still susceptible to drought. In Hogarth's time there, the country experienced three severe dry periods, including the great drought that gripped the entire country from 1895 to 1904. At Anna Creek, the effects of drought were still being felt in 1909, with stations destocking or freighting in feed. That year Hogarth bought 900 tonnes of hay to keep his sheep going. He also saw his flock reduced from 50000 to 11000, and would have lost more but for a massive effort by the station's staff.

Remarkably, while other stations like Commonwealth Hill generally had plenty of feed but a scarcity of water, Hogarth had the opposite problem. 'We have plenty of water,' Hogarth said, 'because we have six artesian wells and four of them overflow, while in the other two the water rises to within 3 feet [90 centimetres] of the surface, and we either pump it or sink trenches so that the fluid can run from the well pipes into troughs.

'I believe we were the pioneers of artesian boring – Mr. "Geology" Brown [a noted rock doctor of the time], I think, has given us that credit. One of the wells supplies over 3000 gallons [13638 litres] an hour, and that is far more than we want, so it has to run to waste into a sandy creek [such bores are now controlled to prevent wastage]. It was about 1873 when we started our artesian well system, and we have never been short of water since then, but, of course, the stock travel long distances to feed. The horses, for instance, often go out about 25 miles [40 kilometres] from the water, and come in to drink every second day.'

The claim that Anna Creek put down its first bore in 1873 may not be accurate. The first artesian bore known to have been sunk is thought to be one drilled at Bourke in 1878.

Hogarth also described the working conditions of his mostly Indigenous staff. There were 110 being paid 'good wages' and doing nearly all the work 'and no one could do it better'. They were employed to drive steam engines, make harnesses, and undertake blacksmithing, carpentry, building, shepherding and shearing.

'I have been good to the natives,' Hogarth claimed, 'and they in return have been good to me.'

Hogarth also had a sense of humour. In another interview given to the *Advertiser* during his visit to Adelaide in 1911, he canvassed the possibility of farming rabbits instead of sheep:

Have we any rabbits? Why, man, they're becoming more plentiful up our way than anywhere else, and it is astonishing to see that lots of people don't go in for rabbit farming in preference to sheep farming. I am quite satisfied that if we sold the whole of our stock and depended entirely on the rabbit for his skin and the meat and meat extract, we would do even better than with sheep and stock because bunny looks after himself. Providence sent the little animal to be a blessing, not a curse, and why don't we make use of him? Sheep may double their number in a year, but rabbits are three or four times as prolific. The rate at which the rabbits breed, the excellence of the fur, the fine quality of the flesh, the cheapness of farming them, and the evident intention of the Almighty that the animal should be a boon to man, makes me think it is our duty to take advantage of its presence.

It doesn't appear that Hogarth went any further with the idea. At the time he was interviewed, he had travelled to Adelaide for an operation and the aging pioneer was looking to retire from the region he had helped establish.

The stations he had built eventually became part of the Strangways Pastoral Company, with shares held by a number of interests. One of those interests was Sidney Kidman. As such his acquisition of Anna Creek appears to have been a gradual process. By 1925, however, Kidman was described as having an absolutely controlling influence in the company, and 30000 shares in Anna Creek in 1926. After that time, the station was generally described as belonging to him. However, the *Centralian Advocate*, reporting the death of one of Kidman's managers, legendary horseman and bushman Archie McLean, in 1953, described Archie as 'the owner manager with Kidman Estates of Anna Creek station on the west side of Lake Eyre for a number of years'. Jill Bowen's extensive biography *Kidman*, written with the assistance of his family, gives no dates for the acquisition.

At the time the Kidman interests took over the station, it may have been in extreme difficulties. A correspondent to the *Adelaide Register* in 1924 described Anna Creek and other places in the north of South Australia as being 'denuded of sheep and cattle by droughts and dogs'. If that was the case, the station may have been ripe for the picking. As explained in other chapters in this book and my chapter on him in *Outback Heroes*, Kidman frequently moved in to buy properties during hard times, when people were trying to cut their losses and sell at any price.

While Kidman may have been more of an accumulator of properties than a developer, he was also building a chain of stations that allowed him to drove stock great distances from northern Australia, much of the way on his own land. His was the prototype for the modern operations of major beef companies that breed in the north, fatten in the Channel Country and elsewhere, and finish on feedlots close to south-eastern markets.

Anna Creek fitted that strategy. When aggregated with the Peake and Macumba stations (and other stations to the north, including Crown Point, as detailed in Chapter 7), it extended for several hundred kilometres along the stock route from northern Australia that passed through Central Australia and terminated at what was the railhead at Marree in the 1880s, Oodnadatta in 1891 and Alice Springs in 1929.

Inevitably, Kidman was criticised for not doing more to develop his properties. The man who pioneered Adria Downs (as detailed in Chapter 8), Bill Brook, didn't hold back when interviewed by Jill Bowen in 1984. According to him, Kidman lost several properties or had parts resumed because he hadn't done enough to improve them, in particular by developing their water supplies. These included Glengyle, Durrie, Innamincka and Annandale.

Bill was referring to events of some years earlier. In 1918, Kidman had been required to improve Glengyle in western Queensland with artesian bores as part of the terms of his lease. He blamed the cost and the difficulty of getting equipment over the sandhills for it not being done. At the time, the lands commissioner at Cloncurry, W. W. Williams, dismissed his excuses and wrote to the Under Secretary for Lands:

> The name of Kidman is a byword in North Queensland for whole-sale devastation of the improvements upon pastoral holdings, and the manner in which many decently improved pastoral leases have fallen into this man's hand to be devastated by neglect, affords ample evidence that the man is worthy of no concessions of any kind and it is necessary to prevent any further areas falling under his control.

By 1981, when part of Glengyle was sold to the Brook family (see Chapter 8) almost nothing had changed. Even then, only one bore had been put down on the Annandale block. However, in explaining how the Annandale block was sold to his family company at that time (also see Chapter 8), Bill Brook's more diplomatic son David suggested the transfer was motivated by goodwill rather than an impatient Lands Department.

Meanwhile, the federal government was in no position to point a finger when it came to neglect. In 1951, the *Centralian Advocate* slammed the condition of the Central Australian railway:

> Following a recent derailment of trucks on a cattle train destined from Alice Springs to Adelaide, near Anna Creek, cattlemen and others in this area have voiced serious concern at the general state of the Commonwealth railway line between here and Port Augusta, at the state of the engines hauling rolling stock, and at the hazard to passengers. One man this week said that after a recent trip from Port Augusta to Alice

Springs, as a first-class passenger, he felt that he should have 'taken out a ticket in Tatts [a lottery ticket] for safe arrival.' He added that he had never travelled in a train which rocked so dangerously. He blamed it on to the condition of what is termed 'the permanent way,' and suggested that the way to Alice Springs was 'not so permanent.'

Quite apart from derailments and other obstructions to the regular passage of traffic on this single vital railway, it has been learnt this week that break-downs in engines have caused untold delay in the despatch of cattle trains from Alice Springs to Adelaide. In one particular case alone – owing to engine trouble and consequent delay in the arrival of trucks – one pastoralist has been feeding more than 500 head of fat cattle for three days, outside of the town, while awaiting transport for his beasts to market. It was estimated on Wednesday of this week that he had already lost £1000 of their value through these delays...

Hardily enough, the Commissioner for Commonwealth Railways (Mr Hannaberry) stated publicly not so long ago that he intended to make this railway pay. Will he now state that he still intends to make it pay at the expense, not only of the Northern Territory cattle growers, but at the expense of the people of Britain, who have been told so many times that 'Beef for Britain' is the aim of the Central Australian cattle growers? It seems to be up to the Commissioner to make this railway line safe soon.

The railway line was just one of the infrastructure problems that beset the region. Roads and communications were also poor. Floods in 1953 caused a breakdown in both during what was described as a 'tribal fight' at Anna Creek. Police took days to travel from Leigh Creek while the only communication with the station was via 'pedal wireless', which by that time was actually powered by the station's generators.

The clash led to the death of one man, and had come about after a group of people not employed at the station went there during heavy rains. Eventually, another man, called Eringa Peter, was charged with

manslaughter and sentenced to 12 months' hard labour. The judge
in the case indicated tribal customs had been a factor in the incident.
It was reported that 'Peter had been challenged to fight. He intended
to spear his opponent in the leg but was struck on the arm. He then
picked up a tomahawk and struck the other native on the head.'

There was another incident based on tribal custom three years
later, when police from Marree investigated the death of a ten-month-
old boy in what was described as 'a native camp near Anna Creek'.
His mother claimed he was the victim of a *kurdaitcha* or spell cast by
'evil-spirit men', and that she and her nephew had also been marked
for death.

A view of life on Anna Creek in the 1970s comes from a school-
teacher who taught there for two years. Peter Caust wrote of his
experiences for *The Australian Women's Weekly* and described how
between 11 and 24 mostly Aboriginal pupils had taught him almost
as much as he had taught them.

He learnt to catch rabbits on the run, hunt goannas and cook
them, although he didn't admit to trying them. When there wasn't
much to do at the station, many of his students pressed him to open
the classroom at night and during weekends, so they could do more
schoolwork.

At other times, he visited Lake Cadibarrawirracanna – the longest-
named lake in Australia – where birdlife was plentiful. He and the
kids swam in waterholes at Douglas Creek, explored the rock for-
mations nearby, visited the natural springs at Coward Springs, and
picked over the ruins of the telegraph stations at Strangways Springs
and the Peake.

The district's major social event at the time, as it still is today, was
the William Creek Gymkhana. The tiny town is 16 kilometres east of
the station homestead and up until the railway line closed in 1980,
was the delivery point for mail and goods for the station.

Peter also described conditions for station workers at the time:

A stockman's life on Anna Creek is not all roses. It is a free and easy-going life but he must live frugally and be prepared for long hours in the saddle and weeks away from the homestead. So the camps can move anywhere on the station, the stockmen's swags are taken on a camel cart driven by the cook. It also carries all his cooking gear. Camels are particularly economical in comparison to the motor car or truck, as grass and water are found in abundance, but not so petrol and diesel fuel.

The stockman's day starts at sunrise or earlier, and ends at sunset. They finish off the day with a roaring fire, stories, and a mug of hot black tea which would warm the cockles of anyone's heart.

Peter's account accords with this writer's experience in the stock camp at Crown Point. Peter also described the experiences of camping out on the station, waking to the sounds of corellas, galahs and crows as the sun came up over the sandhills. In spring, wildflowers put on a dazzling show of variety and abundance, filling the air with their exquisite scent.

However, he also wrote of the loneliness of life on an outback station. He had previously taught in Coober Pedy, 150 kilometres to the west, and frequently went there to socialise with fellow teachers. On one occasion he bogged his mini-Moke and covered the remaining 40 kilometres into town on foot.

'Coober Pedy became a refuge for me in many ways,' he wrote, 'as Anna Creek can be a particularly isolating place in which to spend two years.'

When he finally left the station, the outback had one more surprise in store: a sea breeze. He was still near the centre of Australia but the smell of salty water was coming off Lake Eyre, which lies to the east of Anna Creek.

At the turnoff to the station, I hesitated. I already knew its manager quite well. Norm Sims had been vice-president of the Birdsville Social

Club, while I'd been its secretary, and I'd been very much looking forward to catching up with him and his wife, Stephanie. Now that I was just a few kilometres away, it felt like I should at least call in for a cuppa. In the past, when I'd hesitated over the correct protocol for approaching outback people, I'd been pulled up pretty quick.

'It's never a good time,' they said, when I'd asked if a visit was convenient. 'Just come.'

In the end, fearing that they might be put in an awkward situation, I took a photograph of the sign at the turnoff, got back in the Land-Cruiser and drove on. While I can offer no more information about the modern Kidmans' properties than is available on the company's website or in articles such as 'Kidman Country' in *Outback Magazine,* I can provide some impressions of Anna Creek's manager.

If any young person reading this book is wondering whether Norm Sims would be a good manager to work for, the answer is yes. When I worked with him on a number of fundraising activities, he struck me as one of those quietly capable people who had an extraordinary amount on his plate but still found time to make a substantial contribution to his community.

My recollection is that he inspired such loyalty among his staff that when he left Durrie Station to go to Anna Creek, several went with him. Pretty much the same could be applied to his partner, Stephanie. She is one of those resilient outback women who's warm, friendly and generous with both her time and energy. Both of them were part of the can-do brigade that made all manner of events run smoothly and successfully.

I soon came to an intersection on the public road though Anna Creek. I turned south, passing through William Creek and on to Marree. Along the way were the strange green mound springs that marked the boundary of the Great Artesian Basin, and views of South Lake Eyre, shimmering to the horizon in the late afternoon sun.

Beyond Marree, the weather started turning nasty. The wind picked up as squalls of rain rolled over the road. Dusk was falling as I passed the ghost town of Farina. There was a good campsite there but on a night like that I didn't fancy it.

On through Leigh Creek I drove, finally back on the sealed roads and beyond the risk of being stuck for a couple of days while the unsealed road was closed by rain. I decided to spend the night at Parachilna, a flyspeck town with a remarkably upmarket pub. When I got there I managed to get one bar on my phone and rang my wife.

'You sound really tired,' Michelle said. 'Book yourself one of the best rooms and get a good night's sleep.'

I assured her I would, then booked a cheap donga with a shared bathroom. I reckoned I could sleep just as well for half the price. I treated myself to dinner, though, and ordered a kangaroo schnitzel with a glass of South Australian red. While I waited for my meal, I noticed journalist Paul Lockyer, chopper pilot Gary Ticehurst and cameraman John Bean were wrapping up their day's work over in a corner.

I'd met Paul a couple of years earlier, when he was filming in Birdsville for one of his documentaries on Lake Eyre. I'd spoken on the phone with Gary when I was writing about the 1998 Sydney to Hobart Yacht Race for *Shipwrecks*. I thought about going over and saying hello but they looked like they'd had a long day, and I doubted they were in the mood to network with a virtual stranger. Not that I would be able to bring much to my end of the conversation. They eventually went into the dining room while I ate by myself in the front bar.

I was back on the road at four the next morning. The weather was still pretty wild and the scudding clouds rolled over the rearing peaks of the treeless Flinders Ranges as dawn began to break.

Behind me lay several months of trips and 27 002 kilometres of driving. Ahead lay several months of writing. Within me lay experiences, impressions and revelations about an Australia I might have known existed but had never really understood. I felt incredibly fortunate to have come up with the idea of writing about some of Australia's greatest outback stations and to be backed in doing it by so many.

As I drove through the day, the weather cleared and the sun shone on the spectacularly stark ranges around Yunta and Broken Hill. Every couple of hours I stopped to brew a cup of coffee, then pushed on, thinking I might make it home.

By dark I was so close to the upper Hunter that I was tempted to keep going. I'd just about worn out the Pogues song 'Tuesday Morning', about two parted lovers dreaming about being together. I kept thinking of the Japanese proverb I'd known for years: 'More powerful than a yoke of oxen is the drawing power of a single hair of woman.' It wasn't just a single hair; it was the whole wife.

At seven I tuned the car's radio to ABC NSW and listened to the nightly quiz. I kept the radio on after it ended to catch up with the news. As I drove into the night, I started hearing reports of a chopper crash near Lake Eyre. My first thought was that it was probably a tourist flight, as there were many aircraft in the area taking people to see the wonders of Lake Eyre. No way would it be the helicopter flown by Gary Ticehurst. He was one of the best pilots in the business, with a well-maintained, reliable machine. Nevertheless, it was sobering to think the outback had claimed three lives in an area I had just been.

I drove on and made it home late that night, only to wake to the news that it had been the ABC chopper that had crashed. Paul, Gary and John had all lost their lives. Many Australians were deeply upset by the news. I was certainly one of them.

Opinions may differ about the safety of flying in the outback but while researching this book, some of the pilots interviewed spoke of near misses they'd experienced that had made them better pilots.

After my interview with David Brook (see Chapter 8), we were checking some details when he saw a photo of himself beside his plane in Frances McGinn's book on Birdsville.

He said, 'Bloody hell, I see myself near that plane, I think I'm bloody lucky to be alive; all the things I did in that.'

David's son, Deon, had been killed when the chopper he was flying crashed in 1998, during a routine flight. After completing the text for *Birdsville*, but still living there, I participated in the emergency response at Birdsville airport after an aircraft that had lost a wheel while mustering made a landing on the remaining two.

While working on this book, every time I was about to get into a plane or chopper, I did a risk assessment. Did I trust the pilot and the aircraft? Was I prepared for the consequences of whatever might happen? Only then did I strap in. And every time I left home on another research trip, I said to my wife, 'If anything should happen, please remember one thing: I was doing something I loved.'

Time after time, I'd heard that or similar sentiments echoed. Out in the big country, nearly everyone feels the same way. They're there because they love it.

It's almost impossible to spend time in the outback of Australia and not be touched by it. In the big country, where life is lived on a scale that transcends anything in a cloistered urban landscape, the grandeur of Australia comes with the territory. This I'd realised as more and more of it had passed beneath my wheels.

Along the way I'd also discovered organisations that were world-leading in the way they operated, and as far from the 'she'll-be-right' hayseed stereotype of the bush as it was possible to get.

I'd seen the finely tuned efficiency the big stations strove to achieve, and how susceptible they could be to interruptions to the supply chain, such as that caused by the federal government's ban on live exports to Indonesia. That was ultimately lifted but some months later was followed by a drastic cut in the quota of cattle allowed into Indonesia, whose government was shocked by the realisation that its food security could become the political football of another country. The impact of that on the big country was still to be played out.

I'd developed a healthy respect for the energy and commitment of the young people in the bush. If they're representative of the coming generation, this country is in extremely good hands. In them I'd seen the qualities of character I'd come to admire in many outback people: resilience, reliability and resourcefulness. They don't crack, they don't fail, they always find a way.

On my last afternoon on the road, while waiting for the billy to boil, I thought about what struck me most about what I'd seen, done and learnt.

First, if I could have my life over, I'd spend at least a year working on an outback station. In fact, I'd recommend to any young people reading this that they seriously consider this. It could well be the making of you. Come to think of it, it might still be the making of me.

Second, the time for change in remote Indigenous communities is long, long overdue. Without going into yet another rant, it's time for the excuses to stop and for successful programs to be identified and extended, rather than have their funding cut when there's a change of government, minister or whim. And the 'can-do', 'zero tolerance of bullshit' attitude of big stations could well go a long way to dealing with the 'too-hard' mentality.

Third, my love for the outback, and my country, was deeper than ever. Perhaps it's jingoistic, but I'd seen the vision splendid, the sunburnt country, and taken it into my soul. I only had to close my eyes to see the endless plains of the Barkly, the rugged bluffs of Wave Hill, the verdant lakes of Adria Downs, and yes, even the breast-shaped peaks of Crown Point. All this and more.

I felt privileged to be given access to the wonders of these and other stations. I only hope I've done justice to the special places in the heartland of the real Australia.

REFERENCES

1. A land of opportunity – Bowen Downs Station

'Barcaldine Ballot. Bowen Downs Resumption', *The Brisbane Courier,* 17 May 1930.

'Bowen Downs Blocks, Government's Methods Criticised', *The Brisbane Courier*, 5 January 1929, p 17.

'Bowen Downs Land', *Morning Bulletin*, 18 July 1904, p 6.

'Bowen Downs Poisoning Case', *The Argus*, 24 July 1895, p 5.

'Bowen Downs Poisoning Case', *The Brisbane Courier*, 13 September 1895, p 6.

'Bowen Downs Poisoning Case', *The Brisbane Courier*, 17 September 1895, p 5.

'Bowen Downs Poisoning Case', *The Brisbane Courier*, 19 September 1895, p 5.

'The Bowen Downs Poisoning Case', *The Register*, 13 September 1895, p 6.

'Bowen Downs Poisoning Case', *The Queenslander*, 3 August 1895, p 196.

Buchanan, B., *In the Tracks of Old Bluey: the life story of Nat Buchanan*, Central Queensland University Press, 1997.

Buchanan, G., *Packhorse and Waterhole*, Angus & Robertson, Sydney, 1933.

——, 'Pioneers of the Far North', *The Sydney Stock and Station Journal*, various issues, November 1921–May, 1922.

'Bush Items', *The Worker*, 3 October 1896, p 8.

'Country Mails, The Barcoo', *The Brisbane Courier*, 15 October 1888, p 6.

Holthouse, H., *Up Rode The Squatter*, Angus & Robertson, Sydney, 1970.

'Land Selection at Longreach', *The Queenslander*, 23 July 1904. McCarthy, P., *The Man Who Was Starlight*, Allen & Unwin, Sydney, 1987.

Matthews, R., 'Queensland v. Henry Readford, 11 February 1873 Trial Reenactment', self-published, Roma, 2002.

'Poisoning at Bowen Downs, Fifty-seven Men Affected', *The Brisbane Courier*, 22 July 1895, p 5.

2. The quiet giant – Lake Nash Station

Buchanan, B., *In the Tracks of Old Bluey: the life story of Nat Buchanan*, Central Queensland University Press, 1997.

Costello, M. M. J., *To the Savage Land: the life of John Costello*, Hesperian Press, Carlisle, 1930.

Durack, M., *Kings in Grass Castles*, Constable and Company, London, 1959.

'The Lake Nash Disaster', *Northern Standard*, 7 September 1934, p 5.

'Lake Nash to the Coast', Morning Bulletin, 29 January 1903, p 3.

Liddle, R., *Historical survey of European settlement on the eastern Barkly Tableland of the Northern Territory*, National Trust of Australia, NT, 1996.

Miller, L. A., 'The Border and Beyond', self-published, Camooweal, 1999.

'No Pay – Not Enough Food or Warm Clothing', *Northern Standard*, 1 July 1949.

O'Neill, S. 'Costello, John (1838–1923)', Australian Dictionary of Biography, National Centre of Biography, The Australian National University: http://adb.anu.edu.au/biography/costello-john-3267: accessed 31 January 2012.

'Slave Labour Used on Lake Nash', *Northern Standard*, 29 September 1950.

3. Heartland – Brunette Downs Station

Buchanan, G., *Packhorse and Waterhole*, Angus & Robertson, Sydney, 1933.

'Drovers' Dispute', *Northern Standard*, 17 June 1930, p 2.

Hill, E., *The Territory*, Angus & Robertson, Sydney, 1951.

McCarthy, P., *The Man Who Was Starlight*, Allen & Unwin, Sydney, 1987.

Makin, J., *The Big Run: the story of Victoria River Downs Station*, Rigby, Adelaide, 1970.

4. The long haul – Alexandria Station

Buchanan, G., Packhorse and Waterhole, Angus & Robertson, Sydney, 1933.

Hill, E., *The Territory*, Angus & Robertson, Sydney, 1951.

'Ingenuity Not Dead in the West', *Townsville Daily Bulletin*, 19 June 1952, p 2.

Liddle, R., *Historical survey of European settlement on the eastern Barkly Tableland of the Northern Territory*, National Trust of Australia, NT, 1996.

'NAPCO leading the way', *Landline* transcript, ABC TV, 28 August 2005.

5. The big run – Victoria River Downs Station

'Biggest Cattle Station', *The Advertiser*, 23 September 1908, p 6.

Bowen, J., *Kidman: the forgotten king*, Angus & Robertson, Sydney, 1967.

Buchanan, B., *In the Tracks of Old Bluey: the life story of Nat Buchanan*, Central Queensland University Press, 1997.

'Fight Against Malaria', *The Queenslander*, 29 June 1933, p 34.

'For Defence. More Aerodromes', *The Courier-Mail*, 19 October 1933, p 14.

'Forecasts End of Open Range Policy', *Northern Standard*, 16 September 1949, p 3.

Gill, T. and Titus, R., *South Australians: profiles of people and places*, Wakefield Press, Netley, 1986.

Hill, E., *The Territory*, Angus & Robertson, Sydney, 1951.

'The Languid North', *Townsville Daily Bulletin*, 2 November 1926, p 3.

Lewis, D., *Murranji Track: ghost road of the drovers*, Central Queensland University Press, Rockhampton, 2007.

McHugh, E., *Outback Pioneers*, Penguin Books, Camberwell, 2008.

Makin, J., *The Big Run: the story of Victoria River Downs Station*, Adelaide: Rigby, 1970.

'Noble Work', *The Brisbane Courier*, 16 September 1932, p 4.

'Nurses From Outback. Life at an A.I.M. Hospital', *Sydney Morning Herald*, 23 February 1929, p 11.

'The Pastoral Industry', *The Register*, 26 August 1906, p 6.

Willshire, W. H., *The Land of The Dawning*, Thomas, Adelaide, 1896.

6. A tale of two countries – Wave Hill Station

Buchanan, B., *In the Tracks of Old Bluey: the life story of Nat Buchanan*, Central Queensland University Press, 1997.

Buchanan, G., *Packhorse and Waterhole*, Angus & Robertson, Sydney, 1933.

——, 'Pioneers of the Far North', *The Sydney Stock and Station Journal*, various issues, November 1921–May 1922.

Carney, M., 'Aurukun learning lessons of NT intervention', *Four Corners* transcript, ABC TV, 2 May 2011: http://www.abc.net.au/news/stories/2011/05/02/3204828.htm?site=indigenous&topic=latest)

Lewis, D., *The Murranji Track, Ghost Road of the Drovers*, Central Queensland University Press, Rockhampton, 2007.

Lingiari, V., Manguari, P., Ngalgardji, G. and Kitgneari, L., 'The Original Wave Hill Mob Letter of 1967', 10 April 1968: http://bar.austlii.edu.au/au/journals/AboriginalLB/1986/41.html.

'Living Quarters at Wave Hill a Disgrace. No Education for Natives,' *Northern Standard*, 26 August 1949, p 7.

Manning, B., 'A Blast from the Past', Vincent Lingiari Memorial Lecture, Charles Darwin University, Darwin, 2002.

'Minister's Party at Wave Hill. Bird Life Seen', *Sydney Morning Herald*, 3 August 1938, p 17.

'Notes of the Week', *Northern Territory Times*, 7 February 1896, p 2.

'Wave Hill Station', *Northern Standard*, 29 April 1938.

'Wave Hill Stock Camp. Blacks Preferred to Whites. You Can Treat Them Rough', *Northern Standard*, 4 September 1936, p 4.

7. Red giant – Crown Point Station

'Alleged Murder of a Prospector by an Aboriginal', *The Register*, 5 August 1903, p 5.

'Andado Station Bore', *The Advertiser*, 29 September 1926, p 13.

Basedow, H., 'Arid Australia', *The Argus*, 5 February 1921, p 6.

McHugh, E., *Outback Heroes*, Penguin Books, Camberwell, 2005.

Madigan, C.T., *Crossing the Dead Heart*, Georgian House, Melbourne, 1946.

'Our Undeveloped Territory', *South Australian Register*, 4 July 1891, p 8.

'Starving Natives', *The Register*, 23 April 1907, p 4.

Sturt, C., *Narrative of an Expedition into Central Australia, Performed Under the Authority of Her Majesty's Government During the Years 1844, 5, and 6: together with a notice of the province of South Australia in 1847*, T. and W. Boone, London, 1849.

8. Heartbreak corner – Adria Downs Station

McGinn, F. G., *Birdsville*, Wayne Cantell, Sydney, 1977.

9. The happiest station – Headingly Station

'Abandoned Station Reoccupied', *Morning Bulletin*, 24 October, p 6.

Barker, H.M., *Droving Days*, Hesperian Press, Perth, 1994.

Bowen, J., *Kidman: the forgotten king*, Angus & Roberston, Sydney, 1987.

Costello, M., *The Life of John Costello*, Dymocks, Sydney, 1930.

'The Lake Nash Disaster', *Northern Standard*, 7 September 1934, p 5.

Waterson, D.B., 'de Satgé, Oscar John (1836–1906)', Australian Dictionary of Biography, National Centre of Biography, The Australian National University: http://adb.anu.edu.au/biography/de-satge-oscar-john-3403/text5165, accessed 31 January 2012.

10. The hot spot – Commonwealth Hill Station

'Among the People', *Adelaide Advertiser*, 11 November 1931.

Massy, C., *Breaking The Sheep's Back*, UQP, Brisbane, 2011.

11. The biggest country – Anna Creek Station

'Archie McLean is Dead', *Centralian Advocate*, 7 May 1954, p 6.

Bowen, J., *Kidman: the forgotten king*, Angus & Robertson, Sydney, 1987.

'The Bruce Gunn Agreement', *The Advertiser*, 2 June 1925, p 15.

Caust, P. 'The Multi-colour Schoolkids of Anna Creek', *Australian Women's Weekly*, 28 April 1976, p 22.

'Concern Expressed at Condition of Rail Line', *Centralian Advocate*, 18 May 1951, p 1.

'Correspondence, Pastoral Leases', *The Adelaide Register*, 29 March 1924, p 13.

'Curiosity Could Spell Death for a Lubra', *The Argus*, 15 November 1956, p 1.

The Floating World: an evocation of old Japan, Universe Books, New York, 1979.

'From the Far North-West', *The Advertiser*, 15 June 1911, p 9.

Muller, M., 'Kidman Country', *Outback Magazine*, Dec/Jan 2011, p 64.

'Native Sent To Gaol For Year', *The Advertiser*, 21 March 1953, p 17.

'Outback Pastoral Lands', *The Adelaide Register*, 9 October 1926, p 13.

'The Peake Railway', *South Australian Advertiser*, 19 December 1887, p 5.

'Rabbit Farming', *The Advertiser*, 15 June 1911, p 11.

'Police Check on Fatal Tribal Clash', *The Advertiser*, 19 February 1953, p 1.

'Scarcity of Feed', *The Register*, 29 March 1909, p 7.

'Terrible Experiences by an Afghan, Inquirer and Commercial News',
    7 December 1894, p 10.

Williams, W. W., Land Commissioner, letter to the Undersecretary,
    Department of Public Lands, 22 July 1921, Queensland State Archives,
    LAN/AF277.

ACKNOWLEDGEMENTS

Most books of this type reel off lists of names of people whose assistance was invaluable, but in this book that list would fill pages. To everyone who gave freely of their time, was patient with my questions, or yanked me out of the way as stock were about to thunder past, a very big thank you.

Particular thanks are due to Ken Ross formerly of Bowen Downs, George Scott of Lake Nash and Peter Hughes of Georgina Pastoral, Henry Burke of Brunette Downs and Troy Setter of AACo, Ross Peatling of Alexandria and Nigel Alexander of NAPCO, Rusty Richter of Victoria River Downs and Paul Holmes á Court of Heytesbury Pastoral, Greg Dakin of Wave Hill and Pam Dearmer of Western Grazing, Don and Colleen Costello of Crown Point, Don Rayment of Adria Downs and David Brook of Brook Proprietors, and Simon Robinson of Commonwealth Hill and Callum McLachlan of Jumbuck Pastoral.

Special thanks, too, to the road train driver who helped me get to Katherine from Top Springs when I was having trouble with a wheel. Guardian angels sometimes wear blue singlets.

As always, I owe a great debt to the team at Penguin Books, who put so much professionalism behind my books that it sometimes doesn't feel right that only one name is on them. They set the standard, I try to keep up.